THE ANATOMY COLORING BOOK

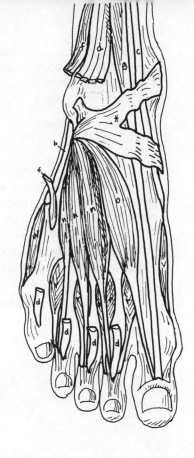

WYNN KAPIT
LAWRENCE M. ELSON

THE ANATOMY COLORING BOOK

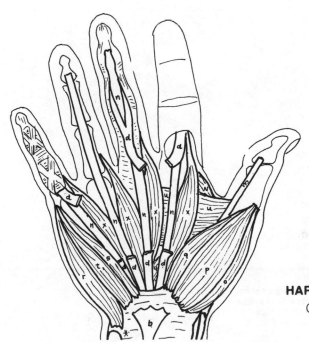

HARPER & ROW, PUBLISHERS, New York
Cambridge, Philadelphia, San Francisco,
London, Mexico City, São Paulo, Sydney

1817

To Larry Elson, my teacher, who provided
the inspiration and collaboration to make
the conception a reality.

Wynn Kapit

For my wife, Joan, with love, whose
positive, sustaining, and buoyant energy
made it possible for me to complete my
contribution to this book, and

For my son, Christopher, with love,
who gave me his 11-year-old perspective
of what coloring books are all about.

Lawrence M. Elson

ABOUT THE AUTHORS

Wynn Kapit, designer and illustrator of the book,
has been a lawyer, graphic designer, art director,
painter, portraitist, and teacher.

Lawrence M. Elson, Ph.D., is the anatomist who
wrote the text for the book. He teaches anatomy
and physiology, and is the author of *It's Your Body*.

The Anatomy Coloring Book

Copyright © 1977 by Wynn Kapit and Lawrence M. Elson

ISBN 0-06-453914-8

83 84 85 86 27 26 25 24 23

CONTENTS

CONTENTS

CONTENTS

CONTENTS

The human body fascinates just about everyone, yet few have the opportunity to study it. Here is a book designed to provide that chance with a minimum of rote memorization and a maximum of self-satisfaction.

Coloring is one of the most effective and pleasant methods of learning. Grade school and high school students can gain familiarity with the basic structural and functional features of the human body by coloring the plates and relating them to their own bodies. College, graduate, and health professional students will find the coloring book particularly helpful in learning and reviewing human anatomy and physiology. Artists can learn the anatomical basis for the beauty of body form. People with specific disorders could color and learn about structures whose malfunction causes their complaint. Physicians, doctors of chiropractic medicine, podiatrists, physical therapists, and other health professionals could employ the coloring book in helping their patients understand their own specific structural dysfunction. Anyone with a more than casual interest in body structure will enjoy the fun of coloring these illustrations of the body and its parts.

This coloring book encourages active learning by coloring 142 plates organized according to body systems. The colorer is first asked to study the "Extremely Important Tips" before starting the plates. It is not necessary to follow the order of presentation of plates; it is recommended that you work through the plates one system at a time, starting at the beginning of that system. It is also recommended that you complete the sections on Introduction to Gross Anatomy and Organization of the Body before going on to the other plates. Within each system, an introductory plate is followed by plates of anatomical structure generally arranged according to body regions (head, neck, upper limb, etc.). Each plate includes coloring notes (CN), which list the number of colors needed and also provide more specific guides than the ones in the "Extremely Important Tips." You color each designated structure *and* its name with the same color, thus enabling you to relate name and structure at a glance. Structural relationships become apparent as visual orientation is developed. Color links between structure and its name leap out in the finished plate. These insights, plus the pride that comes from finishing a plate, provide a rewarding learning experience.

Each plate includes pertinent facts or concepts as space permits. This text portion is written for all colorers and assumes no past academic training in the subject. Some plates may seem intimidating at first glance, even after reviewing the "Extremely Important Tips" and color notes. However, when the various parts are colored, the whole illustration often comes to life and the parts seem to relate with new significance. This same experience can be carried into whole systems when related plates, completely colored, are compared with one another. Appropriate cross references are listed by plate number at the upper right corner of most plates. A pronunciation guide is also included at the back of the book to help with unfamiliar tongue-tripping terms.

The authors are indebted to several people who aided in the creation of this coloring book and whose assistance proved to be of inestimable value. The reviews, criticisms, and suggestions of Drs. Ernest Gardner, Ronald Evans, and William Neff kept us on the track. We thank Howard Boyer, Pat Brewer, and Ann Moru of Canfield Press/Harper and Row, and Paul Quin, for professional guidance and encouragement.

June 1977

Wynn Kapit
Larry Elson

EXTREMELY IMPORTANT TIPS

1. For maximum benefit, a supply of at least 20 colors (including 1 or 2 shades of gray) is desirable, although the plates can be worked with 12 colors including 1 gray. Colored pencils and felt-tip pens are preferable to wax crayons which tend to be messy and coarse.

2. Before beginning to color, look over the entire page, reading coloring instructions, captions, etc. It is not essential to thoroughly understand what you are looking at, but rather to get a feeling for the page and to know what to expect. If you find that certain material, including titles or structures to be colored, are too detailed or technical for your interest, it is recommended that you color them as part of the overall exposure to the subject—even though you are not concerned with memorizing or intimately understanding the material.

3. Color in the order given by the coloring instructions. These will be preceded by the letters CN, which stand for the colors needed for that page (excluding gray). CN will be followed by the actual number of colors needed or by a question mark in situations where because of the excessive number of colors to be used, you will need to repeat a color.

4. You may use any color you wish; however, certain specific colors are directed or suggested for structures which have a consistent color under natural circumstances or are portrayed in color atlases of the body in a consistent color, such as arteries (red), veins (blue), nerves (yellow), lymphatic vessels (green), fat (yellow), muscles (brown), etc. Where several different arteries, veins, nerves, etc. are to be colored, other colors, of course, must be used. As a general rule, use more neutral or light colors for the larger areas, and brighter or darker colors for smaller or more important areas. On occasion, you will be asked to use colors on a plate that were used for the same structures on a previous related plate. In these cases, color their titles first regardless of where they appear on the plate. Then go back to the top of the title list and begin coloring in the usual sequence (down the list in order). This procedure will prevent you from using a color already specified for another structure.

5. Do not color over the heavier outlines, for they are usually the border lines separating areas to be colored. The lighter lines are usually included to suggest texture or define form in an area to be colored; these lighter lines should be colored over. With a transparent marker, they will show through as desired. If you are using colored pencils, they will usually show through; for added dimension, you may wish to draw darker or heavier over these

lined areas to add to a 3-dimensional effect.

6. When you see a small letter following a word or group of words printed in outlined letters, you should *always color in that word or words,* as well as the structure (bone, muscle, etc.) to which it refers. This practice will create a stronger visual link between the structure and its name. It will also aid in learning the spelling of unfamiliar words. It is recommended that you color in these words in the order that they are listed. Where the word or words is followed by an asterisk (✶), it should be colored a middle gray. This will usually apply to subject headings which require careful note and emphasis. If the word or words is followed by a small black dot (•), color it dark gray or black. So as not to confuse titles or names, *use one color for each letter on that particular page.*

Different titles/structures with the same identifying letter but with a small number added on (a^1, a^2, etc.) all receive the same color. Such structures— though different—are sufficiently related to warrant the same color.

There will be times when all the structures to be colored do not have a letter identifying them. This may occur in the case of symmetrical structures, where the unlabeled side is to be colored as well. Or also in the case where one or two labels imply that all should be colored. Occasionally, background structure functionally unrelated to the subject of the plate may not be labeled. Do not color such background structure (in most cases, structure/spaces not to be colored will be indicated by a -¦- symbol).

7. Abbreviations and symbols used throughout are:

M=muscle	Ms=muscles	✶=color gray
N=nerve	Ns=nerves	•=color black
A=artery	As=arteries	n.s.=not shown
V=vein	Vs=veins	-¦-=not to be colored in

The appearance of a ·······˙˙ or ₒₒₒₒₒₒₒₒₒ tailing an artery, vein, nerve, or duct means that structure is deep to (behind) the structure through which the dots pass.

8. Complete the pages of any section in the order given. A broader understanding will then be made possible when you view related pages together. You will find cross-reference page numbers in the upper right-hand corner.

9. A blank backup sheet is provided for you to slip under the page you are coloring.

10. Use the pronunciation guide in the back of the book as a ready reference when coloring and encountering difficult words.

THE ANATOMY COLORING BOOK

TERMINOLOGY

PLATE 1

CN 12

1. Color the four body planes in quiet, pastel colors.
2. Color the anatomical directions (arrows) in bright or dark colors for emphasis.
3. The body itself is not to be colored.

A precise set of terms and planes have evolved to describe positions, relationships, and directions within the human body. To avoid confusion, they must always be related to the standard *anatomical position:* standing erect, palms of the hands forward.

Planes are fixed lines of reference along which the body is often divided (sectioned) to facilitate the viewing of structure. By studying a region from sagittal, transverse, and frontal planes of reference, a 3-dimensional perspective can be obtained.

Terms of *position* and *direction* describe the position of one organ relative to another, usually along one of the three major body planes.

BODY PLANES*
MEDIAN a
The midline plane dividing the body into left/right halves.

SAGITTAL b
The plane dividing the body into unequal left and right parts and parallel to the median plane. The terms medial and lateral relate to this plane.

CORONAL, FRONTAL c
The plane dividing the body into equal/unequal front and back parts. The terms anterior/posterior relate to this plane.

TRANSVERSE, CROSS HORIZONTAL d
The horizontal plane divides the body into upper (cranial) and lower (caudal) parts. Cross/transverse sections are perpendicular to the long axis of the body or other structure and may not be horizontal.

ANATOMICAL DIRECTIONS/POSITIONS*
CRANIAL, SUPERIOR e
These terms refer to a structure being closer to the head or higher than another structure in the body.

CAUDAL, INFERIOR f
These terms refer to a structure being closer to the feet or lower than another structure in the body.

ANTERIOR, VENTRAL g
These terms refer to a structure being more in front than another structure in the body.

POSTERIOR, DORSAL h
These terms refer to a structure being more in back than another structure in the body.

MEDIAL i
This term refers to a structure being closer to the median plane than another structure in the body.

LATERAL j
This term refers to a structure being further away from the median plane than another structure in the body.

PROXIMAL k
Employed with reference to the limbs only, this term refers to a structure being closer to the median plane or root of the limb than another structure in the limb. Such a structure would ordinarily be superior to the other.

DISTAL L
Employed with reference to the limbs only, this term refers to a structure being further away from the median plane or root of the limb than another structure in that limb. Such a structure would ordinarily be inferior to the other.

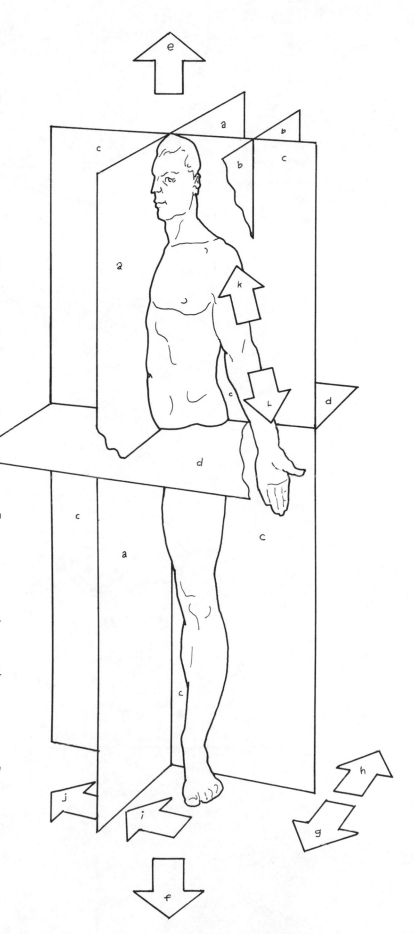

PLATE 2

ORGANIZATION OF THE BODY
THE GENERALIZED CELL *

CN 13

1. As you draw these structures of the cell, remember that the living cell is in motion: the cell membrane is dynamically undulating while absorbing/ejecting materials and vesicles are moving across the cytoplasm. This illustration shows the cell with the action frozen. The pinocytotic vesicles (k), in life, would be gone in a second and new vesicles would be appearing, and so on. The larger intracellular structures probably do not migrate significantly.

2. The endoplasmic reticulum (f) is shown twice, once with ribosomes and once without. The ribosomes should be drawn in a darker color than the ER for contrast.

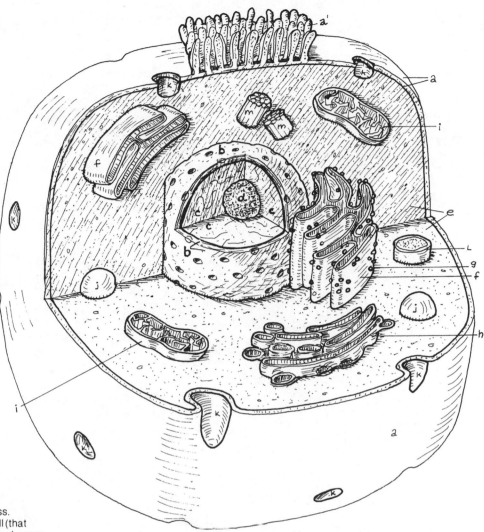

CELL MEMBRANE a
MICROVILLI a'
NUCLEAR MEMBRANE b
NUCLEUS c
NUCLEOLUS d
CYTOPLASM e
ENDOPLASMIC RETICULUM f
RIBOSOMES g
GOLGI COMPLEX h
MITOCHONDRIA i
VACUOLES j
PINOCYTOTIC VESICLES k
LYSOSOME L
CENTRIOLES m

The cell is the fundamental unit of all living things. Its activities constitute what is called life or the living process. It is generally held that anything less complex than a cell (that is, incapable of reproducing, metabolizing, and adapting to changes in environment) is not a cell and is not alive; anything more complex than a cell is a collection of cells. The human body is made up entirely of cells organized into tissues and organs, connective tissue fibers (the products of cells), and fluid. It is cells whose individual functions are magnified in the overall functioning of the body. Breakdown in the proper functioning of cells (whether caused by microorganisms, inherited defects, or injury) is the basis of disease. A cell generally consists of protein (15%), lipids (3%), carbohydrates (1%), nucleic acids and minerals (1%), and water (80%). These compounds make up the working components of a cell, called organelles. Cells all have a basic function: the production of protein (for replacement of parts, for cell work, for export as secretions, and so on). Most cell organelles are involved in this process.

Nucleus : supervises cell activity; consists of protein-coated hereditary material (DNA) in dispersed (chromatin) or condensed (chromosomes) forms, the nucleolus, and a porous nuclear membrane. The DNA holds all instructions for cell activity. The nucleolus produces RNA, some of which conveys the instructions of DNA through the nuclear pores to the cytoplasm.

Cell Membrane/Microvilli/Cytoplasm : The construction of the cell membrane is the same as that of the membranes of several intracellular structures. The cytoplasm is the ground substance of the cell less the nucleus (and its ground substance, nucleoplasm). The free surface of certain cell membranes is often thrown into fingerlike projections (microvilli), which dynamically undulate. They increase the absorptive area of the cell as well as provide a mechanism for receiving/ejecting matter. Within the cytoplasm are:

Endoplasmic Reticulum : layers of flattened vesicles in which protein in various stages of construction may be transported. Often studded with ribosomes (rough ER). Smooth ER is believed to be involved in the production of steroid molecules (estrogen, cortisol, etc.)

Ribosomes : granules of RNA where the actual linking of protein subunits is believed to take place.

Golgi Complex : layers of flattened vesicles whose ends are rounded giving the appearance of a vesicle-budding process. Protein is believed to be stored and concentrated here, contained within the vesicles that bud off to stream through the cytoplasm.

Mitochondria : membrane-lined structures saturated with complex enzyme systems whose activities result in the production of energy for cell operations. Cell respiration (utilization of oxygen and formation of carbon dioxide and water) also occurs here.

Vacuoles/Pinocytotic Vesicles : membrane-lined containers of various compounds in transit through the cell. They may fuse with lysosomes or they may be rapidly incorporated into the cell membrane, which rapidly ejects the contents to the outside extracellular fluid (exocytosis). Introduction of fluids/solids into the cell interior by the same mechanism (endocytosis) is called pinocytosis/phagocytosis (literally, a condition of drinking/eating).

Lysosomes : membrane-lined containers of enzymes, which merge with vacuoles holding certain foreign material or cell debris and disintegrate the contents. The digested contents are usually ejected through the cell membrane.

Centrioles : a pair of barrellike cylinders that are believed to produce during cell division the asters and spindle upon which chromosomes travel to opposite poles of the dividing cell.

The collective and integrated functioning of these various organelles, dependent upon instructions from the operating segments of the DNA, provides for the great variations of cellular activity, including contractions of muscle cells, conduction of electrochemical impulses by nerve cells, secretions of epithelial cells, and formation of connective tissue fibers by fiber-producing cells.

PLATE 3
see also 2

ORGANIZATION OF THE BODY
CELL DIVISION / MITOSIS *

CN 10

1. Complete each phase before going to the next. Reading the appropriate portion of the text will help you understand the meaning of each phase as you draw it. Structures are not repeatedly labeled in each succeeding phase; just color as you did in the preceding phase.
2. Use the same colors for cell membrane, nuclear membrane, nucleolus, and centrioles as were used on the plate of the generalized cell.
3. The colors used for structures e–e² should be strongly contrasted from the colors used for f–f² in order to better perceive how they are arranged and segregated. These colors do not reflect differences in quality of the chromatids/chromosomes.
4. We recommend that you use a gray color for d and d¹ so as not to confuse with structures e–e² and f–f².
5. You can color a line through the spindle fibers (j) rather than color each dot.

CELL MEMBRANE a
NUCLEAR MEMBRANE b
NUCLEOLUS c
CHROMATIN d* / CHROMOSOMES d¹*
CHROMATIDS e / CHROMOSOMES e¹
    CHROMATIN e²
CHROMATIDS f / CHROMOSOMES f¹
    CHROMATIN f²
CENTROMERES (KINETOCHORES) g
CENTRIOLES h
ASTERS i
SPINDLE FIBERS j

A vital characteristic of all living things is the ability to reproduce its kind. Living things are composed of cells, and it is cells that reproduce, in a process of duplication and division called mitosis. Some cells reproduce regularly and frequently (epithelial and connective tissue cells) and others experience division only under specific circumstances, if at all (nerve cells). Failure of certain cells to grow and divide generally constitutes atrophy (without growth). Uncontrolled mitoses constitute cancer.

The drawings primarily reflect changes in the nucleus, because the significance of mitosis lies in the duplication and subsequent division of DNA, the genetic material. Mitosis usually occurs rapidly—within minutes. The period between successive divisions is called *interphase*. It is during this period that the DNA (in chromatin) is doubled preparatory for the next mitosis. The observed nuclear changes during cell division are described by phases:

Prophase: *dispersed chromatin* (d*) begins to thicken, shorten, and coil, forming condensed chromatin or *chromosomes* (d¹*). There are 46 of them. Each chromosome (only 4 are shown for simplification) consists of 2 *chromatids* (e and f) connected by a *centromere* (g). Each chromatid has the equivalent DNA of a chromosome, and will be called a chromosome in anaphase, as you will see. Note in your coloring, that one chromatid (e) of each of the 4 chromosomes is destined for one *daughter cell*, and one (f) is destined for the other daughter cell. As prophase ends, the *nucleolus* disappears and the *nuclear membrane* dissolves. In the cytoplasm, 2 pairs of *centrioles*, having duplicated in interphase, project *asters* of microtubules; the pairs head for opposite poles of the dividing cell.

Metaphase: strands of microtubules (*spindle fibers*) project across the cell center from one pair of centrioles to the other. 46 pairs of chromatids and their centromeres (4 shown here) begin to group on the spindle fibers in the cell center.

Anaphase: the centromeres divide, each daughter centromere attached to one of the two chromatids. The chromatids are no longer paired. They are rightfully called *chromosomes* now (e¹, f¹), and there are 46 of them being drawn to each pole of the dividing cell by their centromere. (4 are shown here going to each of the two poles). Anaphase ends when the new daughter chromosomes arrive at their respective poles.

Telophase: the cytoplasm begins to cleave, pinching the dividing cell into two new cells. In each new cell the nucleolus and nuclear membrane are reconstituted. The chromosomes begin to disperse as the centromeres disappear. The cytoplasmic organelles are segregated into the two daughter cells as the cleavage of the cytoplasm is rapidly completed. The daughter cells, like their "mother cell" before them, will remain in interphase until their "time" arrives.

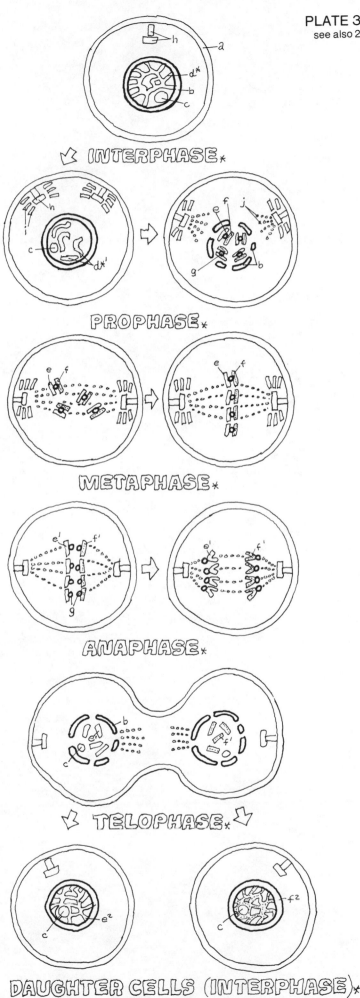

INTERPHASE *

PROPHASE *

METAPHASE *

ANAPHASE *

TELOPHASE *

DAUGHTER CELLS (INTERPHASE) *

PLATE 4

ORGANIZATION OF THE BODY TISSUES / EPITHELIUM*

CN 7

1. Color each block of tissue above the basement membrane. Color across all the cells making up the block.
2. Note that two of the subject headings are to be colored in dark gray or black.
3. Neither the pit of the exocrine gland nor the capillary of the endocrine is to be colored.

Cells of the body are organized into four fundamental tissues: epithelial, connective, muscle, and nerve. *Epithelial* tissues line *all* surfaces of the body: the skin, cavities, ducts, vessels. Epithelial tissues may be a single layer (simple) or several layers (stratified). They are named according to the cell shape on the free surface. Cells of a tissue are held together by the basement membrane and intercellular fibers. These tissues receive their nutrition by diffusion, for they are without blood vessels.

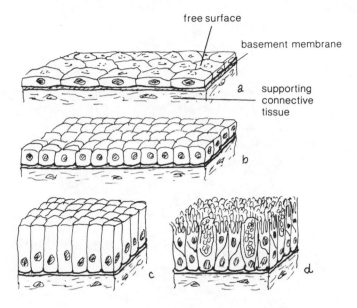

free surface
basement membrane
a
supporting connective tissue

LINING EPITHELIUM.

SIMPLE (ONE LAYER)*
SQUAMOUS a
CUBOIDAL b
COLUMNAR c
PSEUDOSTRATIFIED COLUMNAR WITH CILIA & GOBLET CELLS d

Simple squamous epithelium lines all blood and lymphatic vessels, including the heart, air cells of the lung, and certain tubules of the kidney. Filtration or diffusion occurs rapidly across this thin epithelial sheet. *Cuboidal* and *columnar* cells line glands and the digestive tract and are involved in secretion/absorption. *Pseudostratified columnar* tissue lines the respiratory tract. Its glands secrete mucus, and the cilia stroke the pollutant-laden mucus to the pharynx.

STRATIFIED (SEVERAL LAYERS)*
SQUAMOUS a'
COLUMNAR c'
TRANSITIONAL DISTENDED e CONTRACTED e'

Stratified squamous epithelium lines the skin, oral cavity, much of the pharynx, esophagus, vagina, and anal canal. It protects against wear and tear. *Stratified columnar* is seen in the reproductive tract. *Transitional* epithelium is seen in the urinary bladder, ureters, and kidney. It is capable of distention and contraction in response to changing volumes of urine.

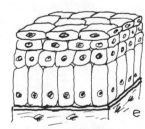

GLANDULAR EPITHELIUM.

EXOCRINE GLAND f

Exocrine glands arise as outpocketings of epithelial tissues. They generally secrete enzymes, mucus, or serous fluid. They are characterized by ducts that open onto the free surface of a cavity or skin. Examples: sebaceous, sweat, mammary, pancreatic. The secretory portions may have one of several shapes (tubular, coiled, alveolar; with one duct or many ducts).

ENDOCRINE GLAND g

Endocrine glands arise like exocrine glands but lose their ducts during development. They are intimately related to capillaries, which conduct their secretory products away. Examples: thyroid, pituitary, adrenal.

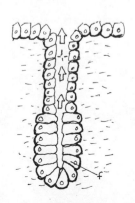
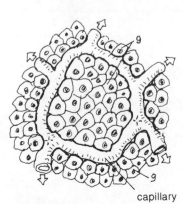

capillary

PLATE 5
see also 8, 9, 48

ORGANIZATION OF THE BODY TISSUES/CONNECTIVE TISSUE * (PART 1)

CN 16
1. The background (matrix, ground substance) for each of the tissues shown is to be left blank except in the cases of hyaline and elastic cartilage where the matrix (p) should be rendered a light blue color.
2. The lipid droplets (h) of the fat cells should be colored yellow. The elastic fibers should be colored black.
3. The connective tissues bone and blood may be drawn on Plates 9 and 48.

The several varieties of *connective tissue* (blood, connective tissue proper, and the supporting tissues of cartilage and bone) serve to connect, support, and bind body structures together. All the epithelial tissues, every single muscle cell, every vessel, every peripheral nerve down to every single axon is ensheathed with connective tissue fibers. Every bone in the body and all the joints among them consist of connective tissues. The components of connective tissues are all basically the same: cells and fibers enmeshed in a ground substance or matrix. The constitution of the carbohydrate-protein matrix, at the microscopic level, appears to be without organized structure (amorphous). The ratio of cells to fibers and/or the density of the matrix determine connective tissue types. For example, blood/lymph has a fluid density with many cells and no fibers. Bone, on the other hand, has a granitelike density with a mineralized matrix, few cells, and many fibers. In all connective tissues except cartilage, there are many blood vessels and nerve processes and perhaps some lymphatic vessels as well. These are not generally shown in these plates.

The semidiagramatic drawings you are coloring here are views of various connective tissues magnified 200-500 times beyond their natural size. Microscopes are required to see such structure, and the tissues are generally stained (colored) with certain dyes to differentiate one structure from another. A section of unstained tissues taken from the body would appear colorless, the outline of structure would be vague, and the detail of structure would be quite difficult to see.

CONNECTIVE TISSUE PROPER.

LOOSE, AREOLAR *

FIBROBLASTS a
MACROPHAGES b
FAT CELL c
PLASMA CELL d
COLLAGEN FIBERS e
ELASTIC FIBERS f

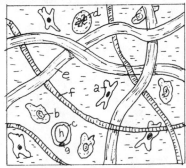

Loose connective tissue is characterized by a viscous matrix, many cells of several varieties, and a loose, irregular arrangement of fibers. The cells of this tissue include *fibroblasts* (which secrete the collagen and elastic fibers), *macrophages* (which engulf bacteria, cell debris, and other foreign matter), *fat cells* (which store fat), and *plasma cells,* lymphocytes, and other white blood cells (all of which defend the body against invasion by microorganisms and other foreign material). The fluid matrix provides a vehicle for the movement of cells from one area to another within the loose areolar tissue. The fibers (which make up most of the tissue mass) consist of linkages of protein that have great tensile strength (*collagen*) or inherent flexibility with capacity for recoil (*elastin*). Loose connective tissue is found under the skin as superficial fascia, supporting the epithelia of the body viscera and cavities, and filling potential spaces throughout the body wall and limbs.

ADIPOSE *

FAT CELL c
NUCLEUS g
LIPID DROPLET h
RETICULAR FIBERS i
CAPILLARIES j

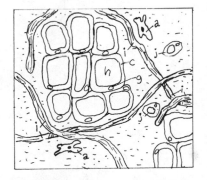

Adipose tissue (fat cells) is a metabolically active tissue that stores fat (a type of lipid) and releases it in response to a variety of nervous and hormonal stimuli. This role of storing potential fuel for metabolic functions is highly significant. Fat cells may also be able to convert carbohydrates into fat. Adipose tissue is found on the surface of certain viscera, in serous membranes, in bone marrow, and in loose connective tissue (especially in the superficial fascia under the skin). In addition to its metabolic role, adipose tissue acts as an insulator (helping to maintain a constant body temperature) and a protective padding in certain locations.

DENSE REGULAR FIBROUS TISSUE *

COLLAGEN FIBERS e
FIBROBLASTS a

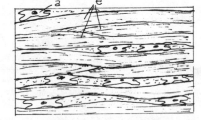

The *dense fibrous tissues* consist of masses of collagenous fibers arranged in parallel (*regular*) or interwoven into a dense matting (*irregular*). Fibroblasts are interspersed among the fibers. Regularly arranged fibrous tissue has great tensile strength (resistance to pulling forces) and makes up ligaments and tendons. Irregular fibrous tissue encapsulates certain organs, cartilage, bone, and supports the epithelial layer of the skin as dermis. Very restricted cell movement is permitted among these dense masses of fibers.

DENSE IRREGULAR FIBROUS TISSUE *

COLLAGEN FIBERS e
FIBROBLASTS a
ELASTIC FIBERS f

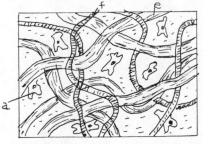

CONNECTIVE TISSUE PROPER.

ELASTIC *
ELASTIC FIBERS f
FIBROBLASTS a

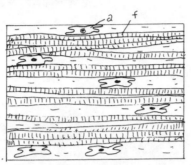

Elastic and reticular tissues, like adipose and others not shown (pigment, embryonic) are specializations of the more common (proper) connective tissues. *Elastic tissue* consists of waves of elastic fibers oriented in parallel with a few fibroblasts here and there. This tissue is found in the walls of most arteries, some veins, erectile tissue, and air cells of the lungs; in certain ligaments; and as isolated fibers in the loose connective tissues.

RETICULAR *
RETICULAR FIBERS L
CELLS OF THE ORGAN m

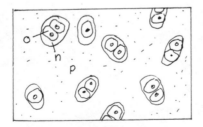

Reticular fibers are actually very small collagenous fibers in loose, irregular array supporting such delicate tissues as liver cells, cells of the lymphatic tissues, and the bone marrow.

SUPPORTING TISSUE.
CARTILAGE *

HYALINE *
LACUNA n
CHONDROCYTE o
MATRIX p

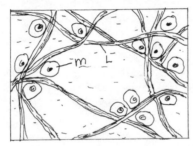

Cartilage consists of a gelatinous *organic* matrix in which stiffening collagenous fibers and the matrix-secreting cells (chondrocytes) are embedded. This resultant mix forms a solid tissue which is weight bearing and yet quite flexible. The cells, often in pairs, reside within spaces of less dense matrix (lacunae) through which they receive their nutrition by diffusion. Unlike other connective tissues, cartilage is without blood vessels (avascular) except within the fibrous sheath surrounding it. *Hyaline* cartilage caps the ends of bones, forms part of the framework of the nose as well as part of the rib cage, and is the principal support for the larynx. The internal framework of the early fetus is largely hyaline cartilage and is later replaced by a bony skeleton.

ELASTIC *
LACUNA n
CHONDROCYTE o
ELASTIC FIBERS f
MATRIX p

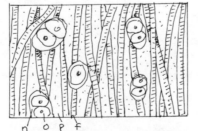

Elastic cartilage is simply hyaline cartilage with elastic fibers and is found in the epiglottis and the external ear.

FIBROCARTILAGE *
CHONDROCYTE o
COLLAGEN FIBERS e

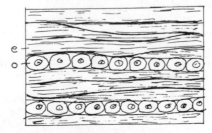

Fibrocartilage, surrounded by matrix and embedded in dense collagenous tissue, is found between the vertebral bodies (discs), the interpubic joint, and in areas of joint capsules and related ligaments.

ORGANIZATION OF THE BODY TISSUES / MUSCLE TISSUE *

PLATE 7
see also 24, 47

CN 8
1. Note the presence of connective tissue (c) surrounding the muscle fibers of each type. The muscle fibers have been pulled apart from one another to demonstrate the connective tissue. It is suggested that a light pastel color be used for the connective tissue and that it be colored before coloring the darker muscle cells.
2. Use dark colors for the nuclei (b) and the intercalated discs (e).
3. Use red for capillaries (f) which are shown in all 3 drawings but are titled only once (under cardiac muscle).

Muscle tissue, consisting of groups of muscle cells (fibers) and their fibrous tissue coverings, is characterized by its ability to shorten by about one-third its resting length in response to nerve, nervelike, or hormonal stimulation. Structurally and functionally, three kinds of muscle fibers can be identi-fied. The connective tissue ensheathing the muscle fibers support the nerves and blood vessels supplying the muscle as well as the muscle fibers themselves. Muscle tissue is quite vascular as muscular contraction creates a heavy demand for oxygen carried by the red blood corpuscles.

VISCERAL/SMOOTH *
SMOOTH MUSCLE CELLS a
NUCLEUS b
CONNECTIVE TISSUE c

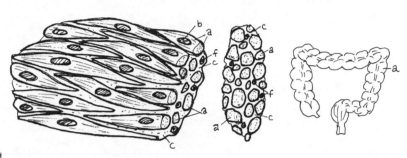

Smooth muscle cells are long and spindle-shaped, have a centrally positioned nucleus, and have no cross striations (smooth). They are found in the walls of organs with hollow cavities (viscera) and serve to propel material along the length of those cavities. Such viscera include urinary, respiratory, and reproductive ducts, blood vessels, and gastrointestinal tract. Smooth muscle action is generally characterized by slow, sustained, rhythmic contractions, as experienced in menstrual cramps (uterine musculature) and stomach cramps. Most smooth muscle contracts in response to certain hormonal stimulation as well as nerve innervation. Its contraction is generally not under voluntary control.

CARDIAC/STRIATED *
CELLS WITH STRIATIONS d
INTERCALATED DISCS e
CAPILLARIES f

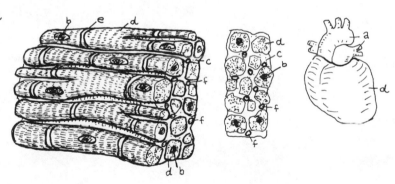

Cardiac muscle cells are characterized by cross striations, definitive junctions between cells (intercalated discs), centrally placed nuclei, and fibers that split (bifurcate) as shown. Layers of interlacing cardiac muscle fibers make up the walls of the heart. Muscle fibers do not generally regenerate well. In obstruction of a major vessel supplying the heart muscle, the muscle tissue in that area dies and is replaced by scar (fibrous) tissue before the neighboring muscle can regenerate. Cardiac muscle fibers contract (beat) spontaneously in association with special impulse-conducting muscle cells—they do not require nerves to *initiate* contraction. Normally, heart rate (rate of contraction) is not under voluntary control, as autonomic (involuntary) nerves *regulate* (not initiate) heart rate.

SKELETAL/STRIATED *
SARCOLEMMA (CELL MEMBRANE) g
MYOFIBRILS h

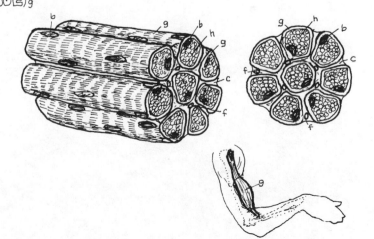

Striated, skeletal muscle cells are long, cylindrical and multinucleated. Their ultrastructure and related fibrous investments may be seen on Plate 24. Skeletal muscles make up the form of the body (glance at Plate 46). They usually attach to bones and in so doing they usually cross a joint (Plate 22). Muscular contraction moves one of the bones at the joint. In this way the skeleton becomes mobile. Skeletal muscle is characterized by rapid, short-term contractions of great strength. Skeletal muscle requires nerve impulses (innervation) to function. In fact, it is metabolically dependent on its nerve supply; for cutting the nerve will cause atrophy and death of the muscle; ultimately the dying muscle will be replaced with connective tissue. Skeletal muscle is under voluntary control.

CN 9 or 18

1. Color the structures of the forearm shown in cross section. Brown is recommended for the muscles. The vessels (h) in the superficial fascia are all veins and should be colored blue. Vessels in the deep fascia include both arteries and veins (red and blue).
2. Color the ligaments, tendons, and periosteum in the knee joint below. It is not necessary to match the colors in the drawing above.
3. Color periosteum (f) a light tan or yellow. Color articular cartilage (t) white or very pale blue.

FASCIAE*
SKIN a
SUPERFICIAL FASCIA b
DEEP FASCIA c
INTEROSSEOUS MEMBRANE d
(LIGAMENT) d
BONES: RADIUS e & ULNA e'
PERIOSTEUM f
MUSCLE g
BLOOD VESSELS h & NERVES i

Most of the body mass is connective tissue in one or more of its various forms: fibrous, cartilage, bone, adipose, etc. The basic unit of these tissues is the fiber: a protein secreted in filaments from cells. It is these collagen fibers that hold the body together in an integrated, "unibody" form of construction. In the forearm or leg, for example, *bones* offer the principal support, and they are largely ensheathed by fibrous *periosteum* which is continuous with the *deep fascia*. This fascia is a thin, fibrous envelope about *skeletal muscle*, supporting it and holding fast *vessels* and *nerves* in transit. Its fibers extend into the muscle mass and give support to individual and small bundles of muscle cells. In the interval between both bones of the limbs, the fibers condense in parallel array to give secure attachment between the shafts. This is the *interosseous membrane* or ligament. *Superficial fascia* is a fat-filled, loose fibrous layer of variable thickness just deep to the skin. A source of fuel in hard times, this fascia acts as an insulator for deeper tissues. It also allows the *skin* some mobility over the deeper fascia-lined muscles (move the skin over the back of your hand to see this). Superficial fascia gives added form to the body as its fat content (and therefore its thickness) is subject to hormonal influence, and its distribution varies fairly predictably between the sexes.

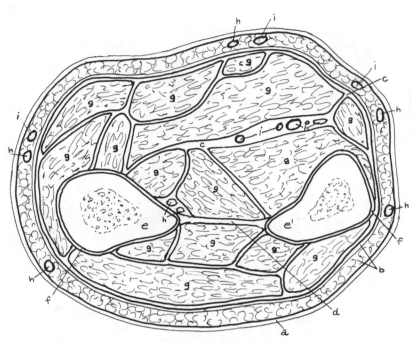

**CROSS SECTION THROUGH
AN IDEALIZED FOREARM**

LIGAMENTS*
THE KNEE JOINT*
FIBULAR COLLATERAL LIG. j
TIBIAL COLLATERAL LIG. k
TIBIOFIBULAR JOINT CAPSULE l
ANTERIOR CRUCIATE LIG. m
POSTERIOR CRUCIATE LIG. n
TRANSVERSE LIG. o
PATELLAR LIG. p
LATERAL MENISCUS q
MEDIAL MENISCUS r
MUSCLE TENDONS s
ARTICULAR CARTILAGE t

Ligaments, tendons, and fibrous capsules are all groups of connective tissue fibers arranged in largely parallel construction, providing great strength and restricted movement. *Ligaments* connect bone to bone. *Tendons* are the fibrous ends of skeletal muscle. They arise from the deep fascia and investing fibers surrounding muscle cells and bundles. *Fibrous capsules* surround joint cavities and are continuous with ligaments and tendons that reinforce or insert into it. In the case of the knee and certain other joints, the socket receiving the rounded condyle is often inadequate, and its perimeter is built up with cartilage discs (*menisci*): thick peripherally, wafer thin centrally. Note the *cruciate ligaments:* they resist excessive movement and slipping of one bone on the other. Synovial joints must exercise freedom of movement within the boundaries of their bony architecture; ligaments, tendons, and joint capsules guarantee that freedom by providing security against rupture and dislocation.

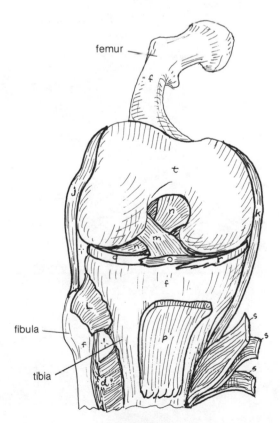

**KNEE JOINT
EXPOSED FROM IN FRONT**
patella and anterior joint capsule
removed and joint flexed

PLATE 9
see also 8, 15, 20

SKELETAL SYSTEM
ANATOMY OF A BONE *

CN 7

1. Color the various structures of this long bone (humerus).
2. Red should be used for both cancellous bone (e) and nutrient artery (h).
3. The epiphysis (a) and diaphysis (b) are represented by a diagram to the far right, and are colored there.

Bones are the supportive framework (skeleton) of the body. The hardest of all living tissues, bone is a connective tissue consisting of a meshwork of fibers and cells (35% by weight) impregnated with calcium salts. Bones are connected at joints and make movement possible, provide sites of attachment for skeletal muscle, are a source of calcium ions for the blood, and form blood cells. Bones may be long (as shown here), short, flat or irregular in shape. Long bones are responsible for stature and reflect most dramatically the phenomenon of growth.

EPIPHYSIS (END)ₐ EPIPHYSEAL LINEₐ'

The *epiphysis* is the end of a long bone; it is largely cancellous and capped with articular cartilage. It is separated from the diaphysis by a variably-sized cartilage plate for about the first 20 years of life. Most bones develop from cartilage models. Bone development occurs in the epiphysis and the diaphysis, and slowly advances toward the intervening cartilage from both ends. The cartilage progressively thins to a line and ultimately disappears and diaphyseal/epiphyseal bone centers meet (end of bone growth).

DIAPHYSIS (SHAFT)ᵦ

The *diaphysis* is the shaft of a large bone. It consists of compact bone with a central cavity. It resists bending forces. The epiphyseal line separates it from the epiphysis. Diaphyseal compact bone develops just before bone replacement of cartilage occurs within the interior of the shaft. It offers support to the developing bone during formation of the central (medullary) cavity.

ARTICULAR CARTILAGEᵪ

The only remaining evidence of an adult bone's cartilaginous past, *articular cartilage* is smooth, slippery, and bloodless, kept moist by the egg-white-like fluid from the synovial lining of the joint cavity. Bones of a synovial joint make physical contact at their cartilaginous ends.

PERIOSTEUMᵈ

Periosteum is a fibrous, cellular, vascular, and highly sensitive life support sheath for bone, providing nutrient blood for bone cells and a source of bone-developing cells during growth and after fracture. It does not cover articular cartilage.

CANCELLOUS (SPONGY) BONEₑ
RED MARROWₑ

Tiny beams of bone forming a latticed truss capable of reorientation, *cancellous bone* resists the stresses of weight and postural changes as well as muscular development. *Red marrow* packs the spaces between beams of certain bony epiphyses and elsewhere. It consists of masses of developing and mature red/white blood cells supported by an array of loose, fine fibers.

COMPACT BONEᶠ

The dense bone of the diaphysis, *compact bone* consists of repeating patterns of solid bone tissue organized into concentric layers. Nutrient blood reaches the bone cells by a system of integrated canals. Cancellous bone is too porous to reflect such regular arrangement.

MEDULLARY CAVITYₒ
YELLOW MARROWₒ

The *medullary cavity* of the diaphysis serves to lighten bone weight and provide space for its marrow. After childhood, blood cell production largely ceases in the marrow of the shaft; such cells are replaced by fat, which is yellow in color.

NUTRIENT ARTERYₕ

Each long bone contains an oblique tunnel in its shaft for the passage of a *nutrient artery*, which enters the medullary cavity and branches throughout, supplying the shaft. Arteries to the epiphyses generally arise from the joint capsule.

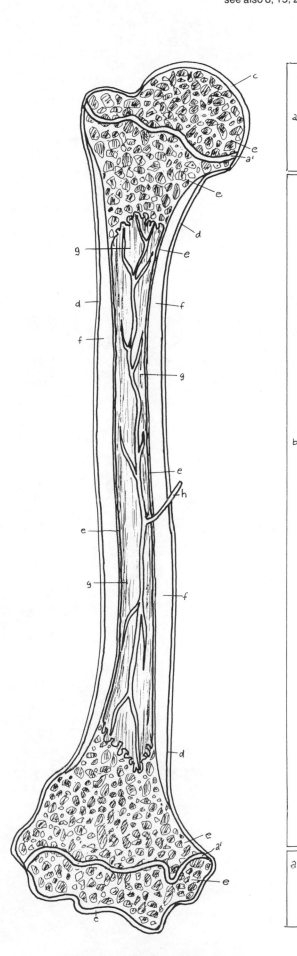

PLATE 10

SKELETAL SYSTEM / CLASSIFICATION *
AXIAL a & APPENDICULAR SKELETON b

CN 2

1. Color the axial skeleton and its titles (in light lines). You may color over the entire rib cage including the space between the ribs.
2. With the second color fill in the appendicular skeleton and its titles (heavier lines).

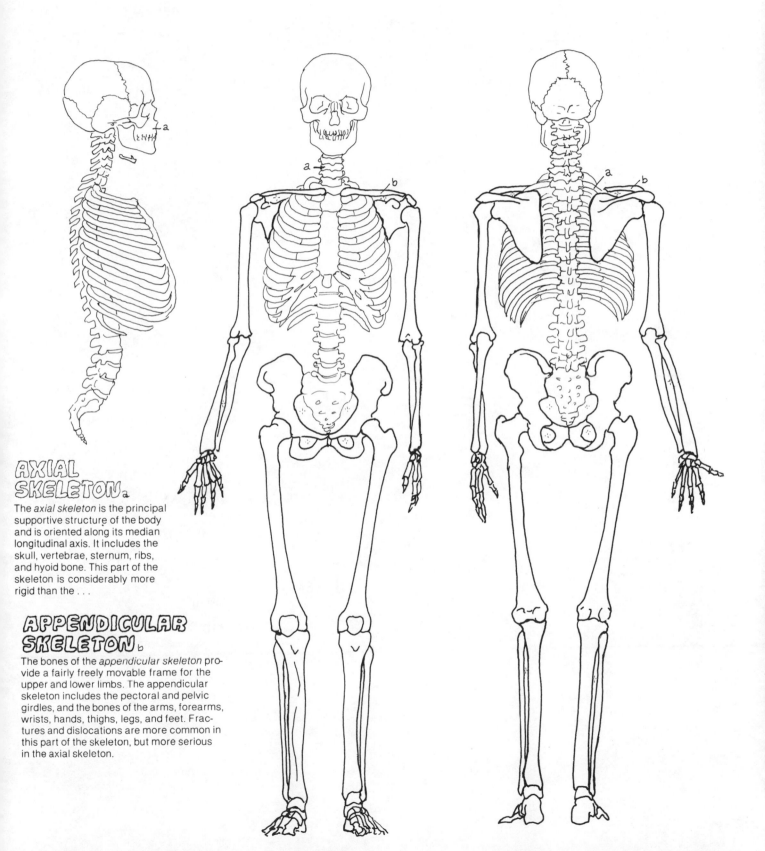

AXIAL SKELETON a

The *axial skeleton* is the principal supportive structure of the body and is oriented along its median longitudinal axis. It includes the skull, vertebrae, sternum, ribs, and hyoid bone. This part of the skeleton is considerably more rigid than the . . .

APPENDICULAR SKELETON b

The bones of the *appendicular skeleton* provide a fairly freely movable frame for the upper and lower limbs. The appendicular skeleton includes the pectoral and pelvic girdles, and the bones of the arms, forearms, wrists, hands, thighs, legs, and feet. Fractures and dislocations are more common in this part of the skeleton, but more serious in the axial skeleton.

PLATE 11
see also 22

SKELETAL SYSTEM
BONES OF THE SKULL*

CRANIAL 8:. OCCIPITAL 1ₐ PARIETAL 2ᵦ FRONTAL 1𝚌
TEMPORAL 2𝒹 ETHMOID 1ₑ SPHENOID 1𝒻
FACIAL 14:. NASAL 2𝓰 VOMER 1ₕ LACRIMAL 2ᵢ
ZYGOMATIC 2ⱼ PALATINE 2ₖ MAXILLA 2ₗ
MANDIBLE 1ₘ INFERIOR NASAL CONCHA 2ₙ

CN 14

1. Work with this plate and the next one at the same time.
2. Save the brightest (darkest) colors for the smallest bones.
3. Work one bone at a time, filling it in where it appears in any of the 7 views shown on this and the next plate.

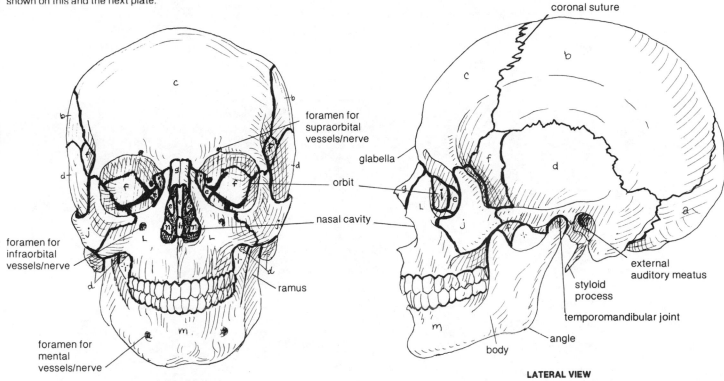

coronal suture

foramen for
supraorbital
vessels/nerve

glabella

orbit

nasal cavity

foramen for
infraorbital
vessels/nerve

ramus

external
auditory meatus

styloid
process

temporomandibular joint

foramen for
mental
vessels/nerve

angle

body

ANTERIOR VIEW

LATERAL VIEW

The *bones of the skull* are rigidly joined at sutures except at the hingelike temporomandibular joint. The *cranial bones* include the flat bones that contribute to the vault for the brain. The *facial bones*, irregular and angular, form the framework of the face. Note how the orbit is created from 7 bones (palatine part is not shown). The frame for the nose is cartilaginous for the most part.

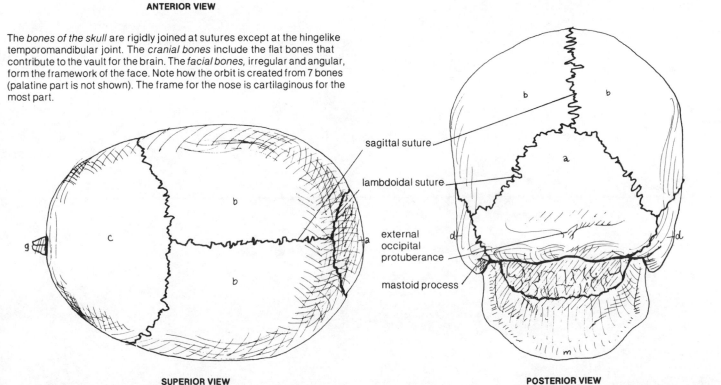

sagittal suture

lambdoidal suture

external
occipital
protuberance

mastoid process

SUPERIOR VIEW

POSTERIOR VIEW

PLATE 12
see also 11

SKELETAL SYSTEM
THE SKULL: ADDITIONAL VIEWS *

CN 10

1. Refer to the preceding plate for bone titles. Use the same colors.
2. Do not color the holes marked (-¦-) in the two bottom views.

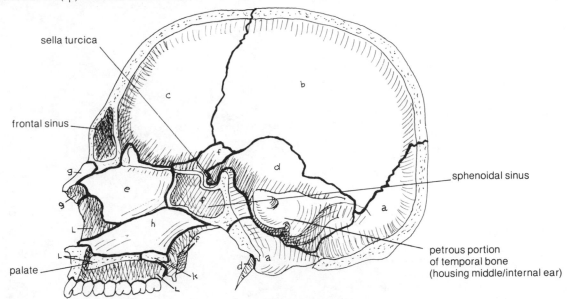

sella turcica

frontal sinus

palate

sphenoidal sinus

petrous portion
of temporal bone
(housing middle/internal ear)

SAGITTAL SECTION

This section shows the interior of the right side. You should be able to make
out the areas concerned with the nasal cavity, the oral cavity, and the brain.
The nasal septum is shown, dividing the nasal cavity into right/left parts.
The cartilaginous part of the septum is not shown, exposing parts of the
right lateral wall of the nasal cavity beyond the septum (g, l).

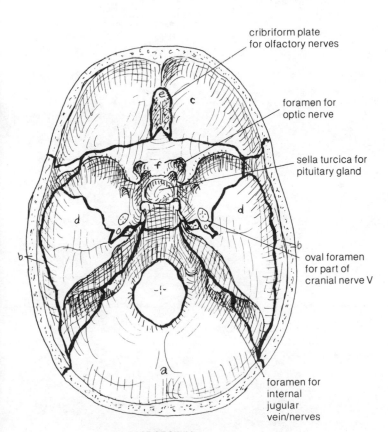

cribriform plate
for olfactory nerves

foramen for
optic nerve

sella turcica for
pituitary gland

oval foramen
for part of
cranial nerve V

foramen for
internal
jugular
vein/nerves

**BASE OF SKULL
INTERIOR VIEW**

In this view the skull cap or calvaria is removed. The brain fits within this vault. You can see where the frontal, parietal, temporal, and
occipital lobes of the brain fit. The many passages (foramina) convey
nerves/vessels into and out of the skull.

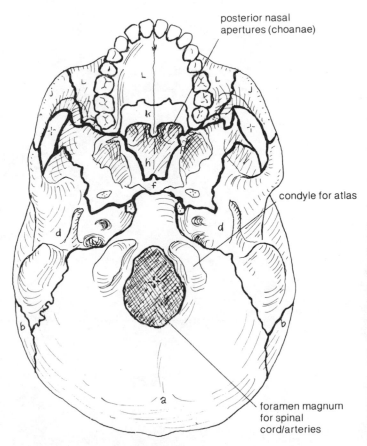

posterior nasal
apertures (choanae)

condyle for atlas

foramen magnum
for spinal
cord/arteries

**BASE OF SKULL
SEEN FROM BELOW**

This surface communicates with the multiple structures of the neck,
e.g., the pharynx (with posterior nasal apertures), first cervical vertebra (atlas), spinal cord, and many vessels, nerves, and muscles.

PLATE 13

SKELETAL SYSTEM
VERTEBRAE & VERTEBRAL COLUMN *

CN 6

1. Color the individual cervical vertebra and the 7 cervical vertebrae in both posterior and lateral views.
2. Do the same for the thoracic and lumbar vertebrae as well as the sacrum and coccyx. Avoid the intervertebral foramina (–¦–) seen in the thoracic and lumbar regions of the column, lateral view. Also avoid the 8 foramina in the sacrum, posterior view of the column.
3. Color in the intervertebral discs.
4. Do not color the skull.

7 CERVICALa

This flexible group of *cervical* vertebrae supports the skull and neck. Holding the head erect develops and maintains its curvature. The 1st and 2nd cervical vertebrae are unique as is the 7th with its prominent spine. The foramina in the transverse processes of C1–C6 transmit the vertebral arteries to the base of the brain. The series of vertebral foramina form a canal for the spinal cord.

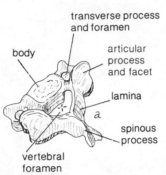

transverse process and foramen

body

articular process and facet

lamina

spinous process

vertebral foramen

a

12 THORACICb

This rather rigid group of *thoracic* vertebrae and the 24 ribs with which they articulate support the thorax. Its prominent curvature is developed in fetal life. Thoracic vertebrae are characterized by long slender spines, heart-shaped bodies, and facets for rib articulation.

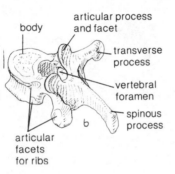

articular process and facet

body

transverse process

vertebral foramen

spinous process

articular facets for ribs

b

5 LUMBARc

These stubby, quadrilateral *lumbar* vertebrae, the most massive of the column, carry a large share of the body weight, balancing the torso on the sacrum. The lumbar curvature results from walking and standing erect. This vertebral group is quite mobile; when lifting from the floor by flexing this group, great pressure is often put on their discs, which may induce their rupture. This may injure the spinal nerves which pass from the spinal cord through the intervertebral foramina.

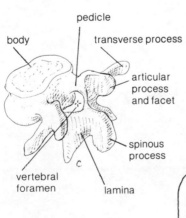
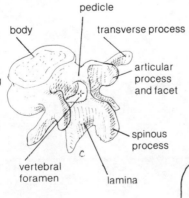

pedicle

body

transverse process

articular process and facet

spinous process

vertebral foramen

lamina

c

SACRUMd

Five *sacral* vertebrae fuse to form this single bone. It transmits the body weight to the hip joints via its articulation with the pelvic girdle.

COCCYXe

Consisting of 2 to 4 fused coccygeal vertebrae, the functionally insignificant *coccyx* represents the vestigial tail of our forebears.

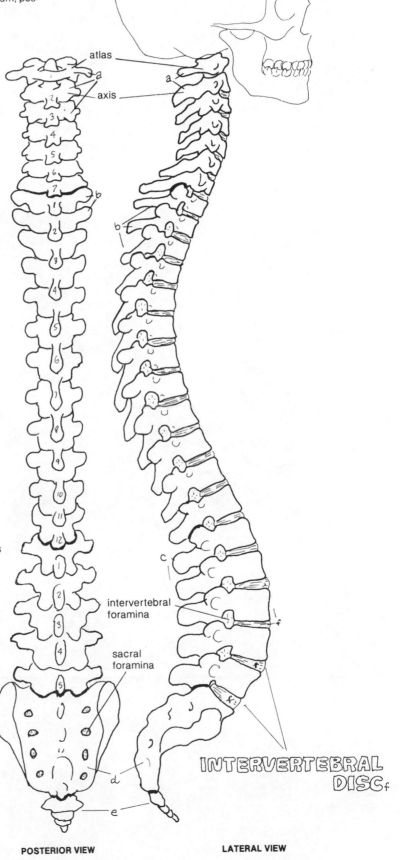

atlas

axis

a

a

b

b

c

c

intervertebral foramina

sacral foramina

d

e

INTERVERTEBRAL DISCf

POSTERIOR VIEW

LATERAL VIEW

PLATE 14
see also 13, 29

SKELETAL SYSTEM / THORAX.

STERNUM: *
  MANUBRIUM a
  BODY b
  XIPHOID PROCESS c

12 RIBS: d
  7 TRUE d
  5 FALSE d
  (2 FLOATING) d'

12 COSTAL CARTILAGES e

12 THORACIC VERTEBRAE f

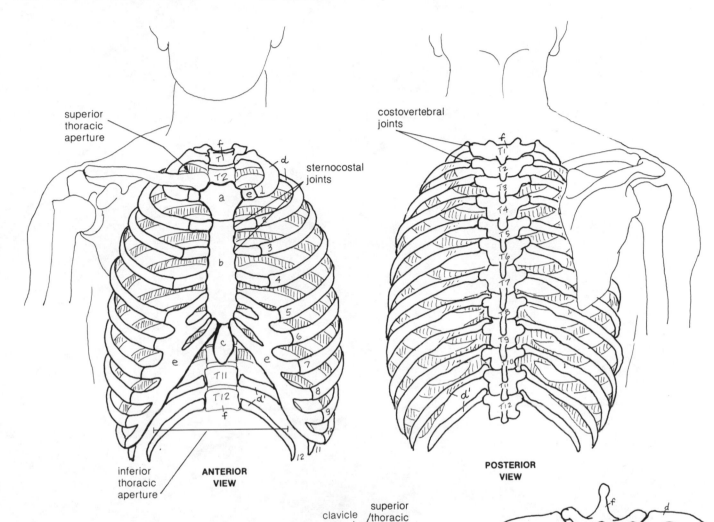

superior thoracic aperture

sternocostal joints

costovertebral joints

inferior thoracic aperture

ANTERIOR VIEW

POSTERIOR VIEW

CN 7

1. Color in the 3 parts of the sternum in front and side views.
2. Color costal cartilages in the same views as above. Color the arrow that shows their upward direction.
3. With one color do each rib carefully, following them around into shaded areas. Color ribs in all views including arrow indicating downward direction.
4. Color the 12 thoracic vertebrae in the back view and front view in the same color as Plate 13. Do not color them in the side view.
5. Color in the 2 diagrams in the right lower corner of the plate.

The *thorax* is a fairly mobile set of structures essential to the function of respiration and harboring such delicate viscera as the lungs and heart. The *sternum* consists of fused bones except between the manubrium and the body (sternal angle), and the body and the xiphoid, where the joints are fibrocartilaginous. Largely cancellous bone covered with a thin compact layer, the sternum contains red marrow and is a convenient site for sampling its blood cell-producing tissue. The *costal cartilages*, joining most ribs to the sternum, add measurable elasticity to the thorax. The upper seven (*true*) ribs join directly with individual cartilages; of the next five (*false*), three join with the 7th costal cartilage, and the last two (*floating*) ribs end in the muscular abdominal wall.

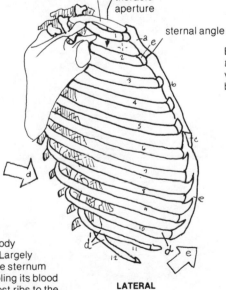

clavicle

superior thoracic aperture

sternal angle

LATERAL VIEW

Each typical rib forms a hinge joint with 2 adjacent *thoracic vertebrae* and their disc: the body and transverse process of one vertebra (shown here), and the body of the upper vertebra.

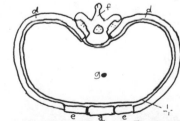

THORACIC CAVITY g.

The thoracic cavity is largely surrounded by a discontinuous set of bone and cartilage. The floor of the cavity is the muscular thoracic diaphragm; above, the cavity is continuous with the neck. Note the extent to which the thoracic vertebra projects into the thoracic cavity.

CN 3
1. Color clavicle in 3 views and the diagram below.
2. Do the same with the scapula.
3. Color the 2 views of the humerus.

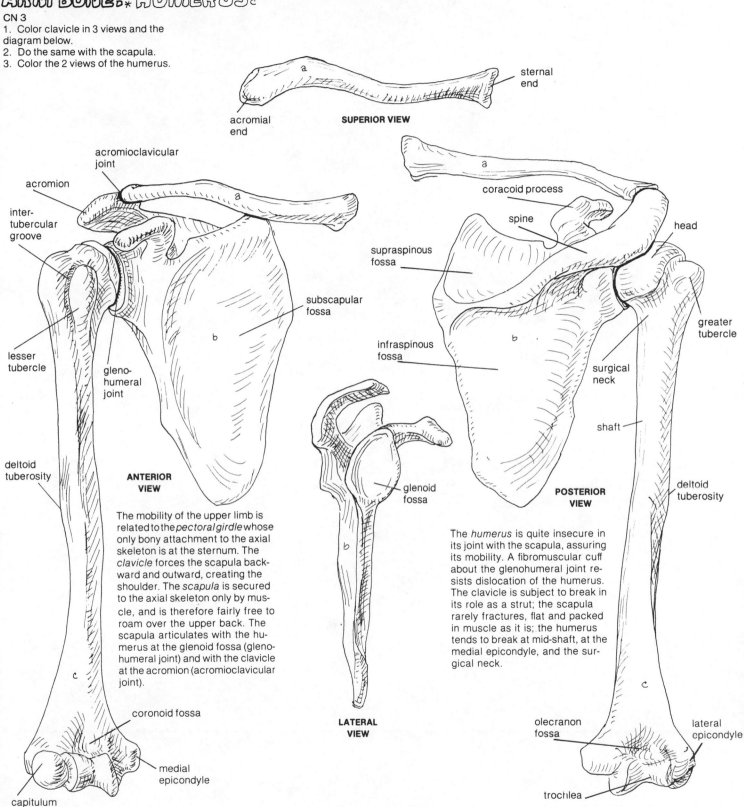

sternal
end

SUPERIOR VIEW

acromial
end

acromioclavicular
joint

acromion

inter-
tubercular
groove

coracoid process

spine

head

supraspinous
fossa

subscapular
fossa

greater
tubercle

lesser
tubercle

gleno-
humeral
joint

infraspinous
fossa

surgical
neck

shaft

deltoid
tuberosity

ANTERIOR
VIEW

The mobility of the upper limb is
related to the *pectoral girdle* whose
only bony attachment to the axial
skeleton is at the sternum. The
clavicle forces the scapula backward and outward, creating the
shoulder. The *scapula* is secured
to the axial skeleton only by muscle, and is therefore fairly free to
roam over the upper back. The
scapula articulates with the humerus at the glenoid fossa (glenohumeral joint) and with the clavicle
at the acromion (acromioclavicular
joint).

glenoid
fossa

LATERAL
VIEW

POSTERIOR
VIEW

deltoid
tuberosity

The *humerus* is quite insecure in
its joint with the scapula, assuring
its mobility. A fibromuscular cuff
about the glenohumeral joint resists dislocation of the humerus.
The clavicle is subject to break in
its role as a strut; the scapula
rarely fractures, flat and packed
in muscle as it is; the humerus
tends to break at mid-shaft, at the
medial epicondyle, and the surgical neck.

coronoid fossa

medial
epicondyle

capitulum

olecranon
fossa

lateral
epicondyle

trochlea

VIEW FROM ABOVE

PLATE 16
see also 15, 17, 18

SKELETAL SYSTEM / UPPER LIMB
FOREARM: ULNA₂ & RADIUSᵦ

CN 2
1. Use colors different from those used on the preceding plate.
2. Color the ulna in the 3 views and the upper diagram, including the arrow indicating its direction of movement.
3. Do the same with the radius.
4. In the small diagrams below, color the radius and the arrows indicating direction of movement.

The structure and arrangement of joints at the elbow and wrist provide considerable mobility for the hand—try it and see. At the elbow, the *radius* and *ulna* form a hinge joint with the humerus. As you can see, the ulna is the larger bone here, and its joint with the humerus limits movement to flexion/extension. At the wrist joint, the radius is the principal bone, and the ulna has no direct contact with the carpus. Here, all movements but rotation are permitted. The basis for rotation of the hand lies in the relationship of the radius to the ulna.

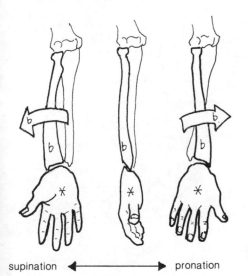

medial epicondyle

supination ⟷ pronation

The radius articulates with the ulna in the two places shown and via a ligament between the two shafts. The radius is free to pivot about the ulna, as you can see, and the hand moves with it due to its joint (radiocarpal) at the wrist. The ulna cannot rotate at all because the nature of the humeroulnar joint will not permit it. As the radius rotates in one direction, it crosses the ulna. Observe the diagram above and place the fingers of your left hand on your right ulna at the olecranon. Have the palm of your right hand facing you. Now rotate your palm so it turns away from you—this rotation movement is *pronation*. Now rotate your palm so that it faces you—this rotary movement is *supination*. Note in the diagram that as the radius goes, so goes the thumb. This is because the radius attaches to the hand on the thumb side. You noticed during these movements, of course, that the olecranon, and therefore the ulna did not move. Practice these rotational movements after drawing in the diagram until you can clearly understand the mechanism.

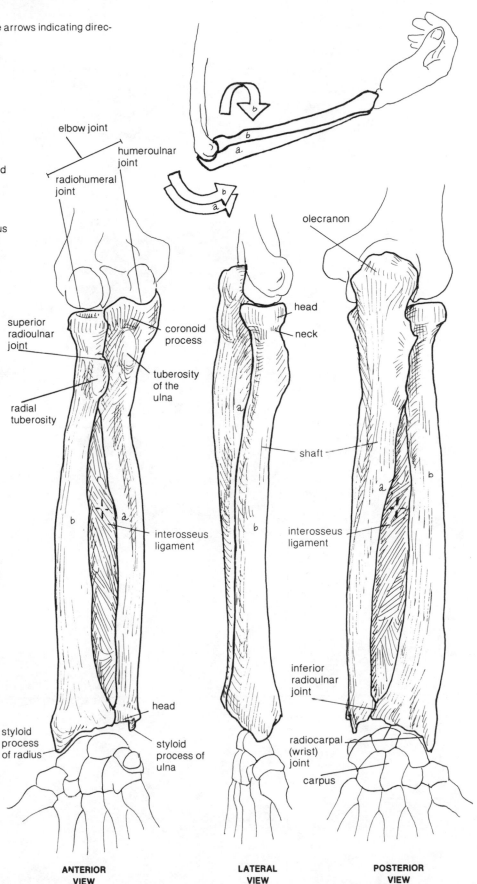

elbow joint

humeroulnar joint

radiohumeral joint

olecranon

superior radioulnar joint

coronoid process

tuberosity of the ulna

head

neck

radial tuberosity

shaft

interosseus ligament

interosseus ligament

inferior radioulnar joint

head

styloid process of radius

styloid process of ulna

radiocarpal (wrist) joint

carpus

ANTERIOR VIEW

LATERAL VIEW

POSTERIOR VIEW

PLATE 17
see also 16, 18, 21

SKELETAL SYSTEM / UPPER LIMB
BONES OF THE HAND *

CN 10

1. Color the 5 metacarpals, using a different color from the preceding two plates.
2. Color the 14 phalanges a different color from the preceding two plates.
3. Color the carpal bones, each a different color. Some colors may
have to be repeated here; if so, space them well apart.

8 CARPAL BONES: *
SCAPHOIDₐ LUNATE♭ TRIQUETRUMᵪ PISIFORM♩
TRAPEZIUMₑ TRAPEZOID₆ CAPITATE₉ HAMATE♄
5 METACARPAL BONESᵢ
14 PHALANGESⱼ

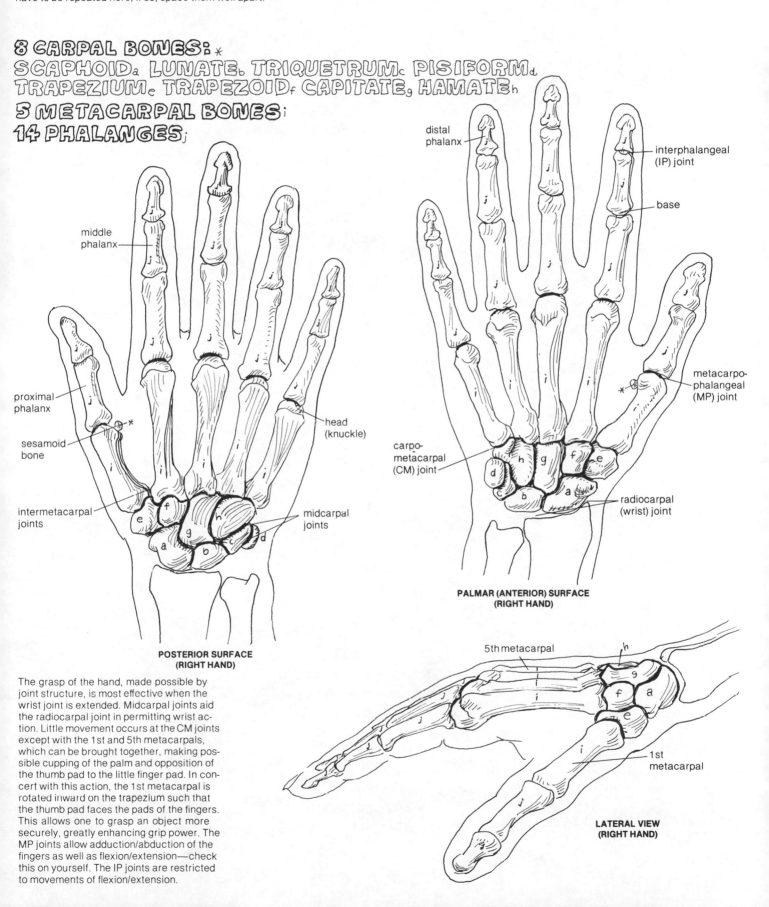

middle phalanx

distal phalanx

interphalangeal (IP) joint

base

proximal phalanx

sesamoid bone

head (knuckle)

intermetacarpal joints

midcarpal joints

metacarpo-phalangeal (MP) joint

carpo-metacarpal (CM) joint

radiocarpal (wrist) joint

POSTERIOR SURFACE (RIGHT HAND)

PALMAR (ANTERIOR) SURFACE (RIGHT HAND)

The grasp of the hand, made possible by joint structure, is most effective when the wrist joint is extended. Midcarpal joints aid the radiocarpal joint in permitting wrist action. Little movement occurs at the CM joints except with the 1st and 5th metacarpals, which can be brought together, making possible cupping of the palm and opposition of the thumb pad to the little finger pad. In concert with this action, the 1st metacarpal is rotated inward on the trapezium such that the thumb pad faces the pads of the fingers. This allows one to grasp an object more securely, greatly enhancing grip power. The MP joints allow adduction/abduction of the fingers as well as flexion/extension—check this on yourself. The IP joints are restricted to movements of flexion/extension.

5th metacarpal

1st metacarpal

LATERAL VIEW (RIGHT HAND)

PLATE 18
see also 15, 16, 17, 20

SKELETAL SYSTEM
BONES OF THE UPPER LIMB:*
CLAVICLE. SCAPULA. HUMERUS. ULNA.
RADIUS. CARPALS. METACARPALS, PHALANGES.

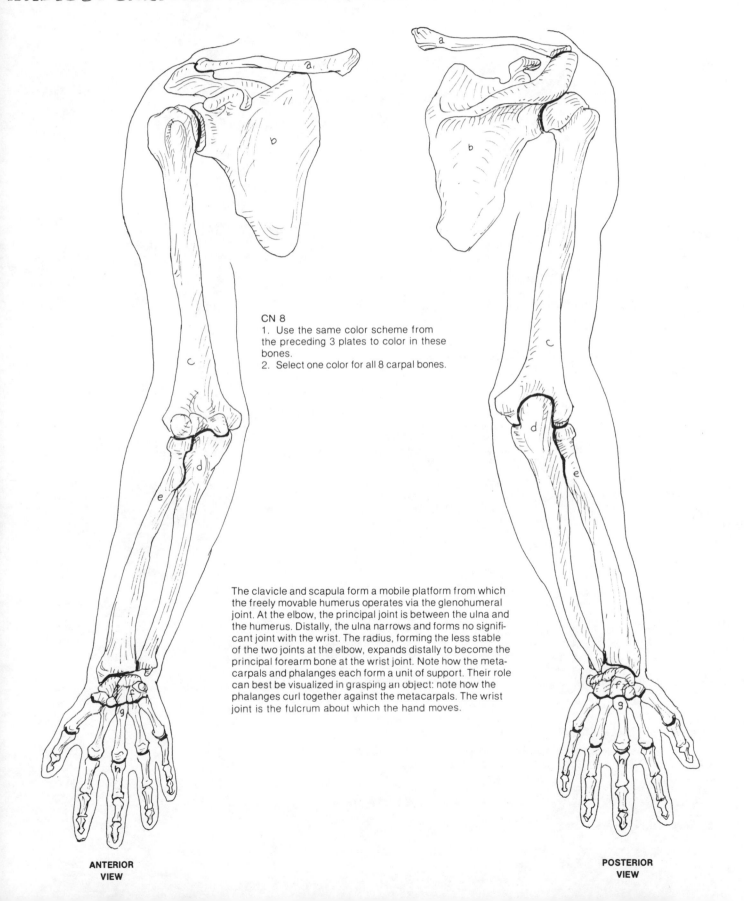

CN 8
1. Use the same color scheme from the preceding 3 plates to color in these bones.
2. Select one color for all 8 carpal bones.

The clavicle and scapula form a mobile platform from which the freely movable humerus operates via the glenohumeral joint. At the elbow, the principal joint is between the ulna and the humerus. Distally, the ulna narrows and forms no significant joint with the wrist. The radius, forming the less stable of the two joints at the elbow, expands distally to become the principal forearm bone at the wrist joint. Note how the metacarpals and phalanges each form a unit of support. Their role can best be visualized in grasping an object: note how the phalanges curl together against the metacarpals. The wrist joint is the fulcrum about which the hand moves.

ANTERIOR
VIEW

POSTERIOR
VIEW

PLATE 19
see also 13, 15, 20

SKELETAL SYSTEM / LOWER LIMB
PELVIS & PELVIC GIRDLE*
2 ILIUM. 2 ISCHIUM. 2 PUBIS. SACRUM. & COCCYX.

CN 6

1. Color the various lettered bones, avoiding the spaces marked open (-¦-), use same colors for sacrum and coccyx as were used on Plate 13.
2. Select a new color for the lower right diagram, and carefully fill in the male pelvis, drawn in light lines. To do this, color along the inside of each border line, following them around completely. Then fill in the area between the borders. Leave the female pelvis blank.

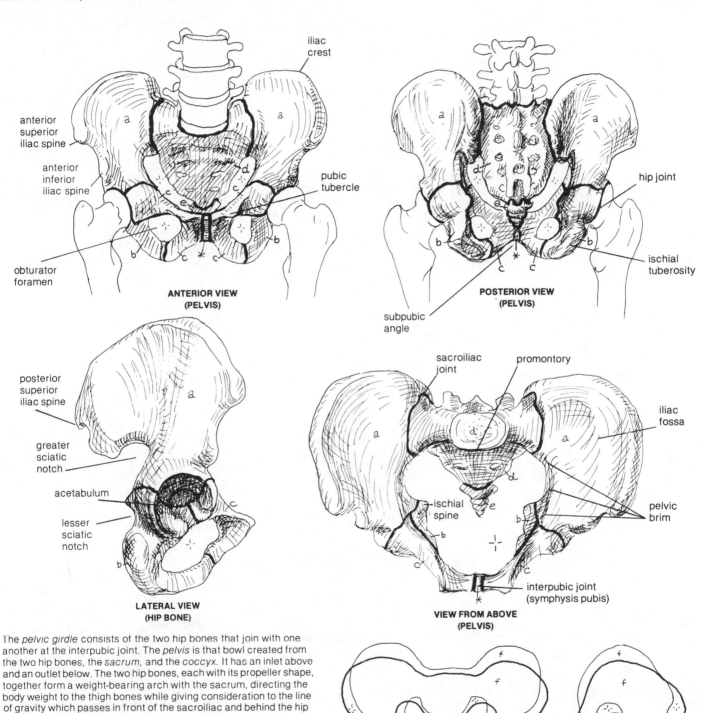

iliac crest

anterior superior iliac spine

anterior inferior iliac spine

pubic tubercle

obturator foramen

ANTERIOR VIEW (PELVIS)

hip joint

ischial tuberosity

subpubic angle

POSTERIOR VIEW (PELVIS)

posterior superior iliac spine

greater sciatic notch

acetabulum

lesser sciatic notch

LATERAL VIEW (HIP BONE)

sacroiliac joint

promontory

iliac fossa

ischial spine

pelvic brim

interpubic joint (symphysis pubis)

VIEW FROM ABOVE (PELVIS)

MALE / FEMALE

The *pelvic girdle* consists of the two hip bones that join with one another at the interpubic joint. The *pelvis* is that bowl created from the two hip bones, the *sacrum,* and the *coccyx.* It has an inlet above and an outlet below. The two hip bones, each with its propeller shape, together form a weight-bearing arch with the sacrum, directing the body weight to the thigh bones while giving consideration to the line of gravity which passes in front of the sacroiliac and behind the hip joints without a bend. Unlike the arm bones with respect to the pectoral girdle, the thigh bones find solid security in the acetabula of the hip bones within which they balance the weight of the body.

The pelvis retains the pelvic viscera in its cavity, which is continuous with the abdominal cavity. The *male* and *female* pelves differ considerably; principally, the female cavity is rounder and wider in all dimensions. This larger pelvis can more easily accommodate a developing fetus, especially as it traverses the birth canal in the pelvic outlet.

PLATE 20
see also 8, 15, 19, 21

SKELETAL SYSTEM / LOWER LIMB
THIGH:* FEMUR*a*   LEG:* TIBIA*b* FIBULA*c* PATELLA*d*

CN 4

1. Color these three bones and the patella.
2. In the two diagrams demonstrating hip and ankle joint movements, the normal position of the bone or bones is straight up/down. In those bones where a movement has taken place (arrow), color them a little lighter than those in anatomical (normal) position.

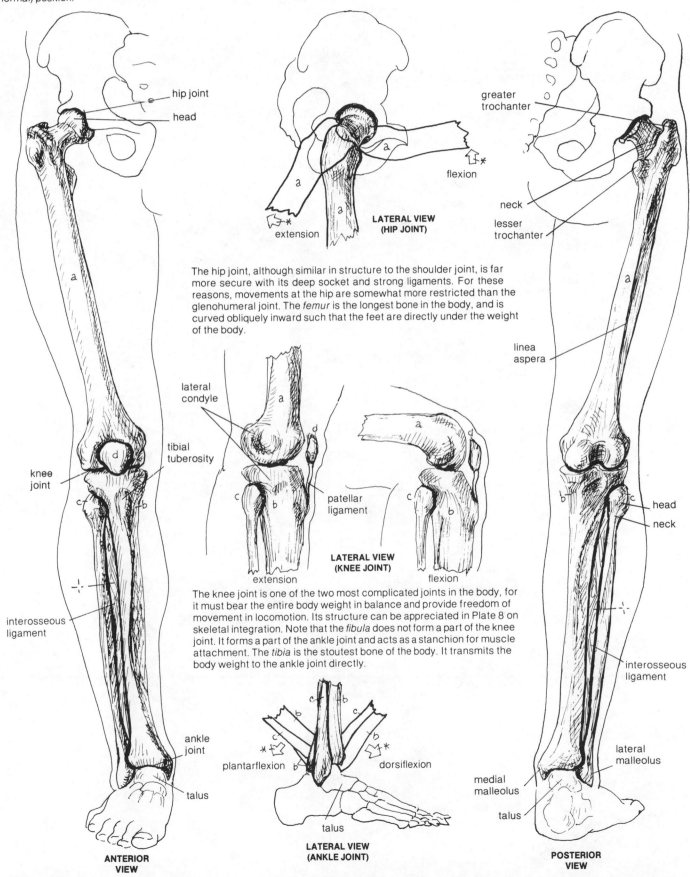

hip joint

head

greater trochanter

flexion

LATERAL VIEW (HIP JOINT)

extension

neck

lesser trochanter

The hip joint, although similar in structure to the shoulder joint, is far more secure with its deep socket and strong ligaments. For these reasons, movements at the hip are somewhat more restricted than the glenohumeral joint. The *femur* is the longest bone in the body, and is curved obliquely inward such that the feet are directly under the weight of the body.

linea aspera

lateral condyle

knee joint

tibial tuberosity

patellar ligament

LATERAL VIEW (KNEE JOINT)

extension

flexion

head

neck

interosseous ligament

The knee joint is one of the two most complicated joints in the body, for it must bear the entire body weight in balance and provide freedom of movement in locomotion. Its structure can be appreciated in Plate 8 on skeletal integration. Note that the *fibula* does not form a part of the knee joint. It forms a part of the ankle joint and acts as a stanchion for muscle attachment. The *tibia* is the stoutest bone of the body. It transmits the body weight to the ankle joint directly.

interosseous ligament

ankle joint

talus

plantarflexion

dorsiflexion

talus

lateral malleolus

medial malleolus

talus

LATERAL VIEW (ANKLE JOINT)

ANTERIOR VIEW

POSTERIOR VIEW

PLATE 21
see also 20, 17

SKELETAL SYSTEM / LOWER LIMB
BONES OF THE FOOT*
14 PHALANGES₀ 5 METATARSALS₆
3 CUNEIFORMS₆ NAVICULAR₄
CUBOID₆ TALUS₇ CALCANEUS₉

CN 7
1. Color in the four views of the foot.
2. In the three diagrams in the middle and at the bottom of the plate, color in the lettered bones only. These bones contribute to the arches of the foot.

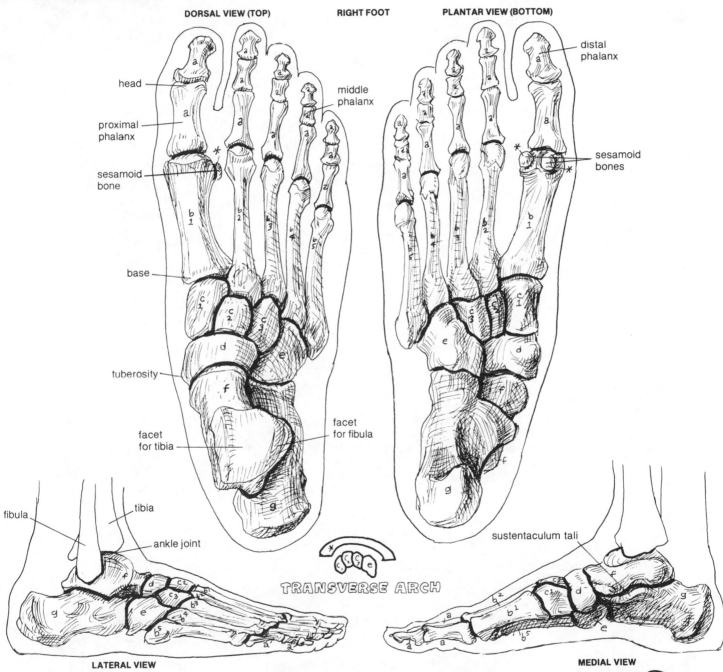

DORSAL VIEW (TOP)   RIGHT FOOT   PLANTAR VIEW (BOTTOM)

head

middle phalanx

distal phalanx

proximal phalanx

sesamoid bone

sesamoid bones

base

tuberosity

facet for tibia

facet for fibula

fibula   tibia

ankle joint

sustentaculum tali

TRANSVERSE ARCH

LATERAL VIEW

MEDIAL VIEW

LATERAL LONGITUDINAL ARCH

MEDIAL LONGITUDINAL ARCH

The *foot* is a mobile, weight-bearing structure. The large tarsal bones and short phalanges relate to this function. The bony architecture, reinforced and maintained by ligaments and influenced by muscles, form *arches*— *longitudinal* and *transverse*. These are important in absorbing shock loads and balancing the body. The longitudinal (medial) arch transmits the force of body weight to the ground when standing and to the great toe in locomotion, creating a giant lever that gives spring to the gait.

PLATE 22
see also 8

SKELETAL SYSTEM
CLASSIFICATION OF JOINTS*

CN 13
1. Color all lettered structures on the plate.
2. Use a dark color for the synovial cavity (f).

Bones are connected at joints (articulations). Joint movements are determined by joint structure. Joint structure is classified as *fibrous, cartilaginous,* or *synovial.*

FIBROUS JOINTₐ

The bones are attached by *fibrous* connective tissue providing little or no movement. Examples: sutures between flat bones of the skull (immovable); interosseous ligaments between bones of the leg and between bones of the forearm (partly movable).

CARTILAGINOUS JOINT꜀

The bones are connected by *cartilage* connective tissue reinforced by fibrous tissue, permitting little or no movement. Example: fibrocartilage discs between vertebral bodies (partly movable); cartilage between epiphysis and diaphysis of developing bone (immovable).

SYNOVIAL JOINT (TYPICAL)*
ARTICULATING BONES꜀
ARTICULAR CARTILAGEₔ
SYNOVIAL MEMBRANEₑ
SYNOVIAL CAVITY (FLUID)f●
JOINT CAPSULE (LIGAMENT)₉

The bones, capped with cartilage, articulate within a *cavity* lined by a *membrane* secreting a viscous *fluid* that absorbs the heat of friction during movement. The *synovial joint* is surrounded by a fibrous *capsule* interlaced with ligaments and tendons.

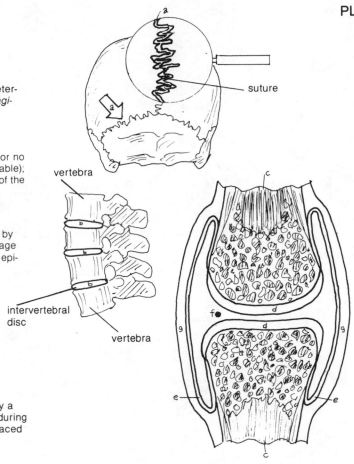

suture

vertebra

intervertebral disc

vertebra

TYPES OF SYNOVIAL JOINTS*

BALL & SOCKETₕ

The ball-like head of one bone fits into the socket-like head of another, permitting all movements. Examples: shoulder and hip joints.

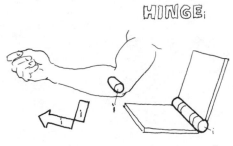

HINGEᵢ

The C-shaped surface of one bone swings about the rounded surface of another. Movement is limited to flexion/extension. Examples: elbow, ankle, interphalangeal joints.

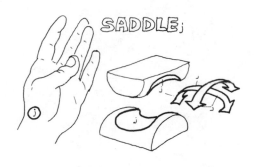

SADDLEⱼ

The concave surfaces of two bones articulate with one another. All movements are possible, but rotation is limited. Example: carpometacarpal joint of thumb.

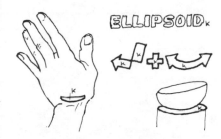

ELLIPSOIDₖ

This is a reduced ball and socket configuration in which rotation is not permitted. Example: radiocarpal (wrist) joint.

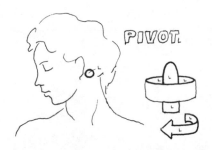

PIVOTₗ

A ring of bone rotates about a process of bone. Movement is limited to rotation. Example: skull on its atlas (1st cervical vertebra) rotates about the odontoid process of the 2nd cervical vertebra.

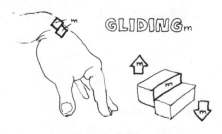

GLIDINGₘ

Two opposed flat surfaces of bone glide across one another. Movement is limited to gliding. Examples: intercarpal joints.

CN 14
1. Color the five parts of a typical skeletal muscle.
2. Color the six types of muscle pattern, using a lighter shade for the tendons.
3. Color the elements of the three lever systems.

A SKELETAL MUSCLE *
BELLY a
TENDON b
APONEUROSIS c (TENDON) c
PERIOSTEUM d
BONE e

The form of the body is largely due to *skeletal muscle*—the voluntary contractile tissue that moves our skeleton about. Skeletal muscle demands large amounts of oxygen and nutrients to sustain itself, and will spasm in their absence. The skeletal muscle you are coloring is a collection of many microscopic muscle cells (fibers) each en-sheathed in a delicate fibrous envelope. As a skeletal muscle ap-proaches its attachment site, the mass of contractile elements (*belly*) ends rather abruptly, while the connective tissue fibers continue on as the *tendon* of attachment, offering astounding re-sistance to pulling tension. Flat tendons are called *aponeuroses*. The collagen fibers of the tendon integrate with those of the *peri-osteum* and the *bone* itself to form a unit construction—a blend resistant to all but the most traumatic forces.

TYPES OF MUSCLES *
FUSIFORM f
UNIPENNATE g
BIPENNATE h
MULTIPENNATE i
BICIPITAL j
TRIANGULAR k

The contractile force of a muscle is partly attributable to the architecture of its fibers. Variations in range and power relate to the configuration of muscle and tendon fibers. Short range but great power and resistance to tension are charac-teristics of *multipennate* muscle where many short muscle fibers attach to shoots of tendon within a small space. In *fusiform* types, the longer the muscle fibers, the greater the range of movement.

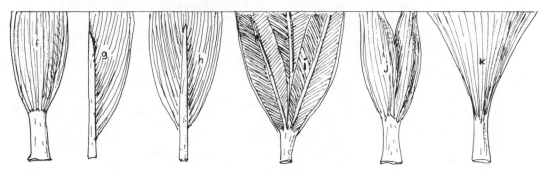

MECHANICS OF MOVEMENT *
FULCRUM L (JOINT) L
EFFORT m (MUSCLE) m
RESISTANCE n (WEIGHT) n

Skeletal muscles employ simple machines, such as *levers*, to increase the effi-ciency of their contractile work. The degree of *muscular effort* required to over-come *resistance* depends upon the force of resistance (weight), and the relative distances from fulcrum to point of resistance (L–n) and from fulcrum to point of muscular effort (L–m). The position of the *fulcrum* (L) relative to points (m) and (n) determines the class of the lever system in use.

1ST CLASS LEVER *

The fulcrum (joint) always lies between the effort (muscle) and the resistance (weight). This is the most efficient class of lever. With a constant weight, the longer the distance L—m, relative to the dis-tance L—n, the less muscle effort required.

2ND CLASS LEVER *

The resistance always lies between the fulcrum (joint) and the effort (muscle), such as when push-ing/lifting a wheelbarrow. In this case, the longer L—m distance relative to the shorter L—n distance provides a good mechanical advantage for the muscle lifting the body weight onto the heads of the metatarsals.

3RD CLASS LEVER *

The muscular effort is placed between the weight and the joint, providing the least efficient mechani-cal advantage. To compare 3rd and 2nd class levers: lifting a 50-lb box with your arms takes significantly more muscular effort than lifting your 150-lb body by standing on the heads of your metatarsals.

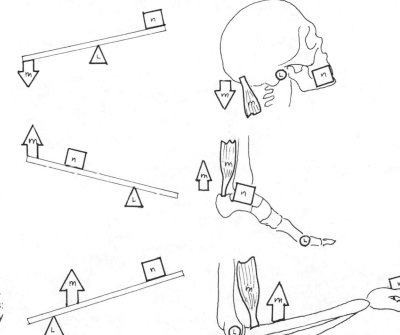

PLATE 24
see also 7

MUSCULAR SYSTEM
STRUCTURE OF SKELETAL MUSCLE*

CN 12
1. Color (b) and (c) the same color. Note that the myofibrils (f), seen in full length as well as in cross sections of the muscle belly, receive the same color as the A band in the diagram below. The large arrow below the myofibril points to the magnified view of the myofibril showing its various bands and lines.
2. Color the diagrams below, describing the contraction of the myofibrils. Note that the H band (h) falls in the center of the A band and is colored separately. Note also that the Z line (j) falls in the center of the I band and is colored separately.
3. Note that the sarcomere (i) and its arrows (*) are to be colored gray.

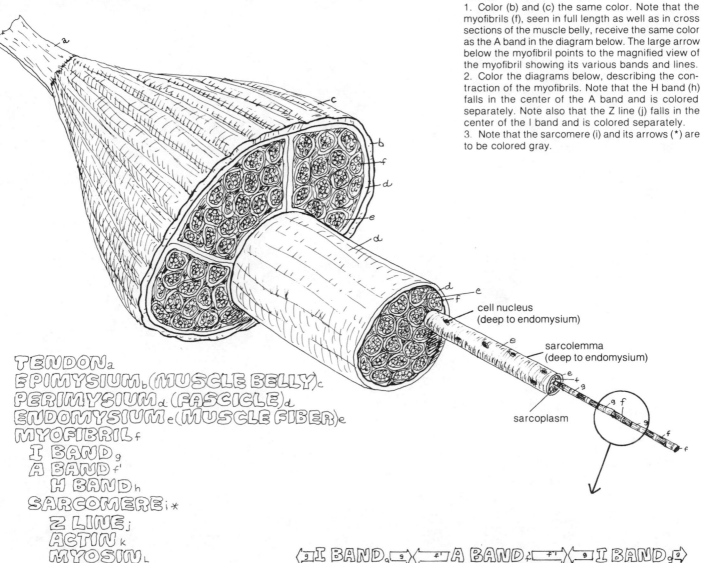

cell nucleus
(deep to endomysium)

sarcolemma
(deep to endomysium)

sarcoplasm

TENDON a
EPIMYSIUM b (MUSCLE BELLY) c
PERIMYSIUM d (FASCICLE) d
ENDOMYSIUM e (MUSCLE FIBER) e
MYOFIBRIL f
  I BAND g
  A BAND f'
    H BAND h
SARCOMERE i *
    Z LINE j
    ACTIN k
    MYOSIN L
    CROSS BRIDGES m

A *skeletal muscle* consists of bundles (*fascicles*) of muscle cells (*fibers*) each wrapped in their connective tissue sheath (*epimysium, perimysium, endomysium,* respectively). As the skeletal muscle approaches its attachment site, the muscle fibers end; and connective tissue continues on as the *tendon.* A muscle cell consists of several nuclei administering a mass of myofibrils in the cytoplasm (sarcoplasm) within the boundaries of a cell membrane (sarcolemma). *Myofibrils* have been shown to be a collection of *myofilaments* arranged in a pattern. The basic unit of this pattern is the *sarcomere* (*). Within the sarcomere, the dark and light areas are called *bands* (I, A, H), and these are created by the relative arrangements of the filaments *actin* (j) and *myosin* (k). When a skeletal muscle fiber contracts, the actin filaments within a sarcomere slide toward each other, past the myosin filaments, breaking and remaking *cross bridges.* The myosin filaments do not move. Therefore, one would expect the A bands to have a constant length during contraction, while the I and H bands would shorten. In this way, the *Z lines* are brought closer together, and the overall muscle cell length shortens by about one-third of its resting length.

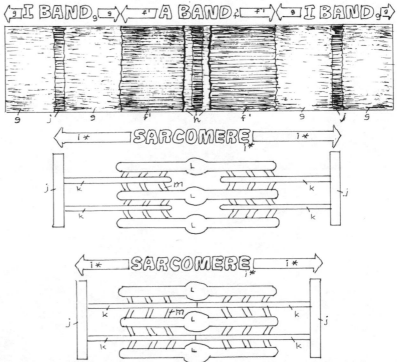

I BAND g — A BAND f f' — I BAND g

SARCOMERE i*

SARCOMERE i*

CN 14

1. Color the muscles creating the pleasant expression on the left side, using bright, warm, and cheerful colors. Color only the lettered muscles.
2. Do the same on the right side using somber, bluish colors.
3. Color the remaining facial muscles (m, n, o), which do not contribute to the above expressions, gray.
4. Color the major muscles of mastication (p, q) a neutral color (e.g., brown) on both sides of the head and in the diagram at lower right. Add 2 new colors for the other masticatory muscles (r, s) shown at lower left.
5. At lower right, color the muscles of facial expression gray (*). Color the muscles of mastication as above.

The *muscles of facial expression* generally arise from bone or cartilage and insert into the superficial fascia or one of the sphincter muscles of the orbit (b) and mouth (m). These are very fine, delicate muscles over which the nervous system has quite precise control, as you are well aware, for how many myriad expressions can *you* create? The mouth is the most mobile structure of the face, so most facial muscles insert at its sphincter (m). As you draw each muscle, try contracting it on yourself while looking into a mirror and see what develops. These muscles are mostly innervated by the facial nerve; should this nerve become damaged, the muscles on the affected side become flaccid and the skin droops, particularly about the eye and mouth, somewhat as drawn on the right side.

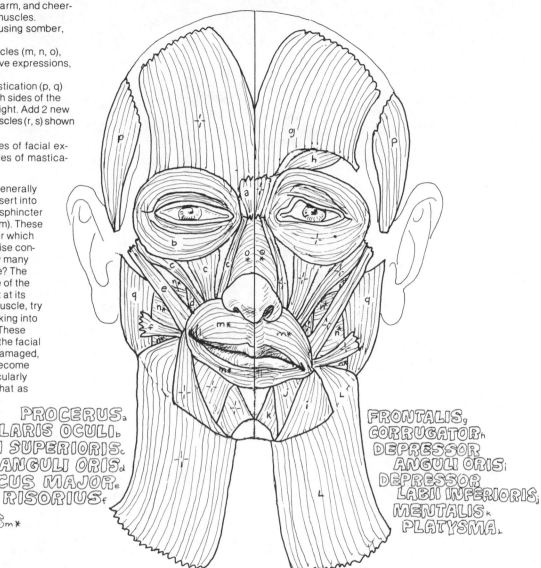

PROCERUS_a
ORBICULARIS OCULI_b
QUADRATUS LABII SUPERIORIS_c
LEVATOR ANGULI ORIS_d
ZYGOMATICUS MAJOR_e
RISORIUS_f

ORBICULARIS ORIS_m*
BUCCINATOR_n*
NASALIS_o*

FRONTALIS_g
CORRUGATOR_h
DEPRESSOR ANGULI ORIS_i
DEPRESSOR LABII INFERIORIS_j
MENTALIS_k
PLATYSMA_l

MUSCLES OF MASTICATION.
TEMPORALIS_p
MASSETER_q
MEDIAL PTERYGOID_r
LATERAL PTERYGOID_s

temporomandibular joint

INTERIOR VIEW OF LEFT MANDIBLE

The *muscles of mastication* are the chewing muscles, for they all insert on the mandible. The two major muscles are shown at right; the two deeper muscles are shown above. The hingelike temporomandibular joint allows movements of elevation and depression of the mandible and some protrusion, and side-to-side action as well. Only the *lateral pterygoid* takes a role in depression of the mandible, as gravity clearly plays a major role here. We all recognize intuitively that it seems to take energy at times to keep our mouths shut—indeed, it has an anatomical basis.

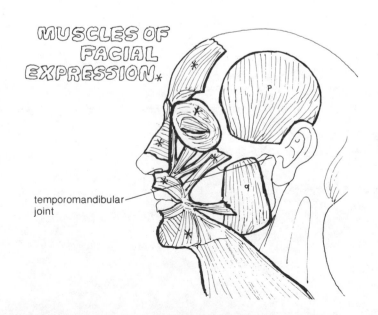

MUSCLES OF FACIAL EXPRESSION*

temporomandibular joint

PLATE 26

MUSCULAR SYSTEM
THE NECK *

CN 5

1. Color the sternocleidomastoid (a) and directional arrows in the diagram at right and in the illustration below. Color its title.
2. Color the suprahyoid muscles in one color and the hyoid bone in a brighter color. Then color the infrahyoid muscles in another color, then the muscles of the posterior triangle with one color. Color their titles too.
3. Color the two triangles in the diagram to the right (*1, *2) gray, and also their titles on the left side of the plate and below on the right.

The *neck* is an exceedingly complicated area from any perspective, and the muscular arrangement is no exception. Shown here are the more superficial muscles of the neck fitted within two triangular areas and the landmark muscle sternocleidomastoid. Not shown are the deep muscles anchoring the skull and cervical vertebrae, most of the deep muscles of the back and neck, and the intrinsic muscles of the larynx and the tongue.

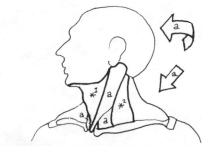

STERNOCLEIDOMASTOID a

The *sternocleidomastoid* is an important muscle in rotation, flexion, and even extension of the head. This muscle is a key structure as it separates anterior and posterior triangles of the neck. The critical carotid arteries, internal jugular veins, and vagus nerves run deep to these muscles.

ANTERIOR TRIANGLE OF THE NECK *1

The *anterior triangle* is bordered by the mandible above, the sternocleidomastoid muscle laterally, and the median plane of the neck. Triangular subdivisions are also named within. This region has many important nerves and vessels in residence.

SUPRAHYOID MUSCLES b
STYLOHYOID b1
DIGASTRIC b2
MYLOHYOID b3
HYOGLOSSUS b4

The *suprahyoid muscles* generally attach the hyoid bone to the floor of the tongue and the mandible. They influence movements of the tongue and hyoid bone during swallowing, and together with the infrahyoid muscles, stabilize the hyoid bone. Vessels/nerves to the tongue and the submandibular salivary gland reside in this region.

HYOID BONE c

The *hyoid* bone is suspended from the styloid processes of the skull by the stylohyoid ligaments and is stabilized by the supra- and infrahyoid muscle groups. It provides a mobile site of attachment for muscles acting on the tongue and the larynx.

INFRAHYOID MUSCLES d
STERNOHYOID d1
OMOHYOID d2
THYROHYOID d3
STERNOTHYROID d4

trapezius muscle

clavicle

sternum

clavicle

POSTERIOR TRIANGLE OF THE NECK *2
SPLENIUS CAPITIS e1
LEVATOR SCAPULAE e2
SCALENUS: ANT. e3 MED. e4 POST. e5

The *infrahyoid* muscles generally arise from the sternum, thyroid cartilage of the larynx, or the scapula (omo-) and insert on the hyoid bone. These muscles resist elevation of the hyoid bone during swallowing and act to depress the larynx during vocalization. Important nerves and vessels transit this area including those enroute to the thyroid gland.

The *posterior triangle* is crossed by important vessels/nerves to the upper limb. Its posterior border is the trapezius muscle; its anterior border is the sternocleidomastoid muscle; and its base is the clavicle. Muscles of this region arise from the skull and cervical vertebrae and head for the ribs (*scalenes*), scapula (*omohyoid, levator scapulae*) and the cervical/thoracic vertebral spines.

PLATE 27
see also 13, 14

MUSCULAR SYSTEM/THE TORSO
DEEP MUSCLES OF THE BACK & NECK.

CN 18

1. Color the various muscles listed below. Note that the deepest muscles are represented on the left side of the spinal column.
2. Color all the suboccipital muscles at the base of the skull and related areas in the diagram below.
3. Color external intercostal muscles and title to the far right.

The *deep muscles of the back* serve to stabilize the multiple bones of the vertebral column (short muscles spanning 1 or 2 vertebrae); influence posture of the back and curvatures of the column; and extend (long muscles), laterally flex (long and short muscles), and rotate (short muscles) all or part of the vertebral column. They largely fill the "gutter" between the angle of the ribs and the vertebral spines. They are supplied by segmental nerves (posterior rami of spinal nerves) and not from nerve plexuses. These muscles lie deep to the muscles of the upper limb which arise on the back.

SERRATUS POSTERIOR:a
SUPERIOR a INFERIOR b

These exceedingly thin muscles are often missed in dissection, and their function is not clear. Although they insert on the ribs, their effect on respiration is negligible. They are the most superficial of the deep back muscles.

SPLENIUS:*
CAPITIS c CERVICIS d

These are known as the "bandage" muscles, specifically referring to the *capitis,* which holds down the deeper muscles of the neck. They are important movers of the head, extending and rotating it in concert with the opposite sternocleidomastoid muscle.

ERECTOR SPINAE: s
SPINALIS e LONGISSIMUS f
ILIOCOSTALIS g

These are the principal movers of the back and the most probable source of muscular spasms and pain in the low back. They are thick, quadrilateral muscles in the lumbar region, splitting into large bundles (spinalis, etc.) to ribs, upper vertebrae, neck, and head in their ascent. They extend and laterally flex the vertebral column.

TRANSVERSOSPINALIS:.
SEMISPINALIS:*
CAPITIS h CERVICIS i THORACIS j
MULTIFIDUS k ROTATORES L
LEVATORES m

This group of muscles are largely rotators of the column, as they generally run from the transverse processes of one vertebra to the spine of the vertebra above or they may span 3 or 4 vertebrae. The *semispinalis* are the largest muscles of this group, which also extends the vertebral column.

INTERTRANSVERSARII n
INTERSPINALIS o

These very small muscles, deep to the larger overlying musculature, extend (*interspinalis*) and laterally flex the vertebral column.

NUCHAL LIGAMENT p

This is a sail-like ligament, whose "mast" is the midline of the occipital bone of the skull and whose "boom" is the spines of the cervical vertebrae. It "sails" in the trough of the cervical curvature with the posterior neck muscles finding attachment at the flat surfaces of the "sail." This ligament resists passive flexion of the head.

SUBOCCIPITAL MUSCLES q

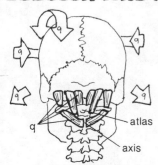

These small muscles set deep in the posterior neck rotate the atlas (C1 vertebra) on the axis (C2) (the skull moves with the atlas). They also extend the skull on the atlas. They are considered postural muscles rather than prime movers.

atlas

axis

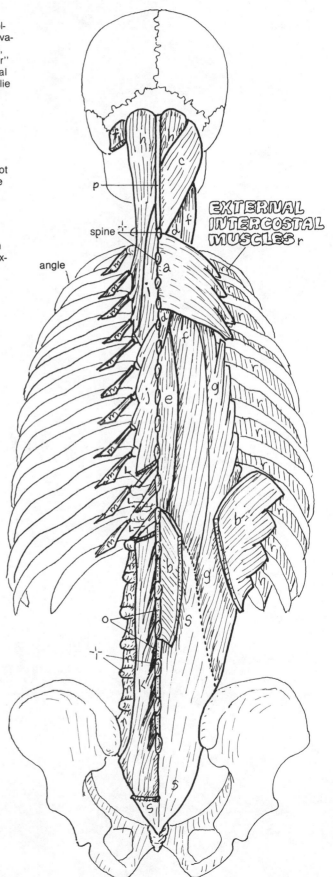

spine

angle

EXTERNAL INTERCOSTAL MUSCLES r

PLATE 28

MUSCULAR SYSTEM / THE TORSO
MUSCLES OF THE ANTERIOR ABDOMINAL WALL*
& INGUINAL REGION*

CN 8

1. Color the layers of the abdominal muscles below. In a, c, and d, note that the central portion of each muscle is an aponeurosis that contributes to the sheath of the rectus abdominis. The sheath/aponeurosis should be drawn in a lighter version of the color applied to each of the fleshy sides of the muscle. These fleshy or muscle fiber parts are indicated by heavier shading. In the drawing below, a view of all four muscles and the aponeuroses making up the sheath are shown.
2. The horizontal tendinous intersections of rectus abdominis should also be lighter.
3. In each drawing, leave the linea alba (white line) blank.⁖
4. Color the cremaster muscle in the diagram below the same color as the internal oblique of which it is an extension.
5. Color the remaining structures of the inguinal region.

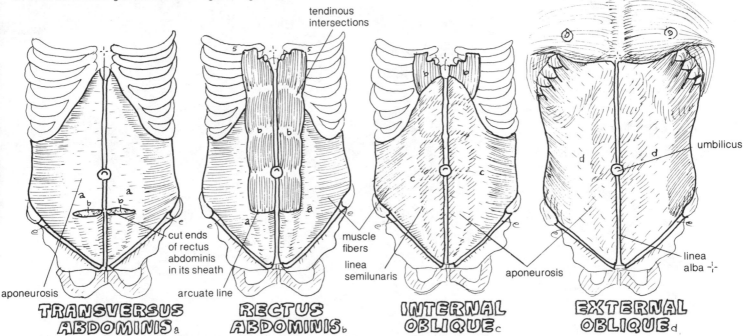

tendinous intersections

aponeurosis

cut ends of rectus abdominis in its sheath

arcuate line

muscle fibers

linea semilunaris

aponeurosis

umbilicus

linea alba ⁖

TRANSVERSUS ABDOMINISₐ   **RECTUS ABDOMINIS**ᵦ   **INTERNAL OBLIQUE**ᶜ   **EXTERNAL OBLIQUE**ᵈ

In general, the muscles of the *anterior abdominal wall* are similar to the intercostal muscles of the thoracic wall in terms of orientation. The deepest muscle is *transversus abdominis,* which corresponds to the very thin innermost intercostal muscle. Transversus encloses the lower fibers of rectus, then adds to the posterior layer of the sheath of the rectus. *Rectus abdominis* arises in segments connected by flat tendons, is enclosed in a *sheath* contributed by the *aponeuroses* of the other 3 abdominal muscles, and is a questionable flexor of the vertebral column. The fibers of *internal* and *external oblique* are oriented 90° to one another and correspond to the internal and external intercostal muscles, respectively. These muscles are active in compression of the abdominal contents, as in straining, and contribute to flexion and rotation of the torso. All these muscles become active in sit-up exercises.

INGUINAL REGION*
INGUINAL LIGAMENT ₑ CREMASTER M. c'
SUPERFICIAL INGUINAL RING ғ
SPERMATIC CORD ɢ
FUNDIFORM LIGAMENT OF PENIS ₕ

The *inguinal region* is the lower medial portion of the abdominal wall and is significant because the spermatic cord transverses the wall obliquely in its trek from pelvic cavity to the scrotum. This creates a potential defect in the abdominal wall at the site of transit—the inguinal canal. Under pressure, loops of intestine or intraabdominal fat can herniate through the deep ring and into this canal, causing some discomfort. It is potentially dangerous for a loop of intestine and its blood vessels can be trapped and choked within the canal. As the *spermatic cord* (sperm duct, blood vessels) traverses the abdominal wall, it takes a representative layer from each of the three muscles. These contribute to the coverings of the spermatic cord. The *cremaster muscle,* one of the coverings, is an extension of the internal oblique and has a slight lifting effect on the cord and testis, an effect best elicited in children. The female inguinal region is similarly constructed, except that a fibrous ligament passes through the canal instead of a duct and vessels.

SHEATH OF THE RECTUS ABDOMINIS:•
APONEUROSES OF*
TRANSVERSUS ABDOMINIS ₐ
INTERNAL OBLIQUE ᶜ
EXTERNAL OBLIQUE ᵈ

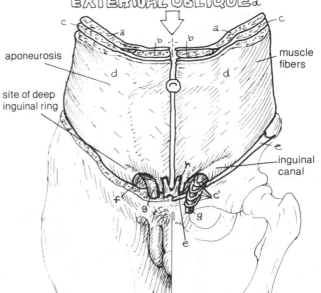

aponeurosis

muscle fibers

site of deep inguinal ring

inguinal canal

PLATE 29
see also 14, 77, 89

MUSCULAR SYSTEM / THE TORSO
MUSCLES OF THE POSTERIOR ABDOMINAL WALL *
THORACIC DIAPHRAGM & INTERCOSTAL MUSCLES *

CN 12

1. Color the muscles of the posterior abdominal wall (a–e) in both anterior and posterior views.
2. Color the intercostal muscles and the diaphragm. To set apart diaphragm muscle from its tendon, lighten the area of the central tendon (h¹).
3. Color the other lettered structures (i–L), using red for k & k' and blue for i & i'.

ILIOPSOAS: d
PSOAS MAJOR a
PSOAS MINOR b
ILIACUS c
QUADRATUS LUMBORUM e
INTERNAL INTERCOSTAL f
EXTERNAL INTERCOSTAL g
DIAPHRAGM h
CENTRAL TENDON h'

The *intercostal muscles* occupy the spaces between the ribs and are important muscles of respiration. They change the dimensions (volume) of the thoracic cavity thereby creating pressure changes within. The anterior portion of the external intercostal muscles is membranous and transparent, and the underlying internal intercostal muscles (f) can be seen through it. The *diaphragm* is a large muscle that seals the inferior thoracic aperture airtight. It contracts during inspiration and relaxes during expiration and is the principal muscle of respiration (see Plate 77 on the Mechanics of Respiration). The diaphragm arises from the xiphoid process, the lower six ribs, and the lumbar vertebrae; the left and right parts of the muscle insert into each other at the broad *central tendon*. The principal artery from the heart to the abdomen (*aorta*), the principal vein enroute to the heart from the abdomen and below (*inferior vena cava*), and the *esophagus* pass through individual openings (*hiatuses*) in the diaphragm.

VENA CAVAL HIATUS; INFERIOR VENA CAVA i'
ESOPHAGEAL HIATUS; ESOPHAGUS j'
AORTIC HIATUS k AORTA k'
12 TH RIB L

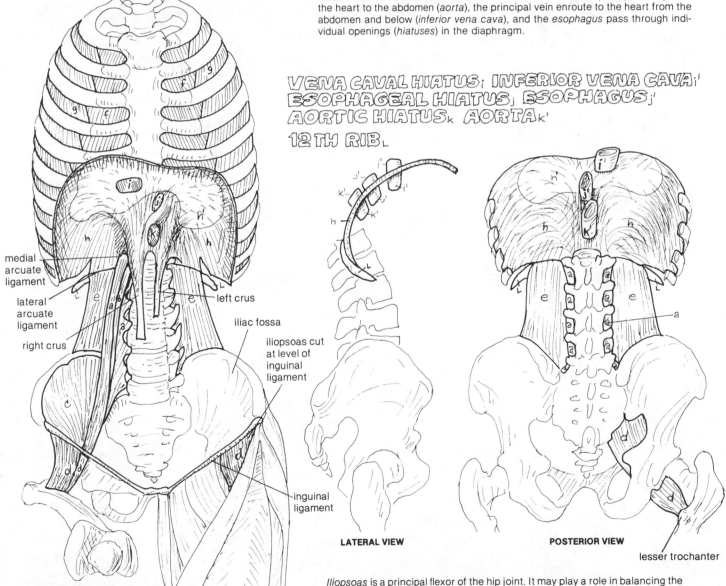

ANTERIOR VIEW

medial arcuate ligament
lateral arcuate ligament
right crus
left crus
iliac fossa
iliopsoas cut at level of inguinal ligament
inguinal ligament

LATERAL VIEW

POSTERIOR VIEW

lesser trochanter

FLEXOR OF THE THIGH d

Iliopsoas is a principal flexor of the hip joint. It may play a role in balancing the torso during sitting. In standing, there is evidence that iliopsoas functions to counteract the tendency of the torso to fall back of the line of gravity, which passes somewhat behind the hip joints. It is certainly an important postural muscle in aligning the lower limb with the body trunk.

PLATE 30
see also 19

MUSCULAR SYSTEM / THE TORSO
PERINEAL MUSCLES & THE PELVIC FLOOR*

CN 12

1. Color the diagram of the perineum, upper left. Then color in structures b, c, d in the male/female illustrations.
2. Color the muscles of the urogenital triangle.
3. Color the muscles of the anal triangle.
4. Color the diagram at lower left showing the relationship of the slinglike levator ani muscle to the urogenital diaphragm.

THE PERINEUM (BOUNDARIES)*
SYMPHYSIS PUBISₐ
COCCYX♭
ISCHIAL TUBEROSITY𝒸
SACROTUBEROUS LIGAMENT𝒹
ISCHIOPUBIC RAMUSₑ

The *perineum* is the region below the pelvic cavity situated within the pelvic outlet. It is bordered by structures a–e. Its floor is skin; its roof is the pelvic diaphragm, the greater part of which is levator ani muscle. This muscle is also the floor of the pelvis. For descriptive reasons, the diamond-shaped perineum is bisected at the *ischial tuberosities* into two triangles: *urogenital* and *anal*.

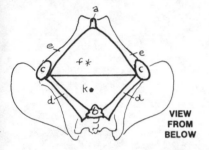

VIEW FROM BELOW

UROGENITAL TRIANGLE f*
ISCHIOCAVERNOSUS₉
BULBOSPONGIOSUS♭
TRANSVERSE PERINEALᵢ
UROGENITAL DIAPHRAGMⱼ

The *ischiocavernosus* and *bulbospongiosus* muscles ensheathe the roots of the erectile bodies of the penis and clitoris and aid in their erection by compressing the bodies and inhibiting venous drainage. Bulbospongiosus also contracts rhythmically in ejaculation, forcing the semen through the urethra of the penis. *Transverse perineal* muscles stabilize the perineal body, which helps anchor perineal structures in place. Muscles in the *urogenital diaphragm* are concerned with micturition (voiding urine) and ejaculation.

ANAL TRIANGLE k•
LEVATOR ANI (PELVIC DIAPHRAGM)ₗ
SPHINCTER ANI EXTERNUSₘ
ANOCOCCYGEAL LIGAMENTₙ

The *pelvic diaphragm*, consisting largely of levator ani muscle, roofs the entire perineum superiorly; however, it is partly covered by the urogenital diaphragm when viewed from below and is best seen in the anal triangle. Its contraction increases intraabdominal and pelvic pressure, aiding in defecating, micturating, and straining in general. It supports the pelvic viscera and is very important in this respect. The *external sphincter ani*, under voluntary control, contracts to close the anal canal and anus and thus prevent defecation.

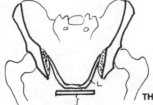

FRONTAL SECTION THROUGH UROGENITAL TRIANGLE

Here you can see the relationship of the *urogenital diaphragm* to the *pelvic diaphragm*. A space exists between the two (anterior recesses of the ischiorectal fossa), which perhaps you can now better visualize in the two main illustrations.

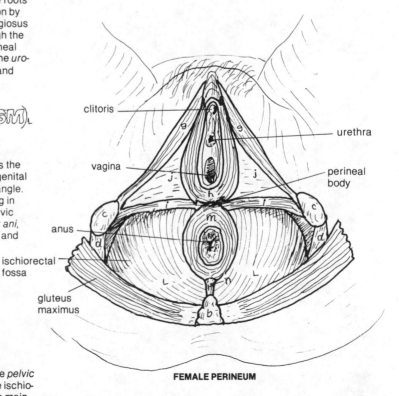

penis

scrotum

anterior recess of ischiorectal fossa

anus

gluteus maximus

MALE PERINEUM

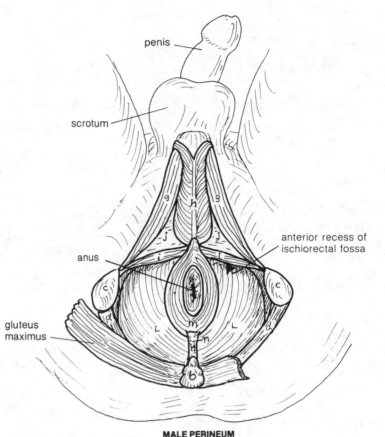

clitoris

urethra

vagina

perineal body

anus

ischiorectal fossa

gluteus maximus

FEMALE PERINEUM

PLATE 31
see also 14, 15, 32, 33

MUSCULAR SYSTEM / UPPER LIMB
MUSCLES OF SCAPULAR STABILIZATION *
TRAPEZIUS a RHOMBOIDS b LEVATOR SCAPULAE c
SERRATUS ANTERIOR d PECTORALIS MINOR e

CN 5

1. This plate and the next 2 plates should be considered together, with different colors for each muscle.
2. Color the five muscles. Include the broken edge of serratus anterior, which represents its insertion at the vertebral border of the scapula on its underside or costal surface.
3. Color the muscles in the lower drawings. The scapulae, clavicles, arrows, and titles in the lower drawings and the scapulae and clavicles in the upper drawings should all be colored gray.

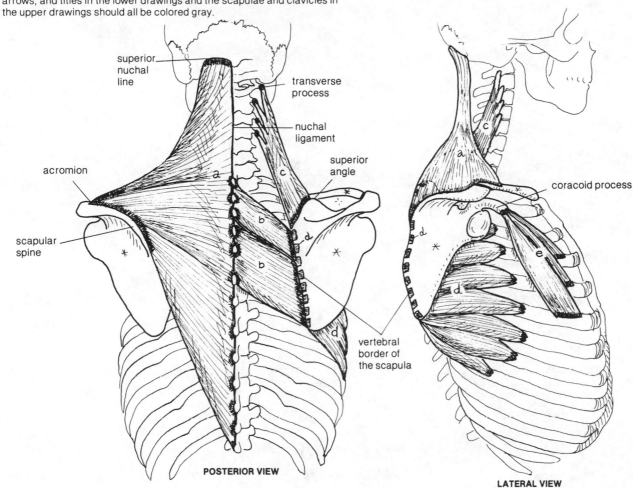

POSTERIOR VIEW

LATERAL VIEW

The muscles you are coloring on this plate are responsible for supporting the scapulae and clavicles. The only bony attachment these bones have with the axial skeleton is at the sternoclavicular joint; thus, they require support. A bonus from this *muscular stabilization* of the pectoral girdle is considerable scapular mobility and, therefore, arm mobility. Muscle groups within an entire muscle are capable of independently contracting or relax-

ing. Thus, as you can see below, the middle fibers of *trapezius* are effective retractors, while the upper fibers elevate and help rotate the scapulae, and the lower fibers are depressors of the scapulae. *Pectoralis minor* assists *serratus anterior* in protraction of the scapula such as in pushing against a wall; it also helps in depression of the shoulder and downward rotation of the scapula.

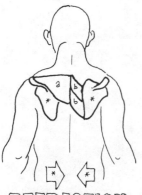

RETRACTION
military posture ("squaring the shoulders").

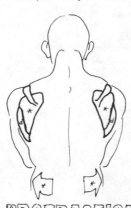

PROTRACTION
pushing with outstretched arms and hands.

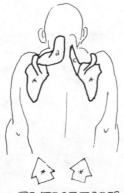

ELEVATION
shrugging the shoulders or protecting the head.

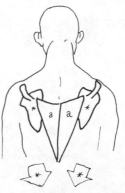

DEPRESSION
straight arms on parallel bars, holding weight.

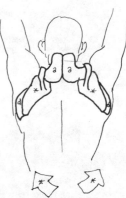

UPWARD ROT.
lifting or reaching over head.

SUPRASPINATUS f
INFRASPINATUS g TERES MINOR h
SUBSCAPULARIS i

CN 4

1. Color the four muscles, directional labels, and arrows. To establish continuity with Plates 31 and 33, use colors different from those used for other muscles shown on those plates.
2. Use the same colors for the cuff diagram at lower right. Use gray for the title.
3. Color the sites of muscular attachment and their titles in their respective colors as you complete Plates 31 and 33. Use the same colors as you use on those plates where possible. Referring to these other plates, study the muscle and its attachments shown here, and try to visualize its function. Muscles titled (p) and (q) appear on P. 34; (o) appears on P. 26.

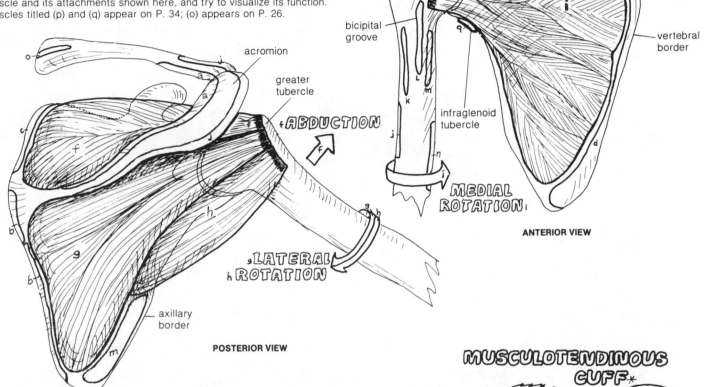

supraglenoid tubercle

glenohumeral joint

lesser tubercle

bicipital groove

infraglenoid tubercle

vertebral border

MEDIAL ROTATION i

ANTERIOR VIEW

acromion

greater tubercle

f ABDUCTION

g LATERAL h ROTATION

axillary border

POSTERIOR VIEW

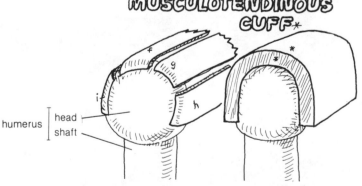

MUSCULOTENDINOUS CUFF*

humerus { head shaft

MUSCULAR ATTACHMENTS: *

TRAPEZIUS a
RHOMBOIDS b
LEVATOR SCAPULAE c
SERRATUS ANTERIOR d
PECTORALIS MINOR e

DELTOID f
PECTORALIS MAJOR k
LATISSIMUS DORSI L
TERES MAJOR m
CORACOBRACHIALIS n

STERNOCLEIDOMASTOID o

BICEPS BRACHII p
TRICEPS BRACHII q

The socket at the glenohumeral joint is too flat to offer any security for the head of the humerus, so the joint must be reinforced by muscle to give active support and still allow a good deal of mobility. The four reinforcing muscles arise from the scapula and cross the joint at the level of the joint to insert on the humerus about the head. The scapula is secured by the five muscles of scapular stabilization and offers a stable platform of origin for these four muscles. As you can see, the muscles and their tendons form a *musculotendinous cuff* around the humeral head. Two of the four (g, h) are lateral rotators; (i) is a medial rotator; hence rotator cuff is a common term for the group; (f) is an abductor of the glenohumeral joint. With the joint secure against dislocation, the many movers of the arm can act to provide almost unlimited mobility. The origins and/or insertions (muscular attachments) of all the movers of the shoulder joint can be visualized with reference to the cuff muscles on this plate. The drawing to its right (to be colored gray *) is a diagramatic concept of the four tendons operating as a cuff.

MUSCULAR SYSTEM/UPPER LIMB
MUSCLES ACTING ON THE SHOULDER JOINT*
DELTOID; PECTORALIS MAJOR k
LATISSIMUS DORSI. TERES MAJOR m
CORACOBRACHIALIS n

PLATE 33
see also 15, 31, 32

CN 5
1. Color these five muscles and the diagrams below.
2. In the diagram on lateral rotation note the presence of infraspinatus (g) and teres minor (h). Use the same colors as on the preceding plate.
3. The fascia/aponeurosis of the latissimus dorsi (L') should be colored in lightly (with same color) to suggest its tendinous nature.

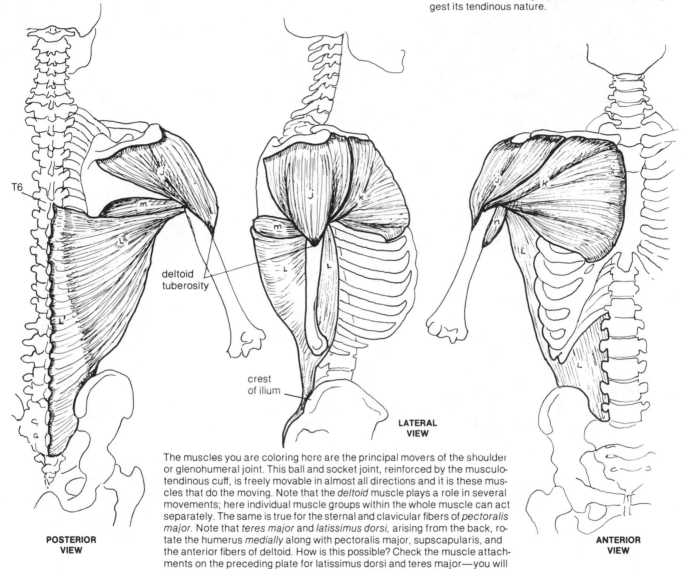

T6

deltoid tuberosity

crest of ilium

LATERAL VIEW

POSTERIOR VIEW

ANTERIOR VIEW

The muscles you are coloring here are the principal movers of the shoulder or glenohumeral joint. This ball and socket joint, reinforced by the musculotendinous cuff, is freely movable in almost all directions and it is these muscles that do the moving. Note that the *deltoid* muscle plays a role in several movements; here individual muscle groups within the whole muscle can act separately. The same is true for the sternal and clavicular fibers of *pectoralis major*. Note that *teres major* and *latissimus dorsi,* arising from the back, rotate the humerus *medially* along with pectoralis major, supscapularis, and the anterior fibers of deltoid. How is this possible? Check the muscle attachments on the preceding plate for latissimus dorsi and teres major—you will see that these muscles insert on the *anterior* aspect of the humerus. Just below the axilla, these muscles cross from the back to the front of the humerus, between the humerus and the lateral chest wall. This makes them medial rotators, and not lateral rotators as you may have first suspected. In the diagrams below, biceps brachii (weak flexor of the shoulder joint) and triceps brachii (weak extensor of the shoulder joint) are not shown.

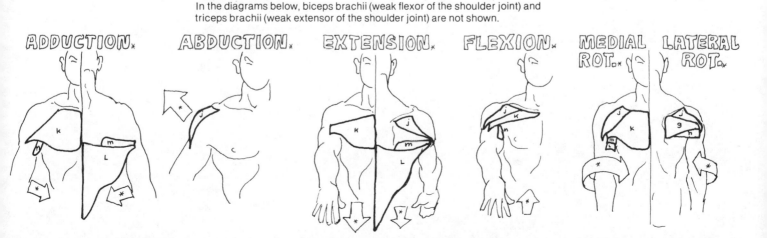

ADDUCTION* ABDUCTION* EXTENSION* FLEXION* MEDIAL ROT.* LATERAL ROT.*

CN 8
1. Color the four flexors, then their attachments in the diagram to the left.
2. Do the same with the extensors, shading the tendon of triceps lightly (e').
3. Color the 2 supinators, the 2 pronators, and the directional arrows. The attachments of supinator are included on the attachment diagrams for flexors.

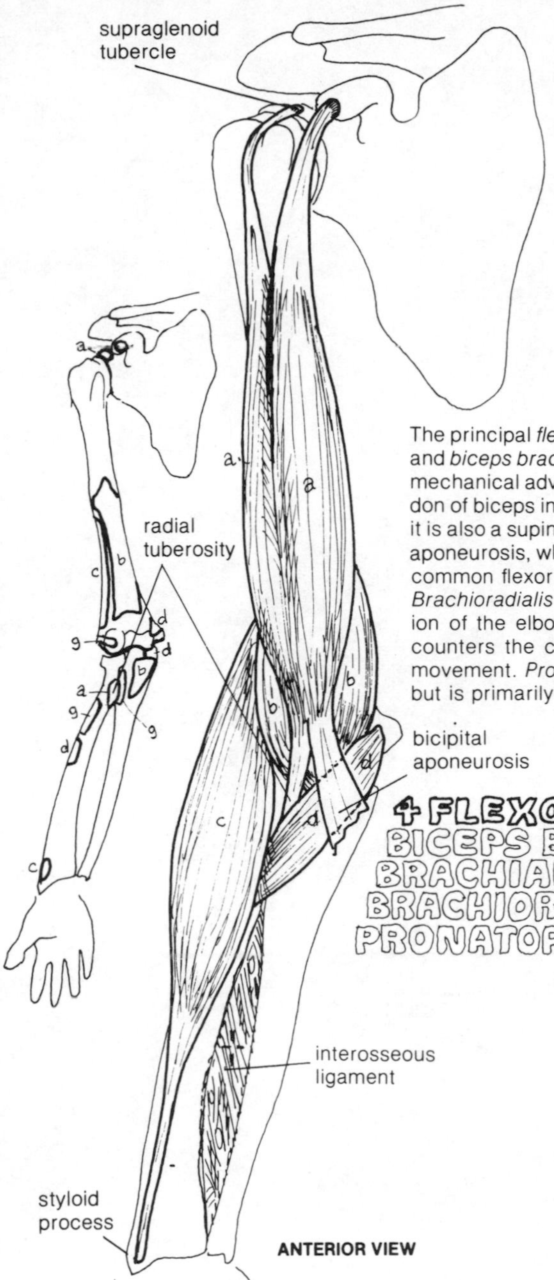

supraglenoid tubercle

infraglenoid tubercle

radial tuberosity

The principal *flexors* of the elbow joint are *brachialis* and *biceps brachii,* of which the former has the best mechanical advantage. Because of the way the tendon of biceps inserts at the tuberosity of the radius, it is also a supinator of the forearm. Note the bicipital aponeurosis, which inserts into the deep fascia of the common flexor group (not shown) in the forearm. *Brachioradialis* has been shown to be active in flexion of the elbow *and in* rapid extension where it counters the centrifugal force produced by that movement. *Pronator teres* assists in elbow flexion but is primarily a pronator.

bicipital aponeurosis

4 FLEXORS:*
BICEPS BRACHII a
BRACHIALIS b
BRACHIORADIALIS c
PRONATOR TERES d

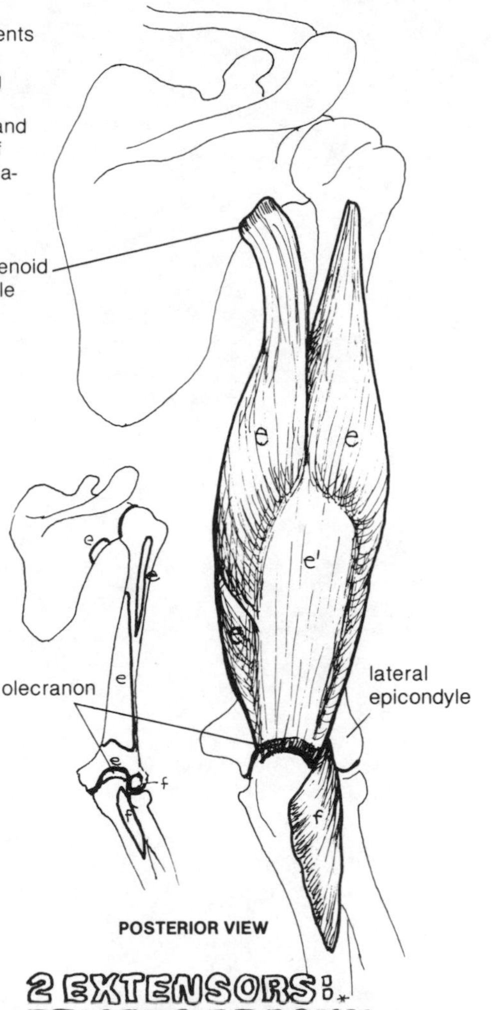

interosseous ligament

styloid process

ANTERIOR VIEW

olecranon

lateral epicondyle

POSTERIOR VIEW

2 EXTENSORS:*
TRICEPS BRACHII e
ANCONEUS f

The principal extensor of the forearm is the three-headed *triceps brachii.* The smaller *anconeus* assists in this function. Like biceps, the triceps is easily felt on yourself.

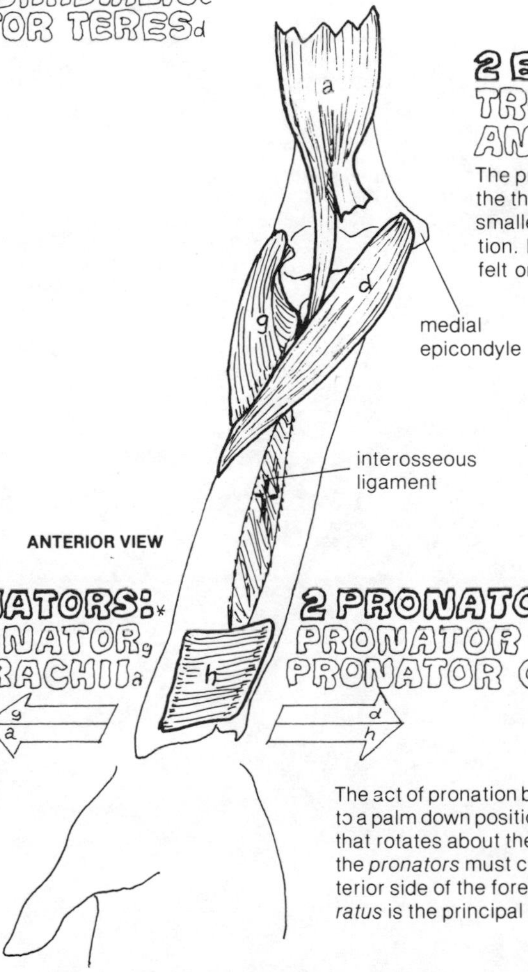

medial epicondyle

interosseous ligament

ANTERIOR VIEW

2 SUPINATORS:*
SUPINATOR g
BICEPS BRACHII a

2 PRONATORS:*
PRONATOR TERES d
PRONATOR QUADRATUS h

Supination is a powerful action, used when tightening the lid of a jar or tightening a screw with a screwdriver. *Supinator,* arising from the lateral epicondyle of the humerus and the lateral surface of the upper ulna (not shown), wraps around the posterior and lateral surfaces of the radius to insert on the lateral aspect of that bone.

The act of pronation brings the palm of the hand to a palm down position. Because it is the radius that rotates about the ulna, it is apparent that the *pronators* must cross the radius on the anterior side of the forearm. The *pronator quadratus* is the principal muscle in this action.

PLATE 35
see also 15, 16, 34, 36

MUSCULAR SYSTEM/UPPER LIMB
MUSCLES ACTING ON WRIST, HAND & FINGERS *

CN 14

1. This plate and the next should be considered and, if possible, colored together.
2. Color the title of flexor digitorum profundus (n) which is too deep to be shown, but whose tendons are colored on the next plate.
3. Notice that the title of extensor carpi radialis brevis is shortened to brevis and it gets a separate color.
4. Color the muscles acting on the thumb, including the arrow representing flexors pollicis longus, which is shown in the flexor view.

EXTENSORS *

The *extensors* arise from the lateral epicondyle and upper parts of the bones and interosseous membrane of the forearm, but on the posterior side, creating an extensor compartment. As you can readily see on your own forearm, the mass of muscle here is less than on the flexor side. The *"carpi" muscles* insert on the distal carpal bones or metacarpals, while the *extensors of the digits* form an expansion of tendon over the middle and distal phalanges to which the small intrinsic muscles of the hand insert. This can best be appreciated in the following plate. The outcropping muscles to the thumb are considered below.

FLEXORS *

The *flexors of the wrist and fingers* take up most of the anterior compartment of the forearm, originating as a group from the medial epicondyle, the upper radius and ulna, and the intervening interosseous membrane. Crossing the wrist joint, the *"carpi" muscles* insert on the distal carpal bones or the metacarpals, while the two *flexors of the digits,* one immediately deep to the other and sharing the same tunnel and sheath, go on to the middle and distal phalanges. *Palmaris longus,* missing in about 10% of the population, merges with the palmar connective tissue (aponeurosis). See the next plate for continuation of digit flexors.

lateral epicondyle of the humerus

medial epicondyle of the humerus

EXT. CARPI ULNARIS e
EXT. DIGITI MINIMI f
EXT. DIGITORUM g
EXT. INDICIS h
EXT. CARPI
RADIALIS
LONGUS i,
BREVIS i'

FLEX. CARPI ULNARIS a
PALMARIS LONGUS b
FLEX. CARPI
RADIALIS c
FLEX. DIGITORUM
SUPERFICIALIS d
FLEX.
DIGITORUM
PROFUNDUS n

POSTERIOR VIEW

ANTERIOR VIEW

anatomical "snuffbox"

ACTING ON THE THUMB *

These four muscles operate the thumb in concert with smaller intrinsic muscles to be drawn on the next plate. *Flexor pollicis* (L. *pollex*=thumb) *longus* is a member of the flexor compartment, lying along side flexor digitorum profundus: its tendon is best seen in the following plate. The two *thumb extensors* and the *abductor* create a small depression in the skin at the base of the thumb, laterally: the anatomical "snuffbox." These 4 muscles insert at the base of the metacarpal and the two phalanges as shown.

EXT. POLLICIS LONGUS j
EXT. POLLICIS BREVIS k
ABDUCTOR POLLICIS LONGUS l
FLEX. POLLICIS LONGUS m

LATERAL VIEW

PLATE 36
see also 17, 35

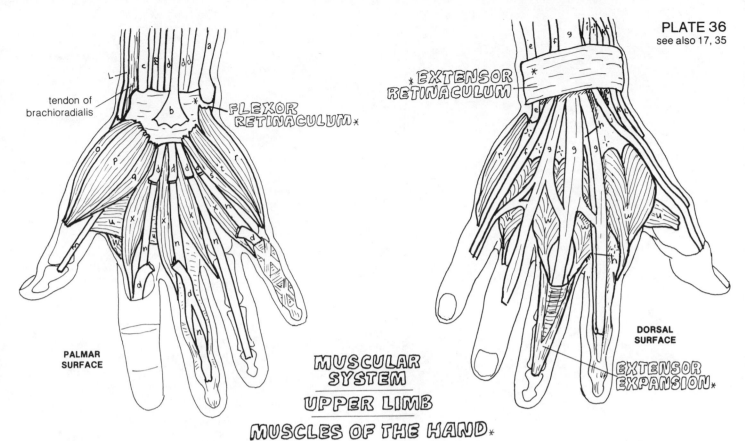

tendon of brachioradialis

FLEXOR RETINACULUM*

PALMAR SURFACE

EXTENSOR RETINACULUM*

DORSAL SURFACE

EXTENSOR EXPANSION*

MUSCULAR SYSTEM
UPPER LIMB
MUSCLES OF THE HAND*

CN 7

1. If you have 7 colors in addition to those used on the previous plate, then color in the tendons of the forearm muscles at the top of the page. Otherwise leave them blank.
2. Color the titles and muscles of the thenar and hypothenar eminences. Use only 3 colors for the six muscles by repeating the hypothenar counterpart of each thenar muscle (o and s, p and r, q and t).
3. Color the deep muscles. The palmar interossei muscles (v) lie too deep in the palm to be seen.
4. Fill in the 6 movement diagrams where indicated. Note that the thumb and its thenar pad are colored gray in the lower 4 drawings.

THENAR EMINENCE*
OPPONENS POLLICIS o
ABDUCTOR POLLICIS BREVIS p
FLEXOR POLLICIS BREVIS q

The complex movement of the thumb results from the integrated action of these *thenar* and adductor muscles, plus the long flexor, abductor, and two extensor pollicis muscles. The thenar muscles arise/insert in the same general area as one another, however, their different orientation orders different functions.

HYPOTHENAR EMINENCE*
OPPONENS DIGITI MINIMI s
FLEXOR DIGITI MINIMI BREVIS t
ABDUCTOR DIGITI MINIMI r

These muscles are complementary to the thenar muscles in attachment and function. The function of opposition is basic to some of the complex grasping functions of the hand.

DEEP MUSCLES*
ADDUCTOR POLLICIS u
PALMAR INTEROSSEUS v
DORSAL INTEROSSEUS w
LUMBRICALS x

Adductor pollicis works in concert with the 1st dorsal interosseous muscle in grasping an object between thumb and index finger. The *interossei* and *lumbrical muscles* insert into the extensor expansion, forming a complex mechanism for flexing/extending the fingers. Additional functions of the interossei can be seen at right.

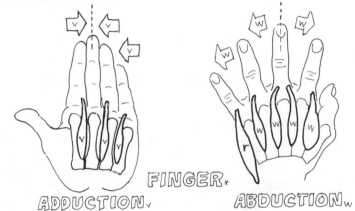

FINGER*

ADDUCTION v

ABDUCTION w

THUMB*

EXT. k

FLEX. q

OPPOSITION*

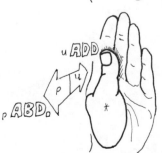

ADD u

ABD. p

CIRCUMDUCTION*

MUSCULAR SYSTEM / UPPER LIMB
SUMMARY OF THE MUSCLE GROUPS *

PLATE 37

CN 8

1. Color the muscles of each functional group with a single color.

The muscles shown are the superficial muscles of the upper limb, many of which can be felt or seen on yourself. The deeper muscles underlying these are not shown.

MUSCLES ACTING ON THE SCAPULA a
MUSCLES ACTING ON THE SHOULDER JOINT b
FLEXORS OF THE ELBOW JOINT c
EXTENSORS OF THE ELBOW JOINT d
FLEXORS OF THE WRIST, HAND & FINGERS e
EXTENSORS OF THE WRIST, HAND & FINGERS f
FOREARM MUSCLES ACTING ON THE THUMB g
MUSCLES OF THE HAND h

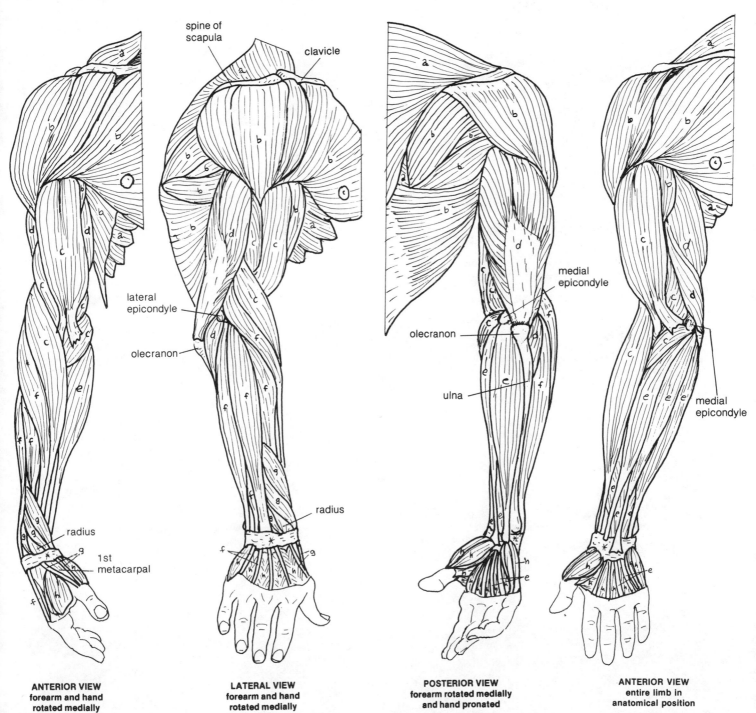

ANTERIOR VIEW
forearm and hand
rotated medially

LATERAL VIEW
forearm and hand
rotated medially

POSTERIOR VIEW
forearm rotated medially
and hand pronated

ANTERIOR VIEW
entire limb in
anatomical position

PLATE 38
see also 19, 39, 40, 41

MUSCULAR SYSTEM / LOWER LIMB
MUSCLES OF THE GLUTEAL REGION*

CN 5

1. Color this and the next 3 plates together, but with different colors.
2. Color the first 4 muscles. Include the attachments and arrows of movement in the diagram at lower right.
3. Color the 6 deep lateral rotators. Use the same color for all 6 muscles, including the attachments and arrows in the diagram.
4. Color the iliotibial tract gray.
5. We recommend that you not color the other lettered muscles of the thigh. The letters correspond to muscles in the following plates, and are in this plate only for reference.

GLUTEUS MAXIMUSₐ
GLUTEUS MEDIUSᵦ
GLUTEUS MINIMUS𝒸
TENSOR FASCIAE LATAE𝒹
6 DEEP LATERAL ROTATORS:ₑ
PIRIFORMISₑ₁
OBTURATOR INTERNUSₑ₂
OBTURATOR EXTERNUSₑ₃
QUADRATUS FEMORISₑ₄
GEMELLUS SUPERIORₑ₅
GEMELLUS INFERIORₑ₆

The muscles of the buttock work the hip joint and, as you can see, are responsible for extending, abducting, and rotating the femur. Tensor fasciae latae, although a part of the flexor compartment of the thigh, is considered a part of the gluteal region because of its attachments and nerve supply. Careful study of the diagram at far lower right after coloring will enable you to understand the function of the gluteal muscles. *Gluteus medius* is an important hip stabilizer and postural muscle because it keeps the hips level when walking or running. *Gluteus maximus*, often an inch or more thick, plays its greatest role in running or climbing. There is a variable amount of fat in the superficial fascia overlying this region, which gives added form to the buttock. The *deep lateral rotators* correspond to some degree with the musculotendinous cuff of the shoulder joint.

ILIOTIBIAL TRACT*

The *iliotibial tract* runs from ilium to tibia and helps stabilize the knee joint. The muscle *tensor fasciae latae* (d) inserts into this fibrous band, tensing it. The tract is a thickening of the deep fascia of the thigh. It-has been dissected away at the level of the buttock to better visualize the musculature.

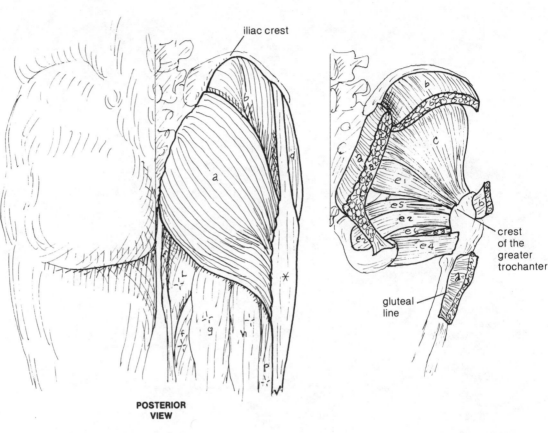

iliac crest

crest of the greater trochanter

gluteal line

POSTERIOR VIEW

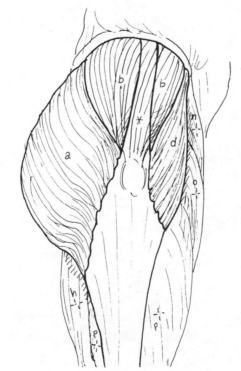

LATERAL VIEW

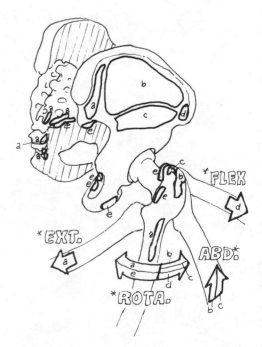

*FLEX
*EXT.
ABD.*
*ROTA.

PLATE 39
see also 20, 38, 40, 41

MUSCULAR SYSTEM / LOWER LIMB
MUSCLES OF THE POSTERIOR THIGH∗
SEMIMEMBRANOSUS f
SEMITENDINOSUS g
BICEPS FEMORIS h
CN 3

1. Color the 3 muscles as well as the diagrams at lower left and lower right.
2. Color the other muscles in the diagrams with their colors used on other plates on the thigh. In the flexor diagram, note that the gastrocnemius muscle in the leg is to be colored gray.
3. Do not color the other lettered muscles as they are in this plate only for reference. Labels correspond to muscles on Plates 38, 40, and 41.

ischial
tuberosity

iliotibial
tract

FLEXORS OF
THE KNEE JOINT∗

Flexion of the knee is attained by a number of muscles crossing the knee joint behind the line of gravity, including one of the adductors (m), a muscle of the anterior thigh (n), gastrocnemius (∗), as well as the hamstring muscles.

long
head

short
head

popliteal
fossa

fibular
head

tibia

EXTENSORS OF
THE HIP JOINT∗

When standing and relaxed, the hip extensors (a, f, g, and h) are generally inactive. When bending the body forward, the hamstrings contract strongly. Gluteus maximus contracts only against strong resistance (climbing). The short head of biceps femoris does not cross the hip joint and is, therefore, not active there.

gastrocnemius

POSTERIOR VIEW

The *muscles of the posterior thigh*, known as the hamstrings (named after a procedure for cutting these muscles in certain domestic animals), are equally effective at both hip and knee joints as extensors and flexors, respectively. The tendons of these muscles can easily be felt and identified at the back of the knee when the knee joint is partly flexed. It is these muscles that restrict extension of the knee during a high kick.

PLATE 40
see also 38, 39, 41

MUSCULAR SYSTEM / LOWER LIMB
MUSCLES OF THE MEDIAL THIGH (ADDUCTORS)*
PECTINEUS;
ADDUCTOR BREVIS;
ADDUCTOR LONGUS k
ADDUCTOR MAGNUS L
GRACILIS m

CN 5

1. Color the 5 muscles below.
2. In the lower figures, color the adductor masses gray. These diagrams show the relationship of the muscle group to the rest of the thigh. In the lower right diagram, the directional arrow (to be colored gray) shows the direction of action of the adductors.

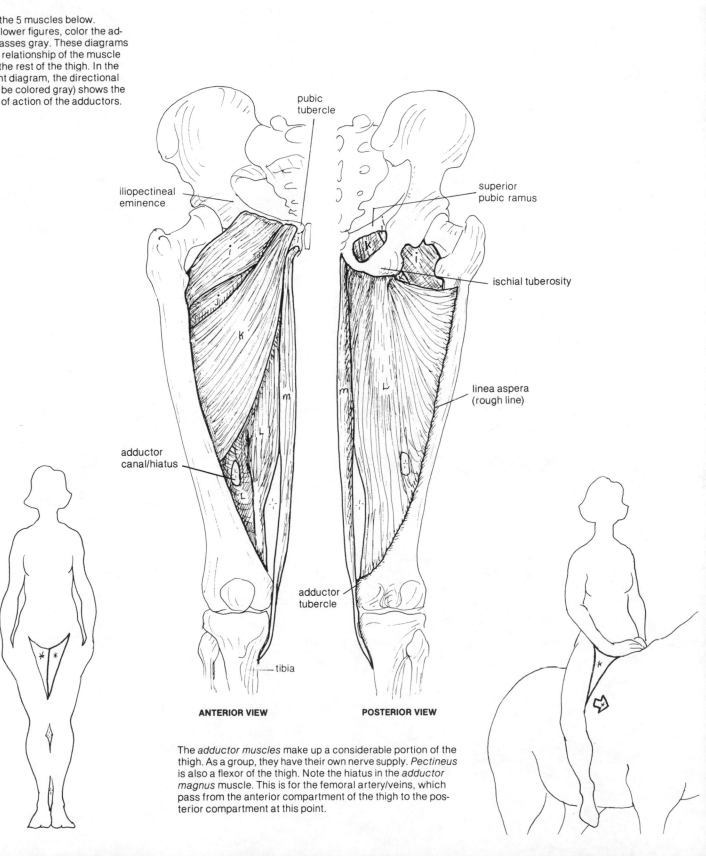

pubic tubercle

iliopectineal eminence

superior pubic ramus

ischial tuberosity

linea aspera (rough line)

adductor canal/hiatus

adductor tubercle

tibia

ANTERIOR VIEW

POSTERIOR VIEW

The *adductor muscles* make up a considerable portion of the thigh. As a group, they have their own nerve supply. *Pectineus* is also a flexor of the thigh. Note the hiatus in the *adductor magnus* muscle. This is for the femoral artery/veins, which pass from the anterior compartment of the thigh to the posterior compartment at this point.

PLATE 41
see also 28, 38, 39, 40, 89

MUSCULAR SYSTEM / LOWER LIMB
MUSCLES OF THE ANTERIOR THIGH∗
SARTORIUS n
QUADRICEPS FEMORIS:∗
RECTUS FEMORIS o
VASTUS LATERALIS p
VASTUS INTERMEDIUS q
VASTUS MEDIALIS r

CN 6
1. Color the sartorius and the 4 muscles of the quadriceps in different colors. Include their participation in the functional diagrams at lower left and lower right.
2. Color the iliopsoas muscle and its title in the diagram at lower right.
3. Color in gray the patellar ligament and the patella.

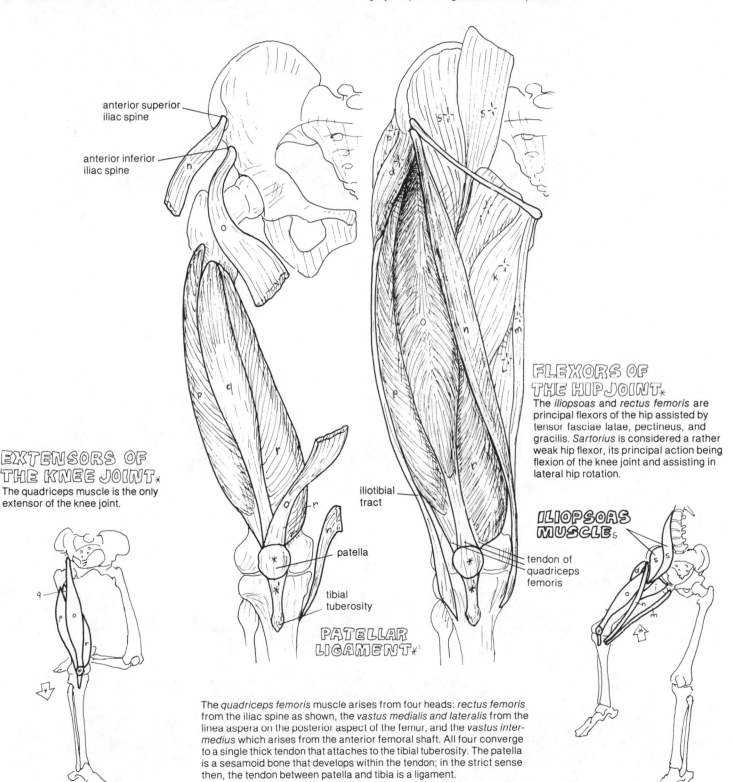

anterior superior iliac spine

anterior inferior iliac spine

iliotibial tract

patella

tibial tuberosity

tendon of quadriceps femoris

EXTENSORS OF THE KNEE JOINT∗
The quadriceps muscle is the only extensor of the knee joint.

PATELLAR LIGAMENT∗'

FLEXORS OF THE HIP JOINT∗
The *iliopsoas* and *rectus femoris* are principal flexors of the hip assisted by tensor fasciae latae, pectineus, and gracilis. *Sartorius* is considered a rather weak hip flexor, its principal action being flexion of the knee joint and assisting in lateral hip rotation.

ILIOPSOAS MUSCLE s

The *quadriceps femoris* muscle arises from four heads: *rectus femoris* from the iliac spine as shown, the *vastus medialis and lateralis* from the linea aspera on the posterior aspect of the femur, and the *vastus intermedius* which arises from the anterior femoral shaft. All four converge to a single thick tendon that attaches to the tibial tuberosity. The patella is a sesamoid bone that develops within the tendon; in the strict sense then, the tendon between patella and tibia is a ligament.

CN 6

1. Color the 2 muscles of the lateral leg in the large drawing at left and in the two diagrams showing attachment and movement.

2. Color the 4 muscles of the anterior leg and in the 3 diagrams showing attachments and function.

ANTERIOR LEG (DORSIFLEXORS)*
TIBIALIS ANTERIOR c
EXTENSOR DIGITORUM LONGUS d
EXTENSOR HALLUCIS LONGUS e
PERONEUS TERTIUS f

These muscles are found in the anterolateral compartment of the leg, as the anteromedial area is taken up by the tibial shaft. They cross several joints and are, therefore, dorsiflexors of the ankle as well as extensors of the toes (L. *hallux* = great toe). *Tibialis anterior* crosses to the medial arch of the foot and is therefore an important invertor of the foot as well as a dorsiflexor of the ankle.

LATERAL LEG*
PERONEUS LONGUS a
PERONEUS BREVIS b

The *peroneal muscles* are principally evertors of the foot (see the eversion diagram), for as you see, the tendons of these muscles pass to the lateral margin and underside of the foot. *Peroneus tertius* is actually part of extensor digitorum, but may play a role in eversion. These muscles may also protect against excessive inversion.

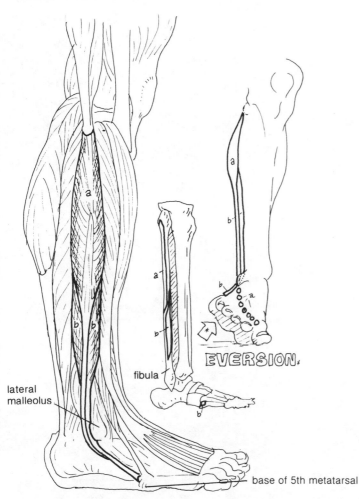

lateral malleolus

fibula

EVERSION*

base of 5th metatarsal

LATERAL VIEW

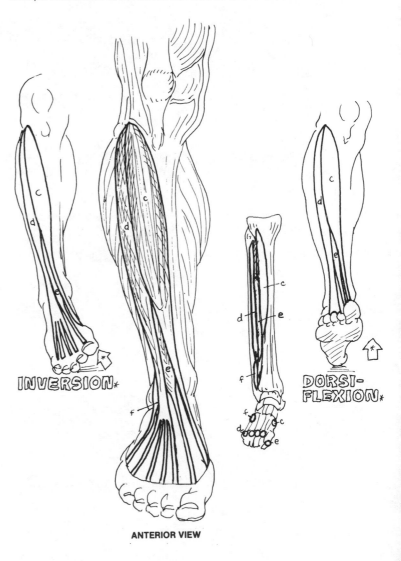

INVERSION*

DORSI-FLEXION*

ANTERIOR VIEW

PLATE 43
see also 20, 42

MUSCULAR SYSTEM / LOWER LIMB
MUSCLES OF THE POSTERIOR LEG *

TIBIALIS POSTERIOR g
FLEXOR DIGITORUM LONGUS h
FLEXOR HALLUCIS LONGUS i
POPLITEUS j
PLANTARIS k
SOLEUS L
GASTROCNEMIUS m

CN 7
1. Using different colors from those on the preceding plate, color each muscle wherever it appears in successive views of the posterior leg. Color the attachments of the muscles, which were cut to show the deeper underlying muscles.
2. In these drawings, the foot is shown with an exaggerated plantar-flexed ankle joint so the plantar tendons can be more easily seen.

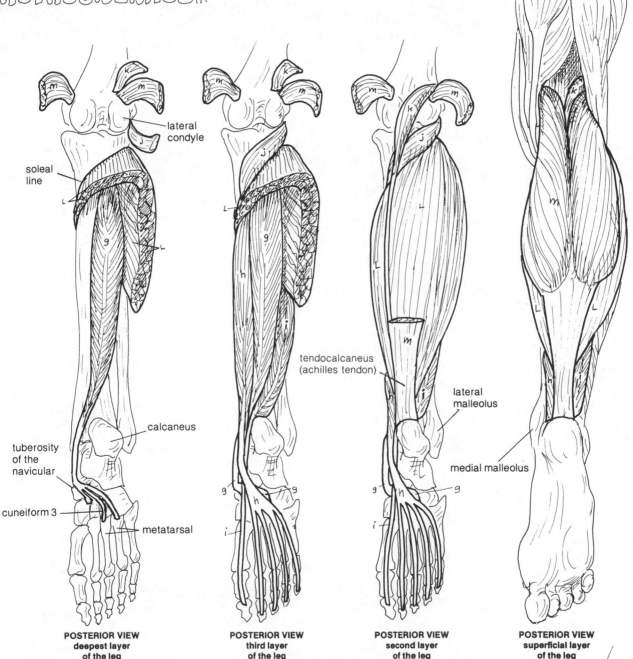

lateral condyle
soleal line
calcaneus
tuberosity of the navicular
cuneiform 3
metatarsal

tendocalcaneus (achilles tendon)
lateral malleolus
medial malleolus

POSTERIOR VIEW
deepest layer of the leg

POSTERIOR VIEW
third layer of the leg

POSTERIOR VIEW
second layer of the leg

POSTERIOR VIEW
superficial layer of the leg

Gastrocnemius (2 heads) and *soleus* form a tricipital muscle that inserts on the calcaneus (as the tendo-calcaneus) and lifts the body onto the heads of the metatarsals (plantarflexion). The other muscles/tendons crossing the ankle joint behind the center of gravity aid in this action. The muscles/tendons to the toes flex the digits (interphalangeal joints) and are so named. The orientation of the insertion of *tibialis pos-*

terior primarily influences the intertarsal joints, making this muscle a prime invertor (see Plate 42), as well as a plantarflexor. Functional use of the terms flexion/extension at the ankle joint is confusing although there is a firm embryological basis for such use. Generally, the terms plantarflexion (flexion) and dorsiflexion (extension) are used for ankle joint movements.

PLANTARFLEXION*

MUSCULAR SYSTEM/LOWER LIMB
MUSCLES OF THE FOOT *

PLATE 44
see also 21, 42, 43

CN 12

1. If about 21 colors are available to you, then use the colors from the preceding 2 plates on the leg to color the tendons of muscles (a–i) wherever they appear on this page. By relating these 3 plates on the leg and foot to each other, you will be going a long way in understanding the many structural relationships here.
2. If you have fewer than 21 colors, leave the tendons (a–i) blank.
3. Color the 12 muscles of the foot starting with the dorsal view and proceeding to the deep layer of the plantar muscles.

The muscles of the hand and foot are generally complementary in structure. However, the foot is structured to support the weight of the body and to provide a mobile platform in a variety of terrains. The hand, with its long fingers and slighter bones, is more of a machine or tool for more precise functions. In the drawing of the dorsal surface, the long flexor tendons have been cut to see deeper structure. Unlike the hand, there are intrinsic short extensor muscles to the phalanges.

The muscles of the plantar surface are arranged in about four layers (3 layers shown here), in conjunction with muscles of the leg that contribute tendons to the foot, create a stable surface yet with considerable mobility. The intrinsic muscles of the foot are largely concerned with stabilizing the joints of the foot when standing or walking/running on any one of many different surfaces.

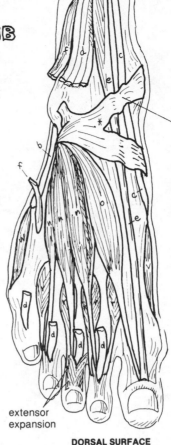

INFERIOR EXTENSOR RETINACULUM *

EXTENSOR DIGITORUM BREVIS n

EXTENSOR HALLUCIS BREVIS o

extensor expansion

DORSAL SURFACE

ADDUCTOR HALLUCIS p
FLEX. HALLUCIS BREV. q
INTEROSSEUS r
FLEX. DIGITI MINIMI BREV. s
OPPONENS DIGITI MINIMI t
QUADRATUS PLANTAE u

ABDUCTOR HALLUCIS v
ABD. DIGITI MINIMI w
LUMBRICALS x

FLEX. DIGITORUM BREVIS y
PLANTAR APONEUROSIS z *

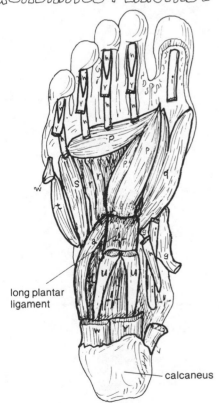

long plantar ligament

calcaneus

PLANTAR SURFACE
deep layer

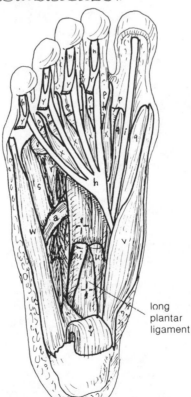

long plantar ligament

PLANTAR SURFACE
middle layer

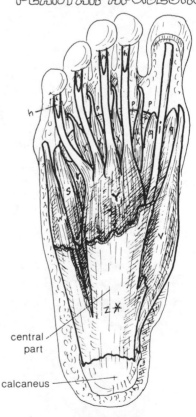

central part

calcaneus

PLANTAR SURFACE
superficial layer

PLATE 45
see also 20, 38–44

MUSCULAR SYSTEM / LOWER LIMB MUSCULAR REGIONS *

CN 8

1. Color all the muscles of each region with a single color.
2. Try to identify each muscle within a region. Note within the hip bone, shown on medial view, two muscles of the gluteal region (lateral rotators) are shown (a').

GLUTEAL a
ANTERIOR THIGH b
POSTERIOR THIGH c
MEDIAL THIGH d
ANTERIOR LEG e
LATERAL LEG f
POSTERIOR LEG g
FOOT h

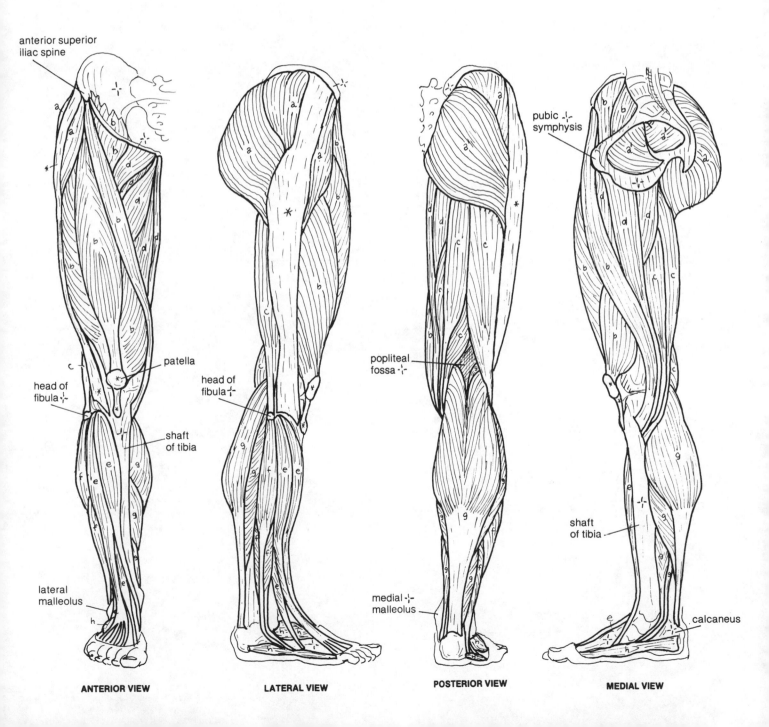

anterior superior iliac spine

patella

head of fibula ⊥

shaft of tibia

lateral malleolus

ANTERIOR VIEW

head of fibula ⊥

LATERAL VIEW

pubic ⊥ symphysis

popliteal fossa ⊥

medial ⊥ malleolus

POSTERIOR VIEW

pubic ⊥ symphysis

shaft of tibia

calcaneus

MEDIAL VIEW

PLATE 46
see also 10

MUSCULAR SYSTEM / REVIEW OF THE BODY RELATED FUNCTIONS*

FLEXORSₐ
EXTENSORS♭
ABDUCTORS𝒸
ADDUCTORS𝒹
ROTATORS𝑒
SCAPULA STABILIZERS𝒻

CN 6
1. Color the 6 areas of related functions of these superficial body muscles.

We have grouped these muscles according to their primary function. Though a muscle may have 2 or more primary functions, we selected one of those functions on the basis of the muscle's location and relationship to the joint it acts upon. When colored, these functional groups will form a visible pattern relating to their particular movement, their location, and the joint they operate.

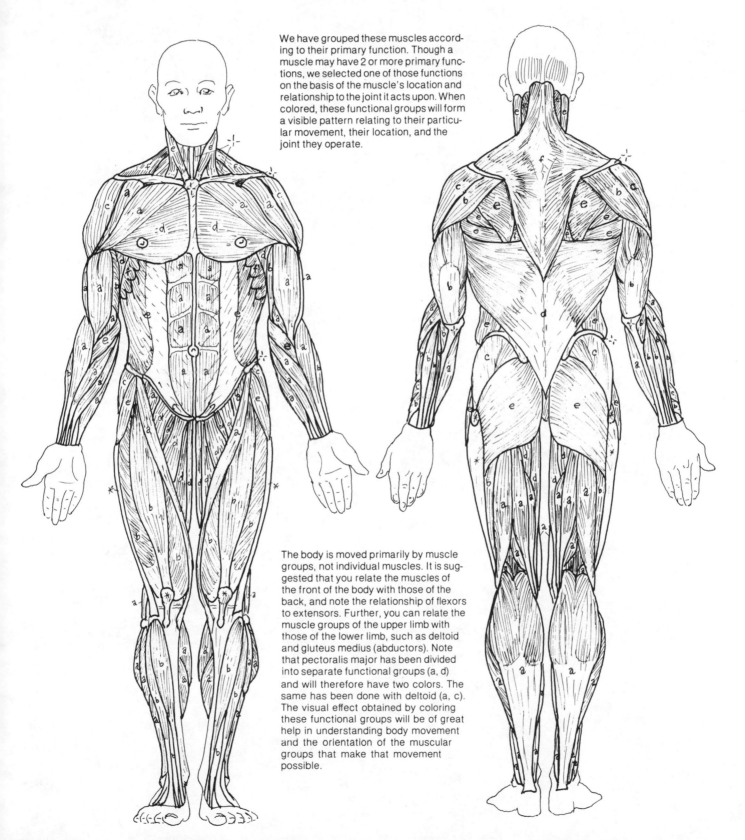

The body is moved primarily by muscle groups, not individual muscles. It is suggested that you relate the muscles of the front of the body with those of the back, and note the relationship of flexors to extensors. Further, you can relate the muscle groups of the upper limb with those of the lower limb, such as deltoid and gluteus medius (abductors). Note that pectoralis major has been divided into separate functional groups (a, d) and will therefore have two colors. The same has been done with deltoid (a, c). The visual effect obtained by coloring these functional groups will be of great help in understanding body movement and the orientation of the muscular groups that make that movement possible.

PLATE 47
see also 5, 6, 7

CARDIOVASCULAR SYSTEM
GENERAL SCHEME OF CIRCULATION *
STRUCTURE OF ARTERY ₐ VEIN ᵦ & CAPILLARY ꜀

CN 7

1. Reserve red for a, blue for b, and purple for c.
2. Color the structures below. As you color each layer, color the corresponding band in the cross section below it.
3. Color the scheme of circulation. Bold arrows are in the arterial flow as well as the pulmonary veins and these vessels should be colored red. The lighter arrows are in the veins as well as the right side of the heart and the pulmonary trunk/arteries; these vessels should be colored blue. Color the capillary areas (c) in purple. The red color reflects the higher degree of oxygenation. Start in the right atrium (marked with an S), fill the area completely with color (blue) and work in the direction of arrow flow.

This is a generalized scheme of the body circulation plan and not anatomically accurate. Use it to see how blood leaves the heart, reaches a body region, distributes nutrients/gases at the capillary level, and returns to the heart.

TUNICA INTERNA *
ENDOTHELIUM ᵈ
AREOLAR AND INTERNAL
ELASTIC TISSUE ₑ

TUNICA MEDIA *
SMOOTH MUSCLE CELLS f
AREOLAR AND EXTERNAL
ELASTIC TISSUE e'

TUNICA EXTERNA *
FIBROUS CONNECTIVE
TISSUE g

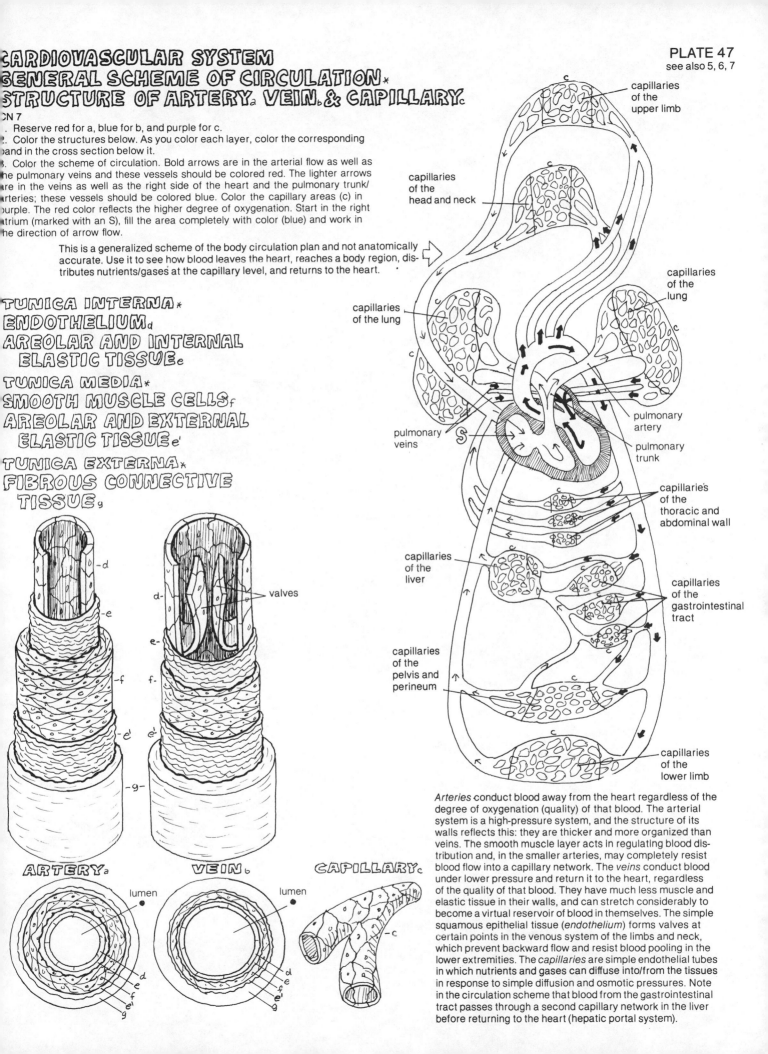

valves

ARTERY ₐ   VEIN ᵦ   CAPILLARY ꜀

lumen   lumen

capillaries
of the
upper limb

capillaries
of the
head and neck

capillaries
of the
lung

capillaries of the lung

pulmonary
veins

pulmonary
artery

pulmonary
trunk

S

capillaries
of the
thoracic and
abdominal wall

capillaries
of the
liver

capillaries
of the
gastrointestinal
tract

capillaries
of the
pelvis and
perineum

capillaries
of the
lower limb

Arteries conduct blood away from the heart regardless of the degree of oxygenation (quality) of that blood. The arterial system is a high-pressure system, and the structure of its walls reflects this: they are thicker and more organized than veins. The smooth muscle layer acts in regulating blood distribution and, in the smaller arteries, may completely resist blood flow into a capillary network. The *veins* conduct blood under lower pressure and return it to the heart, regardless of the quality of that blood. They have much less muscle and elastic tissue in their walls, and can stretch considerably to become a virtual reservoir of blood in themselves. The simple squamous epithelial tissue (*endothelium*) forms valves at certain points in the venous system of the limbs and neck, which prevent backward flow and resist blood pooling in the lower extremities. The *capillaries* are simple endothelial tubes in which nutrients and gases can diffuse into/from the tissues in response to simple diffusion and osmotic pressures. Note in the circulation scheme that blood from the gastrointestinal tract passes through a second capillary network in the liver before returning to the heart (hepatic portal system).

PLATE 48
see also 5

CARDIOVASCULAR SYSTEM
BLOOD & BLOOD CELLS*

CN 12

1. Each of the blood cells shown consists of cytoplasm, nucleus, and granules. Properly stained, they demonstrate several colors. To gain the full effect, each part of the cell (lettered but not named) should be colored as follows: a–pale orange; b–pale blue; c–red; d–reddish purple; e–dark purple; f–light purple; g–golden brown; h–straw (light tan). These colors are consistent with the stains usually employed to observe these microscopic cells.

2. Notice that the granules become larger as you go from neutrophil to basophil. Do not be concerned with covering each granule with the appropriate color.

3. The names of the various leukocytes should be left uncolored.

4. In the right half of the test tube diagram, notice that the areas representing the water portion of the plasma and the leukocytes & platelets portion of blood cell fraction should be left uncolored.

ERYTHROCYTES (RED BLOOD CELLS) a

Erythrocytes are formed in the bone marrow, lose their nucleus, and enter the blood circulation for about 120 days after which they are usually trapped in the spleen and broken down. The circulating RBC is a membrane-lined sac of hemoglobin, which has a powerful affinity for oxygen. Erythrocytes pick up the oxygen in the lungs and release it in the capillaries to the tissues/cells. Erythrocytes are the principal carriers of oxygen in the body, however, they do not normally leave the circulatory system except when they are broken down by the spleen. There are about 5 million RBC's per milliliter of blood (fewer in women).

LEUKOCYTES (WHITE BLOOD CELLS)
GRANULAR LEUKOCYTES *

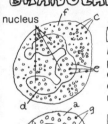

nucleus

NEUTROPHILS

Neutrophils make up about 65% of the total leukocyte population. Arising in the bone marrow, they contain strong enzymes in their granules. They take up bacteria at sites of infection and kill them. Masses of bacteria-stuffed neutrophils are known as pus.

EOSINOPHILS

Eosinophils make up about 3% of the total leukocyte population, and their granules are quite colorful when properly stained. Their precise function is unknown, but their concentration rises during allergic reactions.

BASOPHILS

Basophils make up less than 1% of the white blood cell population, and their dark staining granules are quite characteristic. Their function is not known.

cytoplasm

NONGRANULAR LEUKOCYTES *

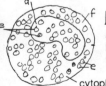

LYMPHOCYTES

Lymphocytes, making up about 30% of the leukocyte numbers, arise from lymph tissues (lymph nodes, thymus, spleen) and bone marrow. Lymphocytes secrete antibodies and assist in rejection of foreign tissue transplants. They are an essential part of the body defense system.

MONOCYTES

Monocytes are the largest of the leukocytes. They can readily enter and leave the circulatory system, and are capable of ingesting bacteria voraciously. These, with the neutrophils and lymphocytes, play an important part in the body defense (immune) system.

PLATELETS b

Platelets, small bits of cytoplasm from giant cells of the bone marrow, are found in the circulatory system at about 250,000 per milliliter of blood. The granules of the platelets are responsible for the clotting mechanism seen at injured blood vessels.

granules

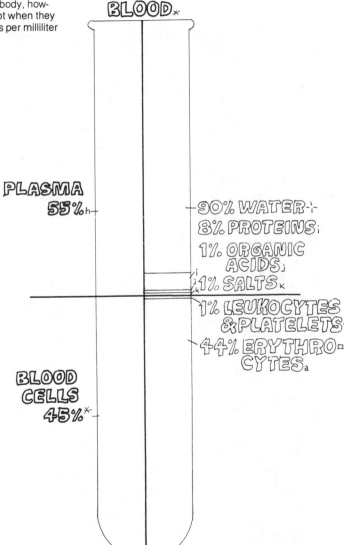

BLOOD *

PLASMA 55% h

90% WATER
8% PROTEINS
1% ORGANIC ACIDS
1% SALTS

1% LEUKOCYTES & PLATELETS
44% ERYTHRO-CYTES a

BLOOD CELLS 45% *

If whole blood is centrifuged in a test tube as shown, the *red cell volume* will settle to the bottom, the *leukocyte fraction* will form a buffy coat on top of that, and the *plasma* will form on top making up 55% of the total volume. The protein content of the plasma (plasma proteins) plays a critical role in the clotting mechanism. Fluid of the blood remaining after clotting is called serum.

PLATE 49
see also 14, 29

CARDIOVASCULAR SYSTEM
THE MEDIASTINUM.

TRACHEA a
ESOPHAGUS b
LUNGS * R □ *¹ L □ *²
DIAPHRAGM c
PHRENIC N. d
PERICARDIUM e

THE GREAT VESSELS & THEIR BRANCHES / TRIBUTARIES.

SUPERIOR VENA CAVA f & TRIB. f¹
INFERIOR VENA CAVA f²
AORTA g & BRANCHES g¹
PULMONARY ARTERIES f³
PULMONARY VEINS g²

MEDIASTINUM.

SUPERIOR h ANTERIOR i
MIDDLE e' POSTERIOR j

CN 14
1. Color red the vessels carrying oxygenated blood (g, g¹, g²); color blue those vessels carrying deoxygenated blood (f, f¹, f², f³).
2. Arteries give off branches (g gives off g¹); veins are formed by their tributaries (f formed by f¹).

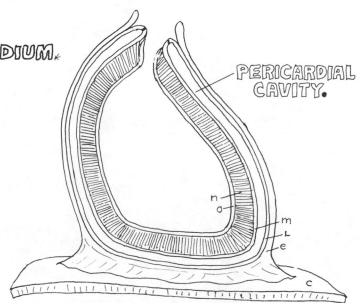

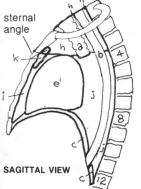

SAGITTAL VIEW

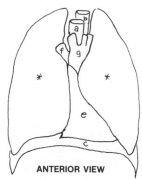

ANTERIOR VIEW

THYMUS GLAND k

The *mediastinum* is a highly populated partition between the lungs. For descriptive purposes, it is divided into the several subdivisions shown at left. The *superior mediastinum* is bordered above by the first rib and below by an imaginary horizontal line running from the sternal angle to the 4th thoracic vertebra. Therein one can find the great vessels of the heart (less inf. vena cava), *trachea, esophagus,* and important nerves including the *phrenic nerves* to the *diaphragm*. The *middle mediastinum* is taken up by the heart and its sac. The *anterior mediastinum* is largely devoid of structure with the exception of the thymus gland, which may extend down from the superior mediastinum in children. The thymus gland is shown on the diagram at far left. The *posterior mediastinum* contains esophagus, descending aorta, thoracic duct, vagus nerves, etc. Note that the floor of the mediastinum is the diaphragm. Note at left the heart is partially covered by the left lung; this is anatomically correct; above, the lung has been retracted on the left side to expose the phrenic nerve.

WALLS OF THE HEART & PERICARDIUM.
FIBROUS PERICARDIUM e
PARIETAL PERICARDIUM L
VISCERAL PERICARDIUM m
MYOCARDIUM n
ENDOCARDIUM o

The heart is enveloped in a three-layered sac (*pericardium*). The inner *visceral pericardium* (epicardium) clothes the heart. At the origin of the aortic arch, this layer turns outward (reflects) to become the *parietal pericardium*. Both these layers secrete a serous fluid which allows the heart to move in its sac without creating friction. The *pericardial cavity* is only potential, as both layers of the pericardium are normally separated by only a thin film of fluid. The *fibrous pericardium* is the outer face of the parietal pericardium; it is fibrous and fatty, and is strongly attached to the sternum, the great vessels, and the diaphragm. It keeps the rhythmically beating heart in its place. The heart itself is composed of an inner layer of simple squamous epithelium (*endocardium*) and the muscular *myocardium*.

PERICARDIAL CAVITY.

PLATE 50
see also 47, 49

CARDIOVASCULAR SYSTEM
CHAMBERS OF THE HEART.

CN 17

1. In both drawings, use red for the heavy-lined arrows (representing the flow of oxygenated blood from the lungs) and numbers. Use blue for the light-lined arrows (deoxygenated blood) and numbers. Start the coloring with the superior vena cava (c) and follow the sequence of titles (direction of blood flow.
2. Save bright or dark colors for f, h, i, j, k, l, p.
3. Color in the arrows in the diagram below, starting in the right atrium (1) with blue, and follow the arrows representing blood flow.

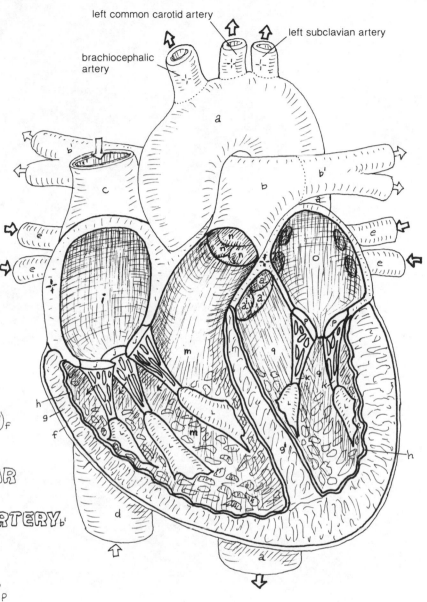

left common carotid artery

left subclavian artery

brachiocephalic artery

SUPERIOR VENA CAVA c
INFERIOR VENA CAVA d

RIGHT ATRIUM i

TRICUSPID VALVE j
CHORDAE TENDINEAE k
PAPILLARY MUSCLE l

RIGHT VENTRICLE m
ENDOCARDIUM h
MYOCARDIUM g
EPICARDIUM
(VISCERAL PERICARDIUM) f
INTERVENTRICULAR
SEPTUM g'
PULMONARY SEMILUNAR
VALVE n

PULMONARY TRUNK b /ARTERY b'
PULMONARY VEINS e

LEFT ATRIUM o

BICUSPID (MITRAL) VALVE p

LEFT VENTRICLE q
AORTIC SEMILUNAR VALVE a'

AORTA a

The *heart* is the muscular pump of the blood vascular system—it is the only one in the system. It has four chambers: two on the right relate to the lungs (pulmonary circulation) and two on the left are concerned with the rest of the body (systemic circulation). Deoxygenated blood from the body enters the *right atrium* and is pumped to the lungs by the *right ventricle* under relatively low pressure. Oxygenated blood returns to the *left atrium* and is pumped to the body tissues by the *left ventricle* under rather high pressure, a fact reflected in the thicker left ventricular walls. The *bi-/tricuspid valves* prevent regurgitation of blood back into the atria; the *semilunar valves* prevent reflux of blood back into the ventricles. The *endocardium* is a continuation of the endothelium which lines all blood vessels: simple squamous epithelium. The *myocardium* is cardiac muscle.

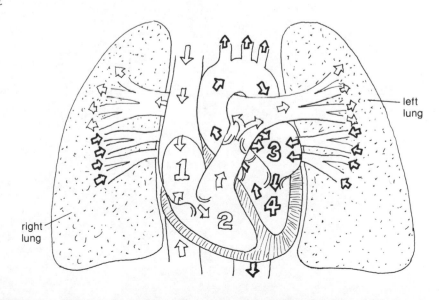

left lung

right lung

PLATE 51
see also 50

CARDIOVASCULAR SYSTEM
CARDIAC CONDUCTION SYSTEM∗

CN 4
1. Color the conduction system in the heart, noticing that a and a′ get the same color.
2. Color the electrocardiogram below, including the various letters.

SA (SINOATRIAL) NODE ₐ
INTERNODAL TRACTS ₐ′
AV (ATRIOVENTRICULAR) NODE ᵦ
AV BUNDLE (HIS) 𝒸
PURKINJE FIBERS 𝒹

Cardiac muscle cells (fibers) are capable of contracting spontaneously; that is, without a nerve stimulus. If all the individual cardiac muscle cells contracted independently without synchrony, no effective pumping action would occur. Enter a network of specialized muscle fibers, which conduct electrophysiological impulses better than they contract. Situated among the regular cardiac muscle fibers, this *cardiac conduction system* is more self-excitable than the cardiac muscle fibers themselves, and therefore controls and synchronizes cardiac muscle contraction. The *SA node* is the most excitable part of the system, therefore it sets the pace ("pacemaker") of impulse conduction. The impulses pass through the atrial musculature or along *internodal tracts* (whose existence is in question) to the *AV node*. Impulses pass from here through the *AV bundle* to the *Purkinje fibers* to the muscles of the ventricles. After a short delay, the SA node fires again and the cycle repeats itself. Each cycle creates a sequence of pumping actions. It is the pumping action of the ventricles which constitutes a heart beat.

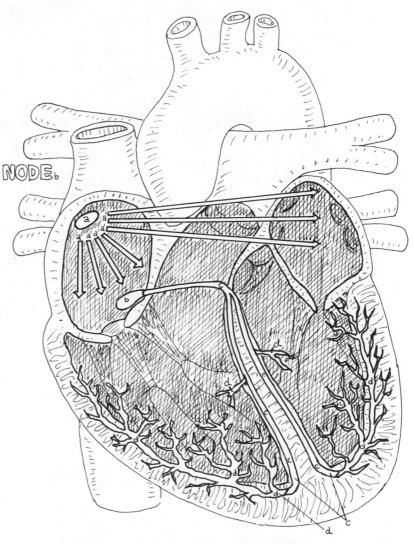

The *ECG* measures the electrochemical activity of the heart. Electrodes are placed at a number of body points and record, in the skin, the voltage and current changes in the heart. The *P* wave is created by impulses passing through the atria from the SA node. Atrial contraction follows immediately. The end of the P wave reflects a delay in impulse transmission at the AV node. The *QRS* wave reflects impulse transmission down the bundle, through the Purkinje fibers and ventricular muscle—a very rapid transmission, as you can see. Ventricular contraction follows immediately. The *T* wave is caused by a recovery of electrical charge in the ventricles, to be followed by another P wave.

ELECTROCARDIOGRAM (ECG) (EKG) ∗

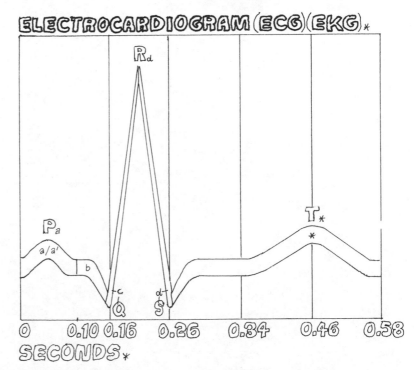

R_d

P_a

a/a′

b

$T_∗$

∗

c

Q

d

S

0   0.10 0.16   0.26   0.34   0.46   0.58

SECONDS ∗

PLATE 52
see also 50

CARDIOVASCULAR SYSTEM
CORONARY CIRCULATION OF THE HEART*

CN 16

1. Reserve the brightest and darkest colors for arteries and veins (n–t).
2. Note that the right atrium and left ventricle are to be colored gray. The other two cavities are left uncolored.
3. The broken lines represent the vessels on the posterior side of the heart, and should be colored.
4. Note the pulmonary artery has been bisected and separated to show the origin of the left coronary artery.

AORTA a
PULMONARY TRUNK b /ARTERY b'
SUPERIOR VENA CAVA c
R. ATRIUM d*
R. VENTRICLE e-¦-
L. VENTRICLE f*
L. ATRIUM g-¦-

THE CORONARY ARTERIES*
R. CORONARY ARTERY h
MUSCULAR BRANCHES h'
MARGINAL BRANCH i
POSTERIOR INTERVENTRICULAR BRANCH j
L. CORONARY ARTERY k
MUSCULAR BRANCHES k'
ANTERIOR INTERVENTRICULAR BRANCH L
CIRCUMFLEX ARTERY m

The *coronary arteries* supply the heart muscle and form a crown (L. *corona*) about the heart. Both left and right arteries arise from small openings in the pockets of two aortic semilunar valves (aortic sinuses). There are insufficient communications (anastomoses) between the two arteries to enable one artery to supply the heart should the other become largely obstructed. Varying degrees of vascular insufficiency occur with obstruction of branches of the *right/left coronary arteries*.

THE CARDIAC VEINS*
GREAT CARDIAC V. n
MIDDLE CARDIAC V. o
MARGINAL V. p
ANTERIOR CARDIAC V. q
SMALL CARDIAC r
CORONARY SINUS s
OBLIQUE t

The *cardiac veins* do not form a complete crown about the heart and, therefore, are not called coronary veins. They generally travel with the coronary arteries. These veins drain the capillary networks of the myocardium and drain into the right atrium by way of the *coronary sinus*. Other small veins may drain directly into the right atrium.

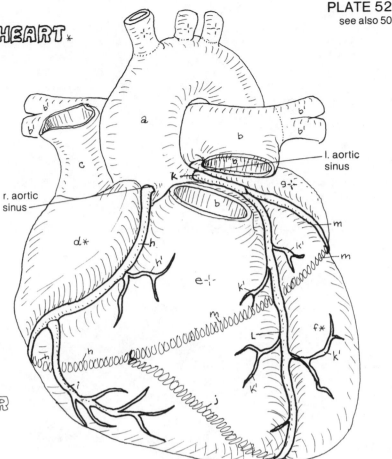

l. aortic sinus

r. aortic sinus

ANTERIOR VIEW

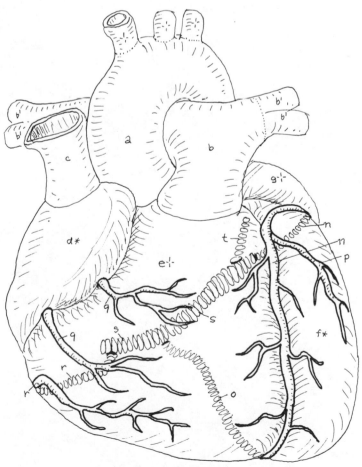

ANTERIOR VIEW

PLATE 53
see also 54, 57

CARDIOVASCULAR SYSTEM
ARTERIES OF THE HEAD & NECK *

CN ?

1. If you need to use the same color for more than one artery, try not to use it for neighboring vessels.
2. The broken lines represent deeper vessels.

BRACHIOCEPHALIC a

R. SUBCLAVIAN b
INTERNAL THORACIC c
VERTEBRAL d
THYROCERVICAL TRUNK e
INFERIOR THYROID f
SUPRASCAPULAR g
TRANSVERSE CERVICAL h
COSTOCERVICAL TRUNK i
DEEP CERVICAL j
HIGHEST INTERCOSTAL k

R. COMMON CAROTID L
INTERNAL CAROTID m
OPHTHALMIC n
EXTERNAL CAROTID o
SUPERIOR THYROID p
LINGUAL q
FACIAL r
OCCIPITAL s
MAXILLARY t
ALVEOLAR BRANCHES: u
INF. n u SUP. n u'
MIDDLE MENINGEAL v
POSTERIOR AURICULAR w
TRANSVERSE FACIAL x
SUPERFICIAL TEMPORAL y

The arteries shown here are the principal vessels supplying the general area of the head and neck. Note that the name of the vessel often indicates its destination. Blood supply to the face comes almost completely from the *external carotid arteries,* as do vessels supplying deeper structures in the head. The *vertebral* and *internal carotid arteries* are the sole supply to the brain; the latter also supplies the orbit. Note the *middle meningeal artery* stemming from the *maxillary:* it supplies the dura mater enveloping the brain and is a relatively frequent site of rupture (epidural hematoma) with a hard fall on the side of the head. Branches from the *subclavian* and lower part of the external carotid supply the neck. These arteries tend to be variable in their pattern. The pulse of the subclavian can be felt behind and somewhat deep to the clavicle; the pulse of the *common carotid* can be felt over the anterior border of sternocleidomastoid; the pulse of the *facial* can be felt over the middle part of the body of the mandible; the pulse of the *superficial temporal* can be felt just in front of the ear. Check Plate 57 and note that the origin of the common carotid and subclavian arteries on the left side of the neck is different from the right.

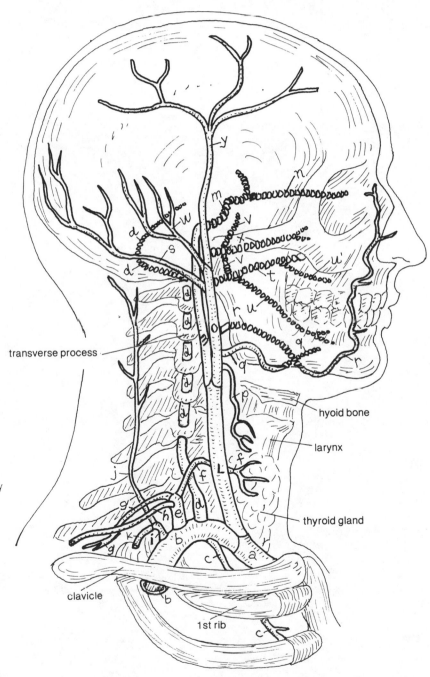

transverse process

hyoid bone

larynx

thyroid gland

clavicle

1st rib

PLATE 54
see also 53, 57

CARDIOVASCULAR SYSTEM
ARTERIAL SUPPLY OF THE BRAIN*

CN 9

1. Color the various arteries in the large illustration as well as the diagram to the far right. The arrows should be left blank.
2. Only arteries b, d, and f appear in the illustrations below.

INTERNAL CAROTID A. c

ANTERIOR CEREBRAL A. b

ANTERIOR COMMUNICATING A. a

MIDDLE CEREBRAL A. d

POSTERIOR COMMUNICATING A. e

VERTEBRAL A. h

ANTERIOR SPINAL A. j

BASILAR A. g

CEREBELLAR (3) A. i

POSTERIOR CEREBRAL A. f

The *internal carotid* and *vertebral arteries* supply blood to the brain. At the base of the brain around the hypophysis (pituitary gland), a number of branches form an anastomotic circle (of Willis), which probably serves to reduce the blood pressure in the smaller branches coming off that circle. Small branches (not shown) coming off the *middle cerebral artery* close to the internal carotid are generally known as "stroke arteries" due to their frequent involvement in cerebral hemorrhages. Functional anastomoses among the vessels at the circle are generally believed to be poor, as occlusion of one of the four major arteries to the brain may cause significant symptoms.

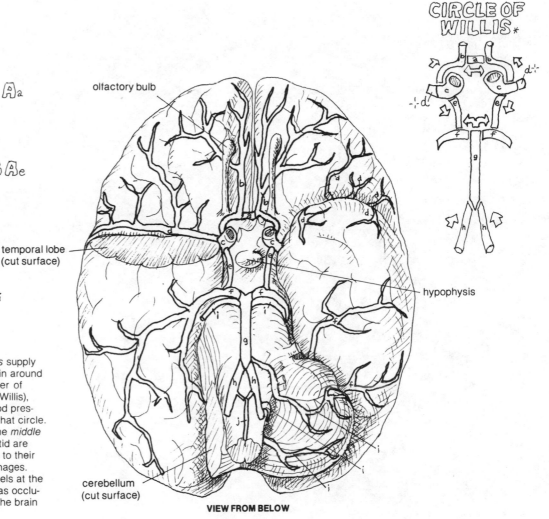

CIRCLE OF WILLIS*

olfactory bulb

temporal lobe (cut surface)

hypophysis

cerebellum (cut surface)

VIEW FROM BELOW

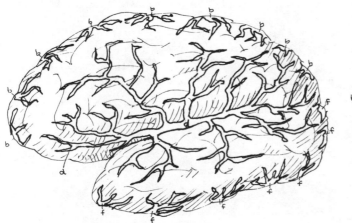

LATERAL VIEW

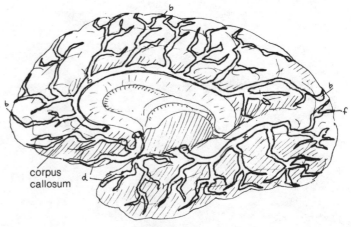

corpus callosum

MEDIAL SURFACE OF RIGHT HEMISPHERE

PLATE 55
see also 18, 57

CARDIOVASCULAR SYSTEM
THE UPPER LIMB / ARTERIES & VEINS*

internal jugular vein

external jugular vein

CN ?

1. When coloring the veins and their names, we recommend you start coloring at the hand and work up to the veins of the neck. Color the small tributaries the same color as the larger veins. Broken lines represent surface veins on opposite side of this anterior view.

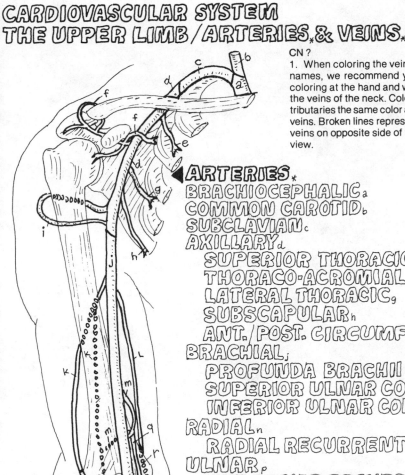

ARTERIES *
BRACHIOCEPHALIC a
COMMON CAROTID b
SUBCLAVIAN c
AXILLARY d
SUPERIOR THORACIC e
THORACO-ACROMIAL & BRANCHES f
LATERAL THORACIC g
SUBSCAPULAR h
ANT./POST. CIRCUMFLEX HUMERAL i
BRACHIAL j
PROFUNDA BRACHII & BRANCHES k
SUPERIOR ULNAR COLLATERAL L
INFERIOR ULNAR COLLATERAL m
RADIAL n
RADIAL RECURRENT o
ULNAR p
ANT. ULNAR RECURRENT q
POST. ULNAR RECURRENT r
COMMON INTEROSSEOUS t
SUPERFICIAL PALMAR ARCH u
PALMAR DIGITAL v
DEEP PALMAR ARCH w

There are several places in the arterial pattern where significant collateral circulation exists, such as around the scapula (not shown), the shoulder, at the elbow, and at the palm. Can you see how blood might get to the forearm if the upper portion of the brachial artery was obstructed? The *subclavian artery* (above the clavicle), the *brachial artery* (medially, against the humerus), and the *radial/ulnar arteries* (at the wrist) can be felt pulsating.

VEINS ▶
DORSAL DIGITAL a & NETWORK a'
BASILIC b
MEDIAN V. OF FOREARM c
CEPHALIC d
MEDIAN CUBITAL e
BRACHIAL f
AXILLARY g
SUBCLAVIAN h
BRACHIOCEPHALIC i

The veins of the upper limb, as everywhere, are quite variable in their pattern. There are generally two sets of veins: deep and superficial. The deep set follow the arteries and are not shown in the anterior aspect of the forearm and lower arm. These deep veins often travel in pairs (venae comitantes; not shown). The superficial veins of the hand and forearm are drained by the *basilic* and *cephalic veins* that travel in the superficial fascia. They, and their tributaries, can often be seen below the skin. The superficial veins of the elbow are frequent sites for blood sampling and administration of intravenous medication.

ANTERIOR
VIEW

ANTERIOR
VIEW

CARDIOVASCULAR SYSTEM
ARTERIES OF THE LOWER LIMB∗

PLATE 56
see also 55, 57

CN ?
1. Work on both views simultaneously.
2. The foot on the right (posterior view) is plantar flexed, showing the sole (plantar surface) of that foot.

inguinal ligament

ABDOMINAL AORTA_a

ABDOMINAL AORTA a
R.COMMON ILIAC b
INTERNAL ILIAC c
OBTURATOR d
SUPERIOR GLUTEAL e
INFERIOR GLUTEAL f
EXTERNAL ILIAC g
FEMORAL h
PROFUNDA FEMORIS i
PERFORATING BRANCHES j
MEDIAL CIRCUMFLEX FEMORAL k
LATERAL CIRCUMFLEX FEMORAL l
DESCENDING BRANCH m
POPLITEAL n
GENICULAR o
ANTERIOR TIBIAL p
DORSALIS PEDIS q
ARCUATE r
DORSAL METATARSAL s
DORSAL DIGITAL t
POSTERIOR TIBIAL u
PERONEAL v
MEDIAL PLANTAR w
LATERAL PLANTAR x
PLANTAR ARCH y
PLANTAR METATARSAL z
PLANTAR DIGITAL 1.

You can gain a good deal of information by comparing the arterial pattern of the lower limb with that of the upper limb. Two important sites of collateral circulation occur about the hip and knee joints. Hip joint problems may relate to inadequate circulation in that area. The arteries about the knee joint (*genicular*) are considered by many to provide inadequate collateral circulation should the *popliteal artery* be obstructed. Note that the gluteal region is supplied largely by *gluteal branches* of the *internal iliac artery* (see Plate 59 on pelvis/perineal blood supply). Arterial pulsations can be obtained from the *femoral* (just below the inguinal ligament) and the *dorsalis pedis* (just below the ankle) as well as the *posterior tibial* (behind the medial malleolus).

ANTERIOR VIEW

POSTERIOR VIEW
(foot in plantarflexion)

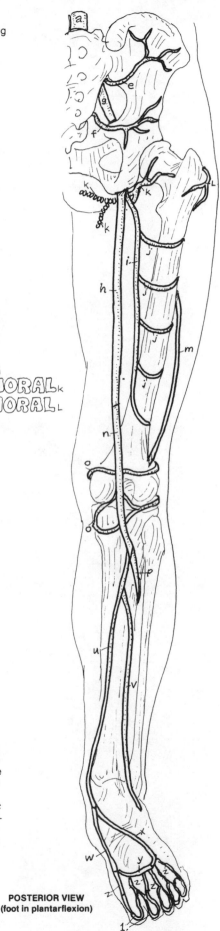

PLATE 57
see also 50, 52, 53, 56, 58

CARDIOVASCULAR SYSTEM
THORACIC & ABDOMINAL AORTA*

CN ?
1. It will be necessary to repeat colors in this drawing.
2. Use bright red for a, a^1, a^2, and a^3.
3. Color the dotted inferior vena cava and its tributaries in gray.

ASCENDING AORTA a
AORTIC SINUSES b

AORTIC ARCH a¹
BRACHIOCEPHALIC c
COMMON CAROTID d
SUBCLAVIAN e
INTERNAL THORACIC f
COSTOCERVICAL TRUNK g
HIGHEST INTERCOSTAL h

THORACIC (DESCENDING) AORTA a²
BRONCHIAL i
ESOPHAGEAL j
POSTERIOR INTERCOSTAL k

ABDOMINAL AORTA a³
INFERIOR PHRENIC l
SUPRARENAL m
CELIAC TRUNK n
L. GASTRIC o
SPLENIC p
HEPATIC q
SUPERIOR MESENTERIC r
RENAL s
TESTICULAR/OVARIAN t
LUMBAR u
INFERIOR MESENTERIC v
MIDDLE SACRAL w

COMMON ILIAC x
INTERNAL ILIAC y
EXTERNAL ILIAC z

The *sinuses* of the ascending aorta become the left and right coronary arteries of the heart. The thoracic aorta (a^2) supplies posterior intercostal arteries (k) to intercostal spaces 3–11. Posterior intercostal arteries for intercostal spaces 1 and 2 come off the highest intercostal artery (h), a branch of the costocervical trunk (g). Posterior intercostal arteries join with anterior intercostal arteries (not shown here; see arteries labeled (o) in Plate 60) derived from the internal thoracic arteries (f) which descend on either side of and deep to the sternum. Note the small *bronchial arteries* supplying primary bronchi and the segmental *esophageal arteries* supplying the esophagus along its length. The *thoracic aorta* passes through the aortic hiatus of the diaphragm.

Branches of the *abdominal aorta* are usually described as visceral and parietal. The major arteries here are visceral, supplying stomach, liver, spleen, kidneys, etc. Parietal branches arise as segmental arteries on both sides, along the length of the aorta supplying the muscles of the posterior abdominal wall (lumbar arteries). Note the arteries supplying the suprarenal glands.

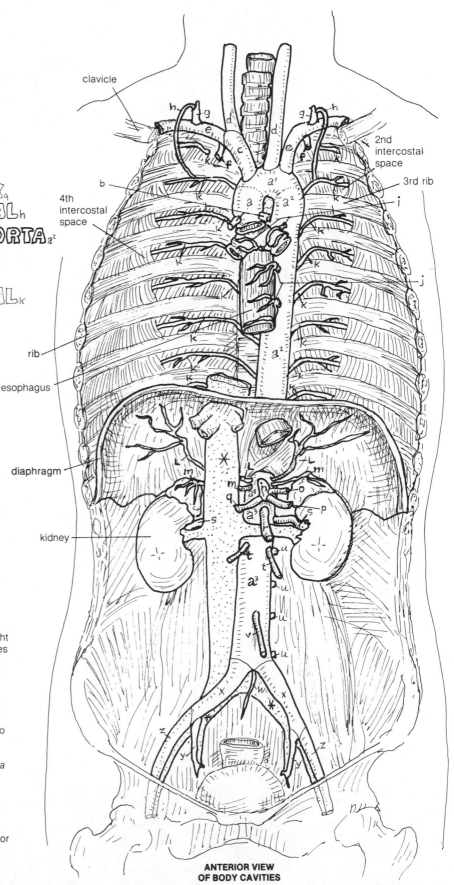

**ANTERIOR VIEW
OF BODY CAVITIES**

PLATE 58
see also 57

CARDIOVASCULAR SYSTEM
ARTERIES TO ORGANS OF DIGESTIVE SYSTEM *

CN 18
1. Save your three brightest colors for a, k, and p.
2. Color the aorta and its terminal arteries (marked with asterisk) gray.

CELIAC TRUNK a
HEPATIC b
L. GASTRIC c
SPLENIC d
R. GASTRIC e
CYSTIC f
GASTRODUODENAL g
PANCREATICODUODENAL (SUP.) h
L. GASTROEPIPLOIC i
R. GASTROEPIPLOIC j

The *celiac trunk* is a very short artery that divides immediately into arteries to the liver, spleen, and stomach. Note the interesting pattern of arteries to the stomach. Only the major branches of these three arteries are shown here. Many of the blood vessels to the pancreas arise from the *splenic artery*.

AORTA & BRANCHES *

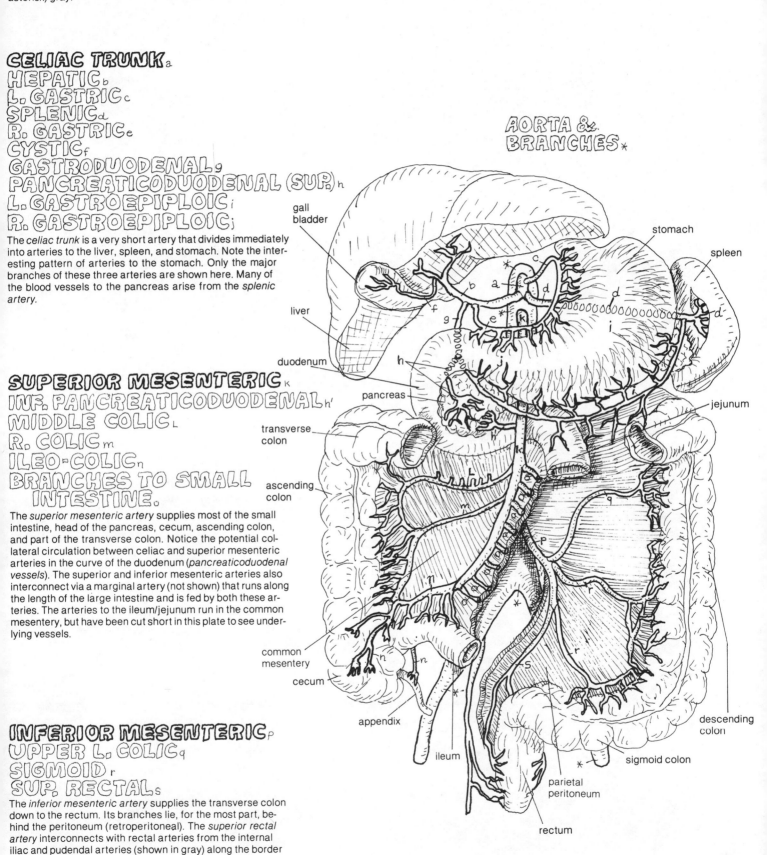

gall bladder

stomach

spleen

liver

duodenum

pancreas

jejunum

SUPERIOR MESENTERIC k
INF. PANCREATICODUODENAL h'
MIDDLE COLIC l
R. COLIC m
ILEO-COLIC n
BRANCHES TO SMALL INTESTINE o

The *superior mesenteric artery* supplies most of the small intestine, head of the pancreas, cecum, ascending colon, and part of the transverse colon. Notice the potential collateral circulation between celiac and superior mesenteric arteries in the curve of the duodenum (*pancreaticoduodenal vessels*). The superior and inferior mesenteric arteries also interconnect via a marginal artery (not shown) that runs along the length of the large intestine and is fed by both these arteries. The arteries to the ileum/jejunum run in the common mesentery, but have been cut short in this plate to see underlying vessels.

transverse colon

ascending colon

common mesentery

cecum

appendix

ileum

descending colon

sigmoid colon

parietal peritoneum

rectum

INFERIOR MESENTERIC p
UPPER L. COLIC q
SIGMOID r
SUP. RECTAL s

The *inferior mesenteric artery* supplies the transverse colon down to the rectum. Its branches lie, for the most part, behind the peritoneum (retroperitoneal). The *superior rectal artery* interconnects with rectal arteries from the internal iliac and pudendal arteries (shown in gray) along the border of the rectum.

PLATE 59
see also 30, 56, 57

CARDIOVASCULAR SYSTEM
ARTERIES OF THE PELVIS & PERINEUM*

CN ?
1. Use a bright color for the internal iliac artery (e). If it is necessary to repeat colors, try to use a separate color for each of the branches of the internal iliac artery.
2. Work both illustrations simultaneously. Only those vessels involved in the rectal anastomoses are shown below.

AORTA a
MIDDLE SACRAL b
COMMON ILIAC c
EXTERNAL ILIAC d
INTERNAL ILIAC e
ILIOLUMBAR f
LATERAL SACRAL g
SUPERIOR GLUTEAL h
INFERIOR GLUTEAL i
OBTURATOR j
INTERNAL PUDENDAL k
INFERIOR RECTAL l
POSTERIOR SCROTAL m
ARTERY TO PENIS n
MIDDLE RECTAL o
INFERIOR VESICAL p
UMBILICAL q
SUPERIOR VESICAL r

The *internal iliac artery* is the principal artery supplying the pelvis and perineum, with some assistance from the inferior mesenteric and femoral arteries. Arterial branches of the internal iliac are usually organized into parietal (wall) and visceral divisions. The actual branching of these vessels is quite variable, and the pattern shown here is considered common. In the female, the uterine and vaginal arteries (not shown) come off the internal iliac; in the male, the arteries to the prostate and seminal vesicles (not shown) come off the *inferior vesical* with a branch off the *superior vesical* going to the ductus deferens (not shown). The external genital structures are supplied by the *internal pudendal* (L. to be ashamed) *arteries.* The *umbilical artery,* conducting fetal blood to the mother via the umbilical cord, dries up to become the medial umbilical ligament in the adult.

RECTAL ANASTOMOSES*
INFERIOR MESENTERIC s
SIGMOID t
SUPERIOR RECTAL u
MIDDLE RECTAL o
INFERIOR RECTAL l

The rectum is a place in which arteries from three different sources often interconnect (anastomosis). Should one or two of these arteries be obstructed, the rectum can still be supplied by the third. Further, blood could flow backward (retrograde) from the *rectal anastomosis* through the *superior rectal artery* to the *inferior mesenteric* and supply organs normally supplied by that artery. This would be effective if the inferior mesenteric artery had become obstructed at its source. Organs supplied by the internal pudendal or internal iliac could receive blood by the same mechanism in the event of certain obstructions.

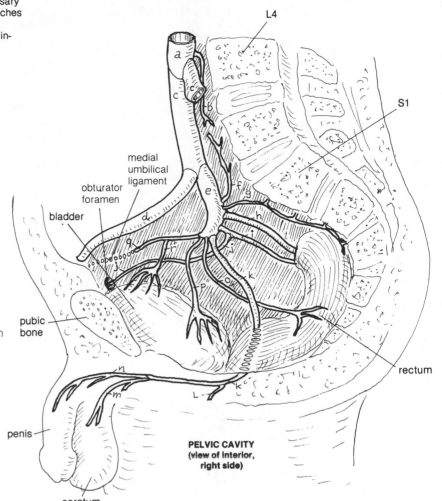

L4
S1
medial umbilical ligament
obturator foramen
bladder
pubic bone
penis
scrotum
rectum

PELVIC CAVITY
(view of interior, right side)

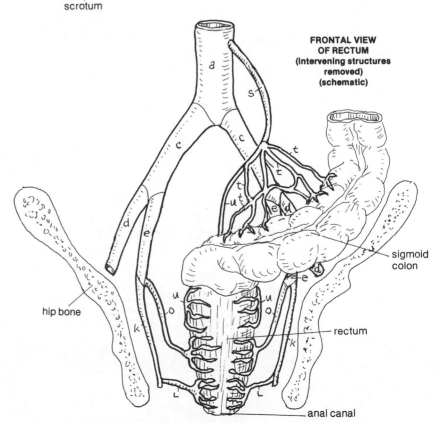

FRONTAL VIEW OF RECTUM
(intervening structures removed)
(schematic)

hip bone
sigmoid colon
rectum
anal canal

PLATE 60

CARDIOVASCULAR SYSTEM
PRINCIPAL ARTERIES OF THE
ARTERIAL SYSTEM *

CN ?

1. Using the preceding plates of the arterial system as reference where necessary, color each artery and write its name in the appropriate space using the same color.

2. The answer key to this plate may be reviewed in the back of the book .

Only the *major arteries* are shown on this plate. The arteries of the limbs are duplicated on each side, but note carefully the arteries of the trunk: the internal thoracic (n) and intercostal (o) arteries are shown on one side only, as are branches of the pulmonary trunk (10). The internal thoracic artery, not shown on a previous plate, gives off the anterior intercostal arteries (o) (between the ribs), which anastomose with the posterior intercostal arteries coming off the thoracic aorta (not shown here). The internal thoracic continues through the anterior abdominal wall (deep to the rectus abdominis) as the superior epigastric (p) and interconnects with the inferior epigastric artery (q) coming off the external iliac (y). This route offers an important collateral route of flow, bypassing the thoracic and abdominal aorta.

a.+a' _____
b _____
c _____
d _____
e _____
f _____
g _____
h _____
i _____
j _____
k _____
L _____
m _____
n _____
o _____
p _____
q _____
r _____
s _____
t _____
u _____
v _____
w _____
x _____
y _____
z _____
1. _____
2. _____
3. _____
4. _____
5. _____
6. _____
7. _____
8. _____
9. _____
10. _____

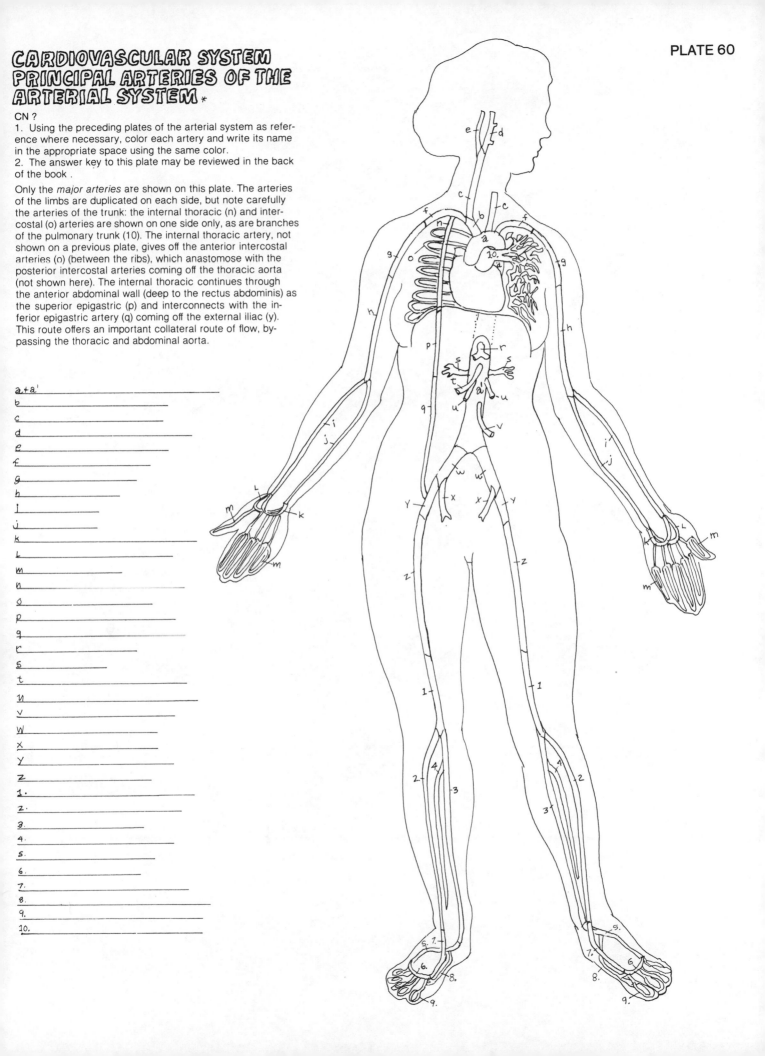

PLATE 61
see also 119

CARDIOVASCULAR SYSTEM
VEINS OF THE HEAD & NECK *
SINUSES OF THE DURA MATER *

CN ?

1. As you color the lateral view of the head, color the sinuses of the dura mater in the illustration below. In the upper drawing, the sinuses are indicated by broken lines (with one exception [i]).

SINUSES OF THE DURA MATER *

SUPERIOR SAGITTAL SINUS a
INFERIOR SAGITTAL SINUS b
GREAT CEREBRAL VEIN c
STRAIGHT SINUS d
OCCIPITAL SINUS e
TRANSVERSE SINUS f
SIGMOID SINUS g
SUPERIOR OPHTHALMIC VEIN h
CAVERNOUS SINUS i
SUPERIOR PETROSAL SINUS j
INFERIOR PETROSAL SINUS k

VEINS OF THE HEAD & NECK *

SUPERFICIAL TEMPORAL V. L
PTERYGOID PLEXUS m
MAXILLARY V. n
RETROMANDIBULAR V. o
POSTERIOR AURICULAR V. p
ANTERIOR JUGULAR V. q
EXTERNAL JUGULAR V. r

ANGULAR V. s
FACIAL V. t
DEEP FACIAL V. u
LINGUAL V. v
SUPERIOR THYROID V. w
MIDDLE THYROID V. x
INTERNAL JUGULAR V. y

DEEP CERVICAL V. z
VERTEBRAL V. 1

SUBCLAVIAN V. 2. AXILLARY V. 3
BRACHIOCEPHALIC V. 4.

The veins draining the brain are tributaries of the large veins (sinuses) in the dura mater, a tough covering of the brain. The internal jugular vein is the principal vessel receiving blood from these sinuses. Should it become occluded, the angular vein (s) (draining the superior ophthalmic vein), the pterygoid plexus, and the suboccipital veins (not shown) offer collateral circulation. The tributaries of the internal/external jugular veins are quite variable and interconnect at a number of places. The internal jugular vein rides with the internal/common carotid arteries, while the external jugular vein can often be seen in the superficial fascia at the side of the neck.

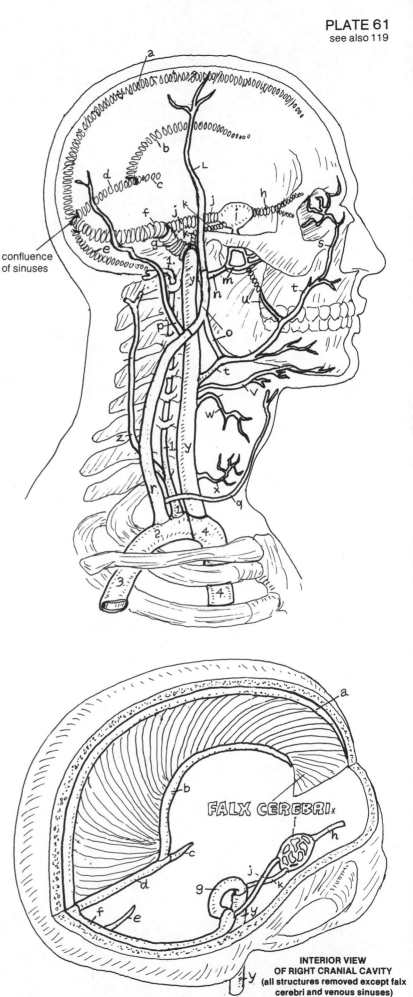

confluence of sinuses

FALX CEREBRI x

INTERIOR VIEW
OF RIGHT CRANIAL CAVITY
(all structures removed except falx cerebri and venous sinuses)

PLATE 62
see also 49, 50, 57, 61, 64

CARDIOVASCULAR SYSTEM
VEINS OF THE FRONT OF THE NECK*
AZYGOS VEIN & TRIBUTARIES*
INFERIOR VENA CAVA & TRIBUTARIES*

CN?

1. Color the aorta and its branches (stippled with tiny dots) gray throughout. Include the diaphragm marked with an asterisk.
2. Certain veins shown in the neck and between the kidneys are connecting veins and do not have to be colored or named.

FRONT OF THE NECK*
INTERNAL JUGULAR a
EXTERNAL JUGULAR b
ANTERIOR JUGULAR c
FACIAL d
MIDDLE THYROID e'
SUPERIOR THYROID e
INFERIOR THYROID f
JUGULAR VENOUS ARCH g
SUBCLAVIAN, R. & L. h
BRACHIOCEPHALIC R. & L. i
INTERNAL THORACIC j
SUPERIOR VENA CAVA k

AZYGOS SYSTEM*
SUPERIOR INTERCOSTAL l'
POSTERIOR INTERCOSTAL l
AZYGOS m
HEMIAZYGOS n
ACCESSORY HEMIAZYGOS n'
ASCENDING LUMBAR o
LUMBAR o'

CAVAL SYSTEM*
INFERIOR VENA CAVA p
HEPATIC q
RENAL r
SUPRARENAL s
PHRENIC t
TESTICULAR OR OVARIAN u
COMMON ILIAC, R. & L. v
MIDDLE SACRAL w
INTERNAL ILIAC x
EXTERNAL ILIAC y

We suggest you compare the veins of the anterior neck shown here with the veins draining the head and neck (Plate 60). The venous drainage of the intercostal spaces and muscles is variable. The first intercostal spaces are drained by the first posterior intercostal veins which drain into the *brachiocephalic* veins. The anterior intercostal veins (not shown) drain into the *internal thoracic* veins. The *azygos vein* is formed by the *r. ascending lumbar* vein and the subcostal vein (lowest intercostal; barely visible; not labeled); the *hemiazygos vein* is formed by the same veins on the left. The azygos vein and its tributaries form a highly significant collateral pattern to get blood back to the heart (via the superior vena cava) should the *inferior vena cava* or the hepatic portal vein become obstructed. Notice the inferior vena cava *does not* drain the digestive tract (see Plate 63 on Hepatic Portal System).

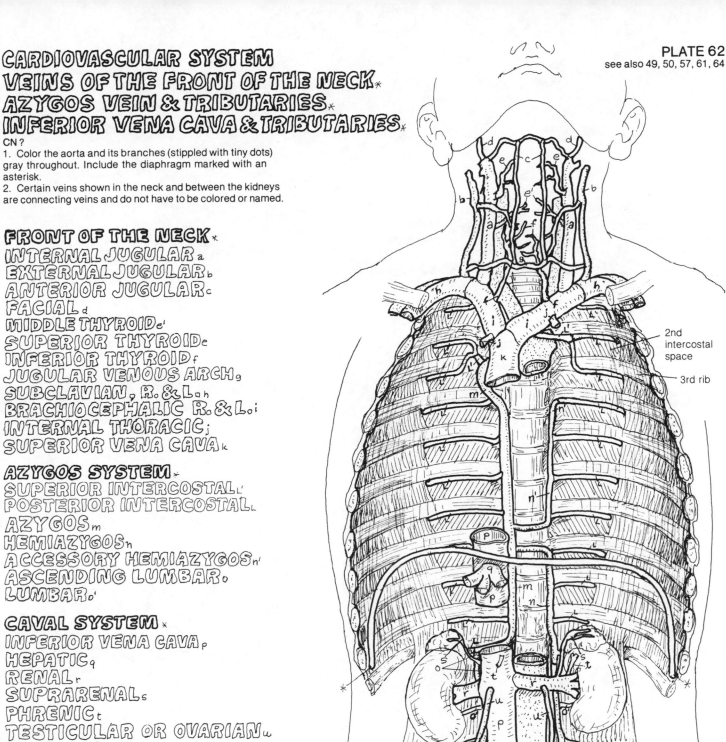

2nd intercostal space

3rd rib

PLATE 63
see also 62

CARDIOVASCULAR SYSTEM
VEINS OF THE LOWER LIMB*

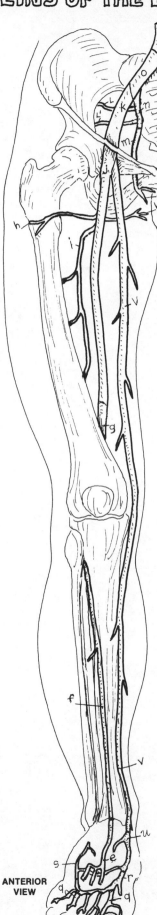

ANTERIOR VIEW

CN 14
1. Color both the anterior and posterior views simultaneously, because certain veins appear on both views.
2. Color all the veins in the small drawing of the leg in the color of the small saphenous vein, except for the portion at the knee labeled (v) (great saphenous vein).

DEEP VEINS*
PLANTAR DIGITAL/METATARSAL a
DEEP PLANTAR VENOUS ARCH b
MED./LAT. PLANTAR c
POSTER. TIBIAL d
DORSAL e
ANTERIOR TIBIAL f
POPLITEAL g
LAT./MED. CIRCUMFLEX FEMORAL h
PROFUNDA FEMORIS i
FEMORAL j
EXTERNAL ILIAC k
SUPERIOR/INFERIOR GLUTEAL l
OBTURATOR m
INTERNAL ILIAC n
COMMON ILIAC o
INFERIOR VENA CAVA p

SUPERFICIAL VEINS*
DIGITAL/METATARSAL q
DORSAL VENOUS ARCH r
LATERAL MARGINAL s
SMALL SAPHENOUS t
MEDIAL MARGINAL u
GREAT SAPHENOUS v

The venous pattern of the lower limb is quite variable. As in the upper limb, the deep veins generally follow the arteries. The superficial veins ride in the superficial fascia and many can be seen in the leg, at the ankle, and in the foot. These veins have valves as do the veins of the upper limb. Because these veins have to overcome the forces of gravity for a considerable distance, their valves often come under heavy stress. Incompetent valves lead to pooling of blood in the lower veins, swelling of veins, and inflammation. Superficial veins are more subject to such problems for they have no skeletal muscles contracting nearby, which helps blood in the deep veins move up (a kind of kneading effect). However, a number of communicating vessels between superficial and deep veins (not shown) allow for venous runoff from the superficial veins, significantly offsetting the effect of incompetent valves.

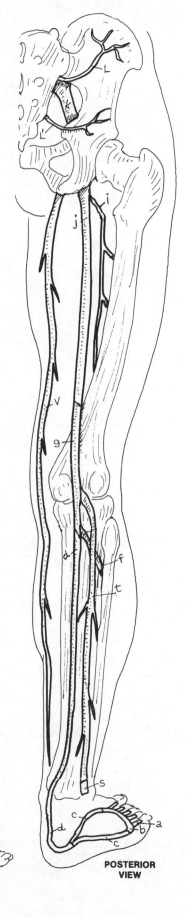

POSTERIOR VIEW

PLATE 64
see also 58, 62

CARDIOVASCULAR SYSTEM
HEPATIC PORTAL SYSTEM⊹

CN 11

1. Note that the tributaries of the portal vein are to receive the same color as the organ they drain (a & a¹, etc.). Color the directional arrows in dark outline with the same color as the vein to which they relate.
2. Use a bright or dark blue for the portal vein (h).
3. Color the inferior vena cava, its tributaries, and the light-line directional arrows gray throughout. Note that where the IVC passes behind the liver it is represented by a dotted line, also to be colored gray. Note the hepatic veins (i) are tributaries of the inferior vena cava and are to be colored gray.

HEPATIC PORTAL SYSTEM⊹
RECTUM a
SUPERIOR RECTAL V a'
LARGE INTESTINE b
INFERIOR MESENTERIC V b'
SMALL INTESTINE c
SUPERIOR MESENTERIC V c'
SPLEEN d
SPLENIC V d'
PANCREAS e
PANCREATIC V e'
GALL BLADDER f
CYSTIC V f'
STOMACH g
L. GASTRO-EPIPLOIC V g'
R. GASTRO-EPIPLOIC V g²
R. GASTRIC V g³
L. GASTRIC V g⁴
PORTAL V & BRANCHES h

Organs of the gastrointestinal tract, the gall bladder, pancreas, and spleen are drained by tributaries of the *hepatic portal vein*. Blood in this vein is discharged into small veins (sinusoids) of the liver, which are surrounded by liver cells. These cells remove digested fats, carbohydrates, proteins, vitamins, iron, etc. from these sinusoids and store them, alter their structure, and/or distribute them to the body tissues. Such nutrients are metered out to small veins in the liver that are tributaries of the *hepatic veins* (i). This blood quickly reaches the heart and is pumped to the tissues. The portal system is so-called because it *transports* nutrients in the venous blood from the capillaries of the intestines to the sinusoids of the liver instead of directly to the heart as do most other veins that drain capillaries.

HEPATIC VEINS i *
INFERIOR VENA CAVA & TRIBUTARIES j *

The *inferior vena cava (IVC)* drains the posterior abdominal wall, the kidneys, ovaries/testes, suprarenal glands, part of the diaphragm, the lower limbs via the external iliac veins, and the pelvis/perineum via the internal iliac veins. It, of course, drains the liver via the hepatic veins. There are a number of interconnections (anastomoses) between tributaries of the inferior vena cava and those of the hepatic portal system. These anastomoses play a life-saving role should the hepatic portal vein become obstructed. In such an event, blood would flow backward through its tributaries to points of interconnection with tributaries of the IVC as well as the azygos vein (P. 62). These would conduct the portal blood to the heart via the IVC/SVC. Points of anastomoses occur between esophageal/gastric veins, lumbar/colic veins, superior/middle/inferior rectal veins, portal/paraumbilical veins (not shown).

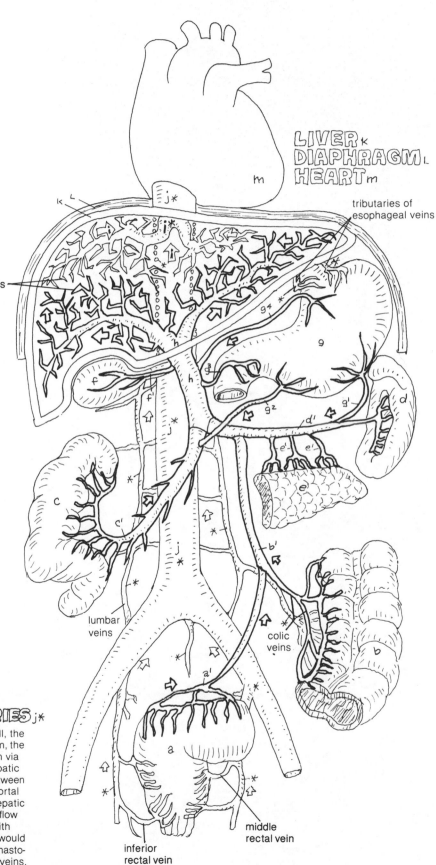

LIVER k
DIAPHRAGM L
HEART m

tributaries of esophageal veins

sinusoids

lumbar veins

colic veins

middle rectal vein

inferior rectal vein

PLATE 65

CARDIOVASCULAR SYSTEM
PRINCIPAL VEINS OF VENOUS SYSTEM *

CN ?

1. Using the preceding plates of the venous system for reference where necessary, color each vein and write its name in the appropriate space using the same color. You may use the same color more than once. Note the figure is in the anatomical position, with palms forward (anterior). Thus, the radial vein, like its arterial fellow, is on the thumb side. Remember in both upper/lower limbs, the dorsal venous network is largely drained by the superficial veins and the palmar/plantar networks are largely drained by the deeper veins.

2. The answer key to this plate may be reviewed in the back of the book.

a _____
b _____ b'
c _____
d _____
e _____
f _____
g _____
h _____
i _____
j _____
....
k _____
L _____
m _____
n _____
o _____
p _____
....
q _____
r _____
s _____
t _____
u _____
....
v _____ v'
w _____
x _____
y _____
z _____
1. _____
2. _____
3. _____
4. _____
5. _____
....
6. _____
7. _____
8. _____
9. _____
10. _____
11. _____
12. _____
....
13. _____

SUPERFICIAL VEINS

DEEP VEINS

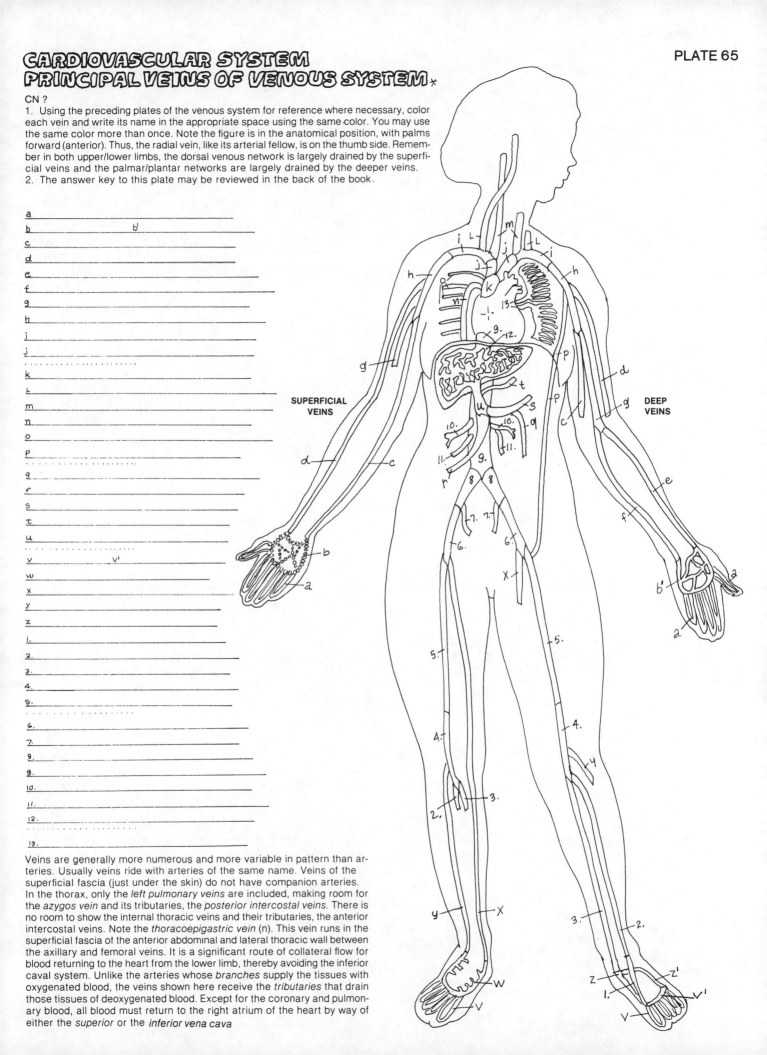

Veins are generally more numerous and more variable in pattern than arteries. Usually veins ride with arteries of the same name. Veins of the superficial fascia (just under the skin) do not have companion arteries. In the thorax, only the *left pulmonary veins* are included, making room for the *azygos vein* and its tributaries, the *posterior intercostal veins*. There is no room to show the internal thoracic veins and their tributaries, the anterior intercostal veins. Note the *thoracoepigastric vein* (n). This vein runs in the superficial fascia of the anterior abdominal and lateral thoracic wall between the axillary and femoral veins. It is a significant route of collateral flow for blood returning to the heart from the lower limb, thereby avoiding the inferior caval system. Unlike the arteries whose *branches* supply the tissues with oxygenated blood, the veins shown here receive the *tributaries* that drain those tissues of deoxygenated blood. Except for the coronary and pulmonary blood, all blood must return to the right atrium of the heart by way of either the *superior* or the *inferior vena cava*

CARDIOVASCULAR SYSTEM
FETAL CIRCULATION *

PLATE 66
see also 47, 50

CN 13

1. Color red all vessels or arrows that are dotted or represented by an a. These represent the flow of oxygenated blood from the placenta (c). Start there.
2. Color blue the light-lined arrows representing the flow of deoxygenated blood draining the organs of the fetus.
3. Color purple all vessels or arrows that are dark-lined or marked b. These represent a mixture of oxygenated/deoxygenated blood. Note the umbilical arteries (b) are included in this group.
4. Color the titles of f, g and note the openings they represent, which obviously cannot be colored.
5. Color structures a–c in the lower illustration to show their relationship to the developing fetus.

PLACENTA c
UMBILICAL V a
UMBILICAL As b
UMBILICUS (NAVEL) d
DUCTUS VENOSUS e
FORAMEN OVALE f
DUCTUS ARTERIOSUS g

The fetus in the uterus (in utero) does not breathe air. Its lungs are deflated. It receives oxygen from the mother by way of the *placenta* and the *umbilical vein* (remember: veins conduct blood to the heart regardless of the quality of that blood). The umbilical vein, traveling in the umbilical cord, passes through the umbilicus, approaches the liver, gives off a branch or two there and becomes the *ductus venosus*, which joins the inferior vena cava. There the oxygenated blood (red) is mixed with venous blood (blue) coming through the liver. The mixed (purple) blood enters the inferior vena cava and into the right atrium, to be mixed again with venous blood returning from the body tissues of the fetus. Happily, the oxygen carrying capacity of fetal hemoglobin (in the red blood corpuscles) is particularly great in comparison with the adult. The lungs are functionless but require a maintenance amount of blood. Two passageways of the fetal heart provide for bypassing the pulmonary circuit: the *foramen ovale* (connecting right and left atria) and the *ductus arteriosus* (connecting pulmonary trunk to the aortic arch). By virtue of these passages (which close soon after birth), the fetal blood is quickly conducted to the left ventricle to be pumped to the body tissues. *Umbilical arteries,* arising from the internal iliac arteries, pass to the umbilicus, through the umbilical cord to the placenta. These arteries and the umbilical vein, ductus venosus, and ductus arteriosus become ligamentous after birth. In the placenta, this fetal mixed blood is reoxygenated with maternal oxygenated blood and recirculated to the umbilical vein. At birth, the umbilical cord is not cut until the newborn has clearly demonstrated functional lungs (crying).

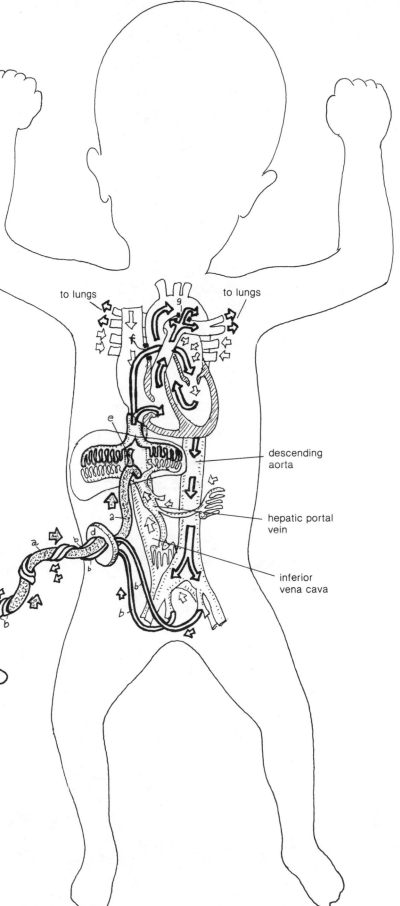

to lungs   to lungs

descending aorta

hepatic portal vein

inferior vena cava

PLATE 67

LYMPHATIC SYSTEM
THORACIC DUCT & TRIBUTARIES *

CN 10

1. Color in all lymph vessels (a) and nodes (b) even where not labeled.

LYMPH VESSELS_a
LYMPH NODES_b
JUGULAR TRUNK_c
SUBCLAVIAN TRUNK_d
R. BRONCHOMEDIASTINAL TRUNK_e
R. LYMPH DUCT_f
LUMBAR TRUNKS_g
INTESTINAL TRUNK_h
CYSTERNA CHYLI_i
THORACIC DUCT_j

right/left internal jugular vein

right/left subclavian vein

right/left brachiocephalic vein

superior vena cava

2nd lumbar vertebra

The body is largely fluid. Fluids of the body require constant circulation, and the pump that maintains this circulation is largely the heart (tissue diffusion pressures can also cause a shift in fluids). The heart drives the fluid of the blood vascular system, and all extravascular fluids of the body must ultimately return to the vascular system to return to the heart. Veins are in the business of returning blood to the heart, thus special fluid "compartments" (of the eye, brain, ear, etc.) generally drain into veins. The lymphatic system of vessels constitutes such a compartment. Arising from veins in the developing embryo and closely associated with veins throughout most parts of the body, *lymphatic vessels* assist veins in their function by draining many of the body tissues and thus increasing the amount of fluid return to the heart. The lymph vascular network does not form a closed loop system like the blood vascular system. Lymph vessels begin as tiny, colorless, unconnected capillaries in the connective tissues. These merge to form progressively larger vessels which are interrupted at various sites by small filtering stations called *lymph nodes*. Lymph vessels ultimately drain into the two principal lymph vessels: *thoracic* and *right lymph ducts*.

Looking like small veins, these ducts pour about 2 liters of lymph into the brachiocephalic veins every 24 hours. The lymph vascular system has no heart of its own, and lymph flow largely depends upon the kneading action of neighboring skeletal muscles alternately contracting and relaxing.

This plate shows the major lymph vessels and their immediate tributaries. Lymphatics of the lower limb, pelvis, perineum and those of the abdominal viscera reach for the *cysterna chyli* via the *lumbar trunks* and *intestinal trunk*, respectively. Just below the diaphragm, the cysterna chyli narrows to become the thoracic duct, which itself drains the *left* thorax. Major tributaries of this duct drain the left upper limb (*subclavian trunk*) and head and neck (*jugular trunk*). The right lymph duct and its immediate tributaries drain the right half of the thorax, upper limb, head, and neck. This lymphatic network has tremendous clinical significance. Interruption of lymph drainage in an area generally creates considerable swelling (edema) due to accumulation of fluids. In addition, the lymph vessels offer a variety of routes for cancer cells to move from one site to another (metastases).

LYMPHATIC SYSTEM
ANATOMY OF A LYMPH NODE a

PLATE 68
see also 67

CN 10

1. Color the various nodes in the figure at right in the same color as the capsule (a) in the large lymph node. The color of the capsule (a) should be the same color used for structures (b) on the previous plate (67).
2. Use red for the artery (h), and blue for the vein (i). Use a dark color for the cortical nodules (e).

CAPSULE a
TRABECULAE a'
AFFERENT VESSEL b
LYMPH SINUSES c
EFFERENT VESSEL d
CORTICAL NODULES/CORTEX e
GERMINAL CENTER f
MEDULLARY CORDS g
ARTERY h
VEIN i

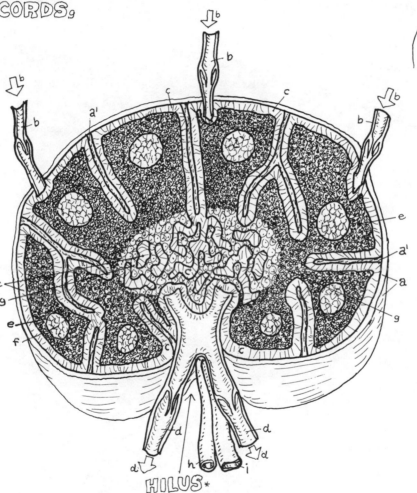

cervical
lymph nodes

sites of lymph nodes
which can be felt
in the superficial fascia
by an examiner.

axillary
lymph nodes

inguinal
lymph nodes

HILUS *

In addition to a network of vessels, the lymphatic system includes a variety of organs generally characterized by a basic unit of structure:lymphocytes and related cells (e.g., macrophages) attached to or free within a delicate framework of reticular fibers and cells. Such masses, ranging from simple to complex in organization, constitute lymphatic tissue. *Lymph nodes*, along with the spleen, thymus, tonsils, nodules, and diffuse lymphatic tissue, make up the lymphatic organs. Normally the size of small kidney beans, lymph nodes are generally found in groups near veins. Small lymph vessels may be seen entering and leaving each node. These lymph filtering devices are organized in the following way. Lymph enters a node through *afferent vessels* that open into the *lymph sinuses* just deep to the *capsule*. These sinuses are a maze of spaces within a net of fine reticular fibers. Lymph percolates through these sinuses, reaching ultimately for the *efferent vessel*. As you can see, the sinuses are supported by *trabeculae* of connective tissue fibers projecting inward from the capsule. In the outer

part of the node, masses of tightly fitted cells (*nodules of the cortex*) surround the lymph sinuses. In the center of these nodules are areas of lighter density, called *germinal centers*, where lymphocytes multiply and proliferate. The inner part of the node is the medulla consisting of lymph sinuses surrounded by cords of cells (*medullary cords*). These cells are largely macrophages, which rapidly absorb such microorganisms as bacteria. These cells, in effect, "strain" the lymph in the sinuses. The cells of the cortical nodules are largely lymphocytes capable of creating complex proteins (antibodies), which, coupled with phagocytic (macrophage) activity, suppress the growth and activity of microorganisms. High concentrations of certain bacteria in the lymph stimulate rapid division of lymphocytes in the germinal centers. Secretion of antibodies by these cells brings about the demise of these bacteria by specific neutralization. Thus, lymph nodes make up an important part of the body defense system, and their enlargement may be an indication of an ongoing disease process.

PLATE 69
see also 67, 68

LYMPHATIC SYSTEM
DEEP & SUPERFICIAL CHANNELS
OF LYMPH DRAINAGE *

CN 14

1. Color the deep lymphatic vessels in the figure on the left. Use colors used for same structures on Plate 67, even though letter identification may differ.

2. In both figures, color the upper right quadrant of the body (the dotted area) gray. This area generally drains into the right lymph duct.

3. Color in the three superficial drainage areas on the left side of the body in the figure at right by coloring the nodes and their respective arrows. If you wish, you can lightly color in the entire area in the same color.

SUPERFICIAL *
CERVICAL NODES l
AXILLARY NODES m
INGUINAL NODES n

DEEP *
RIGHT LYMPHATIC DUCT a
THORACIC DUCT b
JUGULAR TRUNK c
SUBCLAVIAN TRUNK d
BRONCHOMEDIASTINAL TRUNK e
LOWER INTERCOSTAL TRUNK f
LUMBAR TRUNK g
CYSTERNA CHYLI h
INTESTINAL TRUNKS/VESSELS i
VESSELS FROM PELVIS j
FROM LOWER LIMB k

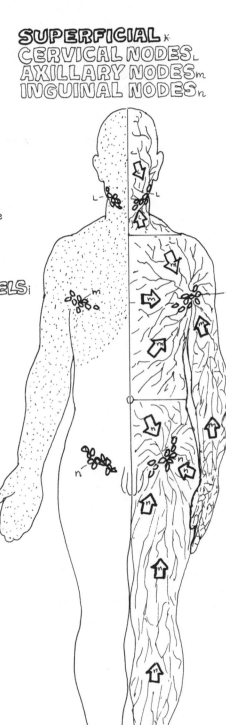

The lymph vascular system has both deep and superficial vessels. The deep vessels generally follow the deep veins, which often travel with companion arteries and nerves. The superficial vessels travel through the superficial fascia, and their related lymph nodes are usually found where large superficial veins flow into the deeper veins. Certain areas are devoid of lymphatic vessels/nodes, such as the brain, spinal cord, bone marrow, and structures generally without blood vessels that receive their nutrition by diffusion (cartilage, epidermis, etc.) In the upper limb, both deep and superficial lymphatic vessels reach for the *axillary nodes*. In the lower limb, both deep and superficial vessels flow into the *inguinal nodes*. In the neck, lymph vessels pass into *cervical nodes* in a variety of places, ultimately passing to deep cervical nodes near the large lymph ducts. The deeper patterns of lymph flow have been described in Plate 67 but are repeated here to enhance perspective of the entire system of vessels.

On the body surface, three sets of lymph nodes can be felt (see figure on right). Occasionally a node or two may be felt behind the knee or at the elbow. Lymph nodes enlarge when an infection is present in their area of drainage, due to a proliferation of lymphocytes in the germinal centers. Thus, enlarged superficial nodes signal that an infectious process may be underway. Lymph nodes may also enlarge when cancer cells migrate in from various lymph channels (metastases) and begin rapidly dividing.

PLATE 70
see also 14

RESPIRATORY SYSTEM
GENERAL SCHEME*

CN 7

1. Color the elements of the respiratory system.

NASAL CAVITYa
PHARYNXb
LARYNXc
TRACHEAd
PRIMARY BRONCHIe
LUNGS, R□f¹ L□f²
DIAPHRAGMg

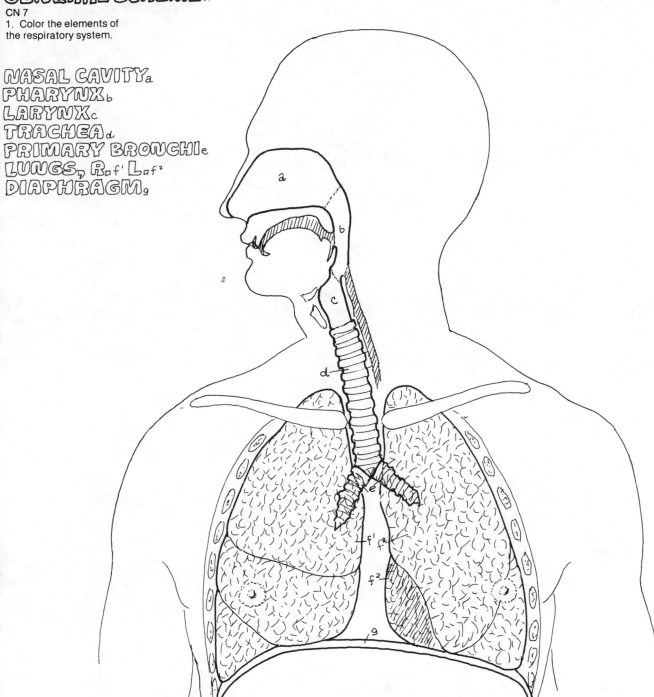

The *respiratory tract* functions to bring atmospheric air to a place where it can readily be absorbed by the blood. In reverse, it can take undesired gases from the blood and exhaust them to the outside. The respiratory tract also helps develop sound, refine that sound into intelligible vocalization, and help maintain acid-base balance of the blood by blowing off carbon dioxide to the outside. In no other place does the outside environment, with all its creatures of microscopic dimension, have such easy access to the sterile interior cavities of the body as it does at the air/blood interfaces of the lung.

Thus, the structure of the respiratory tract includes a fairly adequate defensive capability. Generally, the tract is divided into respiratory tissue, where gaseous exchange actually occurs, and conducting tubes. As you see, most of the tract conducts air. In doing so, it traps foreign matter in mucus, warms the air with heat from nearby underlying blood vessels, and adds water to the air allowing the oxygen to go into solution before it is absorbed by the blood. The following plates consider portions of the respiratory tract in more detail.

PLATE 71
see also 12

RESPIRATORY SYSTEM
THE EXTERNAL NOSE*
NASAL SEPTUM*
NASAL CAVITY*

CN 17

1. Color the various structures in the three drawings. Note in the lower drawing that certain areas to be colored are defined by a dotted border. Color in the remaining area around these structures in gray to complete the nasal cavity (lined with a heavy border).
2. The nasopharynx is not to be colored in.
3. In the bottom illustration, all parts of the cribriform plate (j) should be colored in.

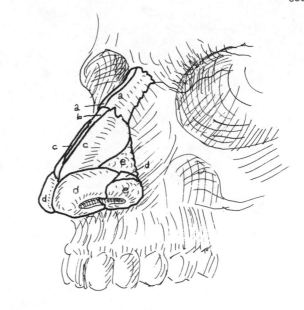

EXTERNAL NOSE*
NASAL BONES a
CARTILAGE OF NASAL SEPTUM b
LATERAL NASAL CARTILAGE c
ALAR CARTILAGE d
FIBRO-FATTY TISSUE e

NASAL SEPTUM*
CARTILAGE OF NASAL SEPTUM b
PERPENDICULAR PLATE OF
ETHMOID BONE f
VOMER BONE g

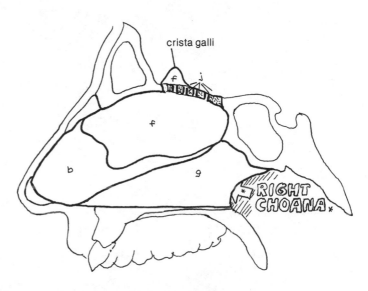

crista galli

RIGHT CHOANA*

NASAL CAVITY*'
FRONTAL BONE h & SINUS h'
SPHENOID BONE i & SINUS i'
CRIBRIFORM PLATE OF ETHMOID j
VESTIBULE OF NOSE k
SUPERIOR CONCHA l & MEATUS l'
MIDDLE CONCHA m & MEATUS m'
INFERIOR CONCHA n & MEATUS n'
HARD PALATE o
SOFT PALATE p

The *nasal cavity* begins with the anterior nasal apertures and ends with the posterior nasal apertures or *choanae*. The nose is a fibrocartilaginous extension of the nasal cavity and septum. The *septum* divides the nasal cavity into right and left *cavities*. It can be felt at the tip of the nose; it ends at the choanae. The *vestibule of the nose* is lined with long hairs (vibrissae) that serve to discourage entrance of foreign bodies. The membranous lining of the nasal cavity (mucosa) is characterized by ciliated epithelial cells which secrete a mucus and whose cilia sweep small particulate matter down into the nasopharynx. The mucosae-lined *conchae* increase the surface area of the nasal cavity and thereby provide more heat and moisture to the passing air. Special epithelial cells at the roof of the nasal cavity are receptive to chemicals in solution by discharging an electrochemical impulse down the lst cranial nerve. The sensation is interpreted in the brain as smell or olfaction. Note the floor of the nasal cavity is the *palate* which is the roof of the oral cavity.

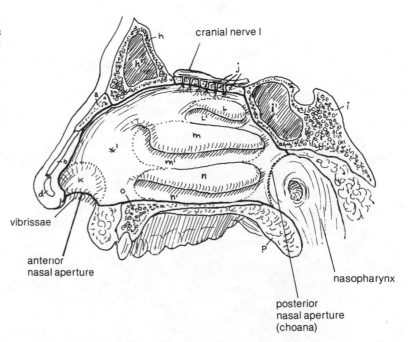

cranial nerve I

vibrissae

anterior nasal aperture

nasopharynx

posterior nasal aperture (choana)

PLATE 72
see also 11, 78, 138

RESPIRATORY SYSTEM
PARANASAL AIR SINUSES*

CN ?

1. You will need some of the colors used on the preceding plate for the same structures seen on this plate. If you have additional colors, use 6 new ones for the added materials. Otherwise use colors from the preceding plate used for structures not shown on this plate.
2. Note that only the frontal (h') and sphenoidal sinuses (i') are to be colored, not the entire bone.
3. Color the arrows indicating routes of drainage. The conchae have been cut away to expose the foramina (holes for drainage flow).
4. Ethmoidal sinuses (t) receive color (j) of Plate 71.

OPENING OF AUDITORY TUBE q
MAXILLARY SINUS r
NASOLACRIMAL DUCT s
ETHMOIDAL SINUSES t
MASTOID AIR CELLS u
NASAL SEPTUM v
NASAL CAVITY *

The skull has a number of cavities in it. You are familiar with some of them (mouth, nose, external ear, orbits), but perhaps not so familiar with others. The frontal, sphenoid, maxillary, ethmoid, and temporal bones have variably sized cavities, all of which directly or indirectly communicate with the nasal cavity. These are the *paranasal air sinuses,* to be distinguished from the venous sinuses of the dura mater. These air sinuses serve to lighten the skull and they add timbre to the voice. They are lined with respiratory-type epithelium, which is continuous with the epithelium of the nasal cavity. The mucus secretions from these epithelial linings pass down canals and enter the nasal cavity just under the conchae (meatuses). Their specific drainage sites are indicated by the arrows. Should these passageways become blocked by inflammation and swelling, the pressure builds within the sinuses to a point where considerable pain can be experienced (sinusitis, sinus headache). Agents that constrict the blood vessels help to reduce the swelling and reestablish proper drainage. The *mastoid air cells* (in the mastoid process of the temporal bone) drain into the middle ear cavity, down the auditory (pharyngotympanic or Eustachian) tube into the nasopharynx adjacent to the nasal cavity. The *nasolacrimal duct* receives secretions from the lacrimal gland which functions to keep the covering (conjunctivum) of the eye moist. These tears drain into slits at the medial aspect of the eyelids, which open into sacs that narrow into the nasolacrimal ducts. These ducts pass downward along the lateral walls of the nasal cavity and open into the meatus of the inferior concha on each side—and that explains how it is that one blows one's nose after one cries. (In the drawing below, the nasolacrimal duct and ducts of the frontal and maxillary sinuses are shown on one side only.)

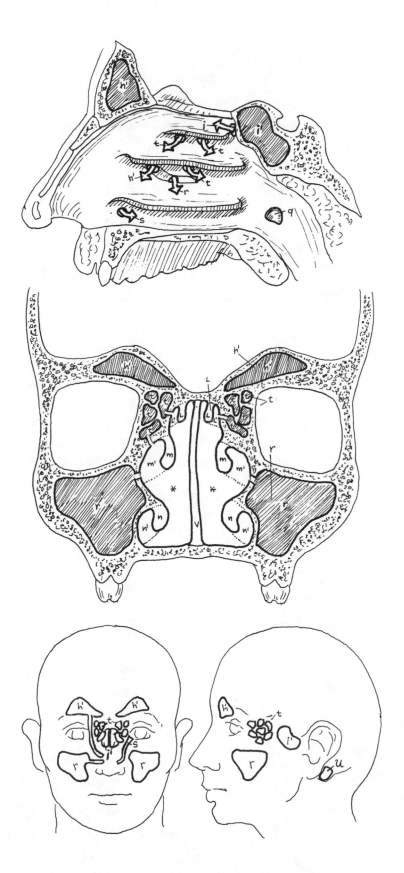

PLATE 73
see also 70, 81

RESPIRATORY SYSTEM
PHARYNX & LARYNX CN 15

1. Some of the structures relating to the titles below are not included in the drawing to the right, but only appear at the bottom.
2. When you complete the lower drawings, try to relate them to the one above (sagittal view of larynx). The lowest set of drawings illustrates the bony, fibrous, and cartilaginous framework of the larynx. The two views of the laryngeal inlet include the mucosal coverings (p, q, s, t) which line that framework.

NASAL CAVITY a*
ORAL CAVITY b*
PHARYNX:
NASOPHARYNX c
PHARYNGEAL TONSIL d
OROPHARYNX e
PALATINE TONSIL f
LARYNGOPHARYNX g
LARYNX:
EPIGLOTTIS h
HYOID BONE i
THYROID CARTILAGE j
THYROHYOID MEMBRANE k
CRICOID CART. l
CRICOTHYROID MEMBRANE m
CORNICULATE CART. n
ARYTENOID CART. o
VESTIBULAR FOLD p
VOCAL FOLD q
GLOTTIS r •
ARYEPIGLOTTIC FOLD s
INTERARYTENOID FOLD t

The *pharynx* is a fibromuscular tube that seems to hang from the walls of the posterior nasal apertures (choanae). It is continuous with the *nasal cavity* and is open to the *oral cavity* anteriorly. Posteriorly it is supported by fascia relating to the vertebral column and the skull (sphenoid bone to about C4 vertebra). Inferiorly, it continues as the *esophagus* behind and the *larynx* in front. Food and air share this common tube. Should air pass into the esophagus it will usually leave where it came in (burp); should food attempt passage through the larynx, a number of mechanisms will be called into action characterized by fits of coughing. This potentially serious possibility is made slight by the complex swallowing mechanism. The *nasopharynx* receives the auditory tube and harbors the *pharyngeal tonsil* (adenoids). If one views the oral cavity with a mirror, the extension of the soft palate (uvula) prevents one from seeing the nasopharynx (see Plate 79). Lined with respiratory epithelium, it is extremely sensitive to the passage of anything but air. The *oral pharynx* contains the *palatine tonsils* in its lateral walls and is lined with the epithelium of the oral cavity: stratified squamous. The *laryngopharynx* is also lined with oral epithelium and is characterized by a pair of pockets or recesses on either side of the laryngeal inlet (not shown).

muscle and fascia

uvula

spine of C1

tongue

base of tongue

ESOPHAGUS u*
THYROID GLAND v
TRACHEA w & CARTILAGE w'

VIEW OF LARYNGEAL INLET FROM ABOVE
vocal folds adducted

VIEW OF LARYNGEAL INLET FROM ABOVE
vocal folds abducted

The *larynx* is supported by a framework of cartilage. Although nearby the larynx, the hyoid bone is not considered part of its intrinsic framework. The *thyroid cartilage* articulates on the *cricoid cartilage* and is attached to the hyoid by the thyrohyoid membrane (ligament). The cricoid fits onto the trachea. The *arytenoid cartilages* articulate with the top of the cricoid and are capable of pivoting on it. The *vocal folds* are mucosa-lined ligaments stretching between thyroid and arytenoid cartilages. They are abducted/adducted by the movement of the arytenoid cartilages. In breathing they are abducted; in coughing (when the pressure is being built up in the thorax, trachea, and lower larynx) they are closed and then released rapidly, creating the explosive cough. During phonation, generally only a thin line of space occurs between the adducted vocal folds, varying somewhat with pitch and volume. The *vestibular folds* (false vocal folds) are fibrous and move only passively.

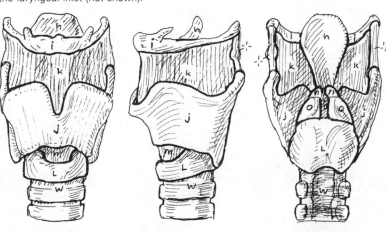

ANTERIOR VIEW

LATERAL VIEW

POSTERIOR VIEW

PLATE 74
see also 49, 70

RESPIRATORY SYSTEM
THE BRONCHIAL TREE*

CN 16

1. When coloring in the respiratory unit, use red for the venule (n) (it is returning oxygenated blood to the heart from the alveolus) and blue for the arteriole (o). You may wish to color the capillary network (between the venule and the arteriole) surrounding the alveolar sac purple to represent gradual oxygenation. Color structures a–f the colors they received on Plate 73, though letter identification differs.

HYOID BONE a
THYROHYOID MEMBRANE b
THYROID CARTILAGE c
CRICOTHYROID MEMBRANE d
CRICOID CARTILAGE e

TRACHEA f

PRIMARY BRONCHI : R. g^1 L. g^2
LOBAR BRONCHI (SECONDARY) h
   R. UPPER LOBAR h^1
   R. MIDDLE LOBAR h^2
   R. LOWER LOBAR h^3
   L. UPPER LOBAR h^4
   L. LOWER LOBAR h^5
SEGMENTAL BRONCHI (TERTIARY) i
   R. UPPER LOBE 3 i^1
   R. MIDDLE LOBE 2 i^2
   R. LOWER LOBE 5 i^3
   L. UPPER LOBE 5 i^4
   L. LOWER LOBE 5 i^5
BRONCHIOLES j
RESPIRATORY
   BRONCHIOLE k
ALVEOLAR DUCT L
ALVEOLAR SAC &
   ALVEOLI m
PULMONARY VENULE n
PULMONARY ARTERIOLE o
LYMPHATIC p

The *trachea* and *bronchi* constitute the lower respiratory conducting tract. The trachea, whose tracheal cartilage rings can be felt in the lower neck just above the sternum, is lined with typical respiratory epithelium. At the level of the 2nd rib's attachment to the sternum (or 4th thoracic vertebra), the trachea divides into two main bronchi, one for each lung. These *main bronchi* disappear within the substance of the lung to divide again into *lobar bronchi,* each serving a lobe. Here the cartilage plates are fragmented, and an increase in smooth muscle is seen in the bronchial wall—muscle that spasms all to often in the view of the asthmatic. Within each lobe of the lung, the bronchus divides into smaller *segmental bronchi,* each of which serves a bronchopulmonary segment. Within a segment, which is bordered by connective tissue and surgically resectable, the segmental bronchus divides into *bronchioles* which serve the lobules. Bronchioles are without cartilage and have a good deal of smooth muscle and elastic tissue in their walls. Within a lobule, bronchioles divide further into terminal bronchioles (not shown/labeled) which give off respiratory bronchioles. The *respiratory bronchiole, alveolar duct and sacs,* and *alveoli* constitute the *respiratory unit* where gaseous exchange occurs. (A group of air cells [alveoli] form an alveolar sac which is served by an alveolar duct). At the respiratory unit level, oxygen is absorbed by the blood and carbon dioxide is released to the air cell from the blood. Three-fifths of the lung volume is blood/blood vessels.

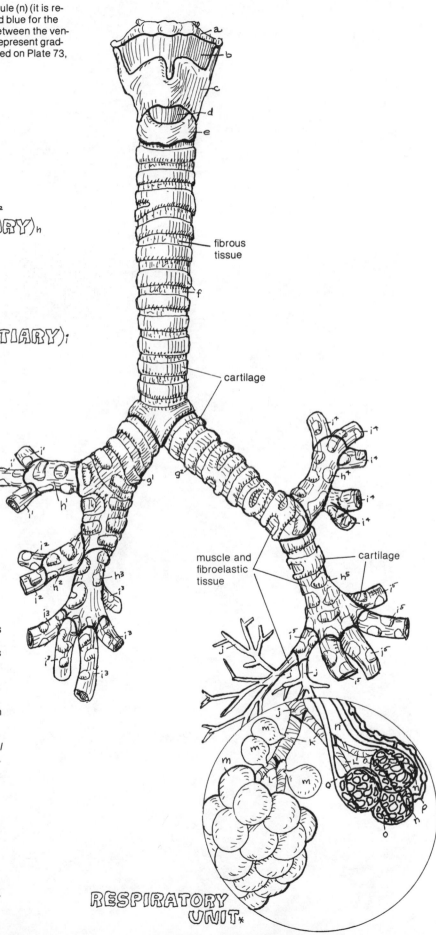

fibrous tissue

cartilage

muscle and fibroelastic tissue

cartilage

RESPIRATORY UNIT*

PLATE 75
see also 14, 49, 74

RESPIRATORY SYSTEM
LOBES & PLEURAE OF THE LUNGS *
LOBES:* R. UPPER a R. MIDDLE b R. LOWER c L. UPPER d L. LOWER e
PLEURAE:* VISCERAL PLEURA f PARIETAL PLEURA g PLEURAL CAVITY h●
LARYNX i TRACHEA j PRIMARY BRONCHI k LOBAR BRONCHI l
SEGMENTAL BRONCHI m BRONCHIOLES n R. LUNG *¹ L. LUNG *²

CN 13
1. Save the brightest or lightest colors for (f) and (g). Black is recommended for (h). Note the four points at which (f) becomes (g).
2. Note that the larynx is drawn in a single color.
3. Use the same colors for (j–n) as you did for these structures on Plate 74, although their letter identification is different.
4. It is not necessary to carefully color in all the bronchioles. They don't appear on drawing to the right due to size limitations.

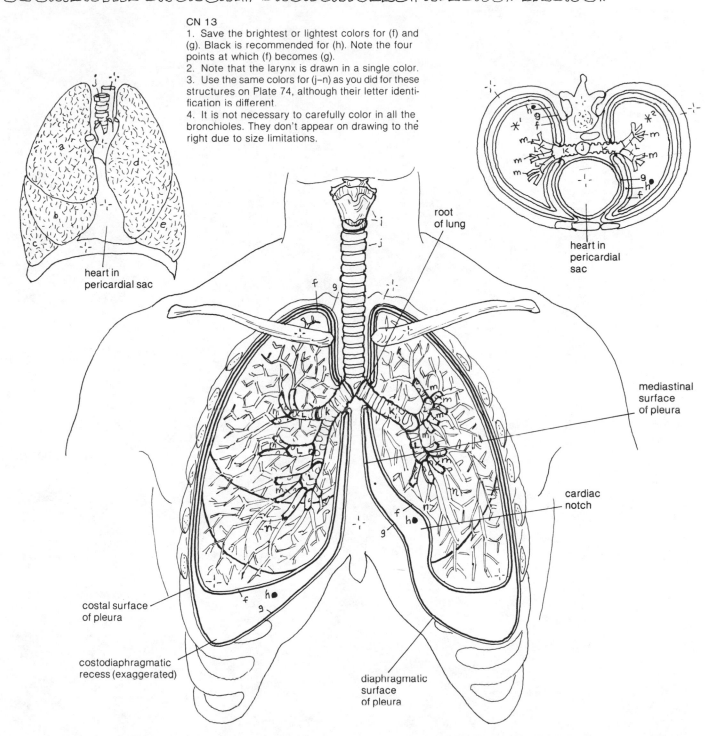

heart in pericardial sac

root of lung

heart in pericardial sac

mediastinal surface of pleura

cardiac notch

costal surface of pleura

costodiaphragmatic recess (exaggerated)

diaphragmatic surface of pleura

The *pleura* is the lining of the lungs and is very much like the pericardium of the heart and the peritoneum of the abdominal viscera. The layer of pleura lining the lungs and which cannot be separated from the lungs is the *visceral pleura*. At the root of the lung, the visceral pleura bends around and out to become the *parietal pleura,* which adheres to the rib cage, diaphragm, and pericardium. The *pleural cavity* is the potential space between the two layers. It is empty except for a thin film of fluid that separates the two layers and allows the lungs to move within their sac without friction. This fluid is secreted by the cells of the pleura. As the thoracic wall heaves in respiration, the lungs move with it. As the diaphragm relaxes during expiration, the lungs move with it, decreasing in size as air is forced out. At this time, the diaphragm forms a dome over the liver, stomach, and spleen, and corners or recesses are created at the angles between diaphragmatic and costal pleurae (and mediastinal and costal pleurae too). At these costodiaphragmatic and costomediastinal recesses, the pleurae extend beyond the lung tissue. Should fluid collect in the pleural cavity due to disease or injury, it can be withdrawn by needle at these places.

RESPIRATORY SYSTEM
MEDIASTINAL SURFACE OF THE LUNGS ✴

CN 17

1. Color the arrows pointing to the various impressions made by structures pressing on the lungs.
2. Use red for (c) and blue for (b).
3. Use the same color for bronchus (a) as you used for primary bronchi (k) on Plate 75.

BRONCHUSₐ
PULMONARY ARTERY♭
PULMONARY VEIN𝒸
APEX𝒹
OBLIQUE FISSURE𝑒
HORIZONTAL FISSURE𝒻
PULMONARY LIG.𝑔

GROOVES MADE BY:
BRACHIOCEPHALIC V.ₕ
SUPERIOR VENA CAVAᵢ
SUBCLAVIAN A.ⱼ
AZYGOS V.ₖ
AORTAₗ
HEARTₘ (CARDIAC IMPRESSION)ₘ
INFERIOR VENA CAVAₙ
TRACHEA ₒ & ESOPHAGUSₒ

DIAPHRAGMATIC SURFACEₚ
CARDIAC NOTCH𝓆

The lungs are light, spongy structures that hug the mediastinum at its lateral aspects (see Plate 49 on Mediastinum). The lungs are quite impressionable, and those taken from cadavers are seen to have various grooves and concavities created by adjacent mediastinal structures. Note in both left and right lungs the root of the lung where *pulmonary vessels* and *bronchi* exit and enter the lung, and relate these areas to the diagrams showing the lateral aspects of the mediastinum. The *pulmonary ligaments* represent the bending (reflection) of the visceral pleura to become parietal pleura. In the right lung (upper diagrams), note the *azygos vein* arching over the root of the lung, the *inferior cava* coming up to the right atrium from below, and the large concavity for the *heart* (m). On the left lung (lower diagrams) relate the arch of the aorta with the marked impression on the lung (L). In both lungs, note how the base of the lungs rests on the *diaphragm*. By studying these impressions on the mediastinal surfaces of the lungs, you will be able to appreciate the relationship of structures in the thoracic cavity.

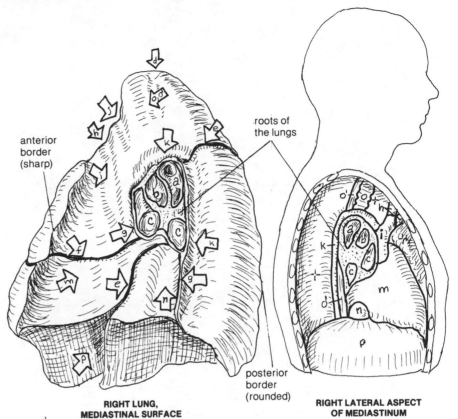
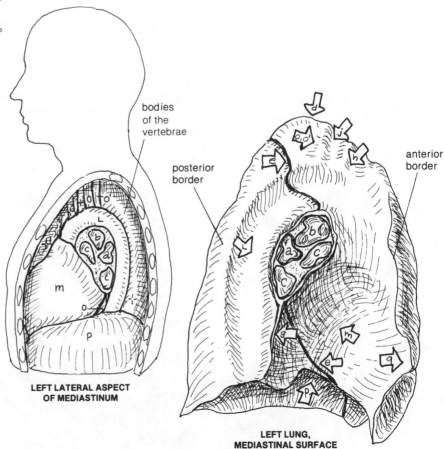

PLATE 77
see also 14, 27, 29, 70

RESPIRATORY SYSTEM
MECHANICS OF RESPIRATION *

CN 5

1. Color the external intercostal muscles and the arrows indicating the direction of their muscular action. Color the arrows indicating the direction of movement of the rib cage gray (*). Do the same for the internal intercostal muscles.
2. Color the lower drawing indicating the expansion of the thorax during inspiration.

INSPIRATION: *
EXTERNAL INTERCOSTAL MUSCLES a
DIAPHRAGM: INSPIRATION b /EXPIRATION b'
EXPANDED THORAX c

EXPIRATION: *
INTERNAL INTERCOSTAL MUSCLES d
THORAX AT REST e

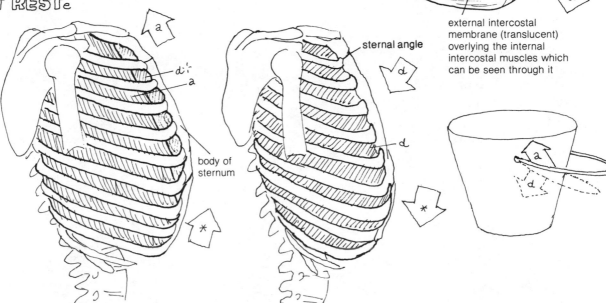

external intercostal membrane (translucent) overlying the internal intercostal muscles which can be seen through it

sternal angle

body of sternum

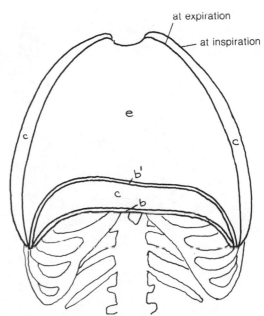

Respiration (breathing) is a somewhat passive phenomenon based on the principle that volume and pressure are inversely proportional; that is, as one goes up, the other comes down. In the case of the thorax, by increasing the size or volume of the thoracic cavity, the pressure within that cavity decreases. The lungs reside within the thoracic cavity, and their cavities (air spaces) are subject to the same principle. These air spaces are open to the outside via the bronchi, trachea, etc. When the pressure within the lungs drops because the thorax has expanded, it drops *relative to* the outside air pressure. Thus we have two areas of unequal pressure connected by tubing (bronchi, trachea, etc.) Air from the area of higher pressure will immediately diffuse into the area of lower pressure; more specifically, air from the atmosphere outside the nose will be drawn into the respiratory conducting tubes and into the air spaces of the lungs. This is called *inspiration.* Conversely, by decreasing the volume of the thorax, the pressure within the lungs will momentarily rise relative to the outside air, and air will diffuse out through the respiratory passages to the outside. This is *expiration.*

The *diaphragm* is responsible for 75% of the respiratory effort. When it contracts, it flattens, increasing the vertical dimensions of the thorax. When it relaxes, it is pushed up by underlying abdominal organs into a slight dome shape, decreasing the vertical dimensions of the thorax. The *external intercostal muscles,* in contraction, pull up the lower ribs. The first rib is fixed. Because the rib cage is wider below than it is above, the *thorax expands* laterally as it rises. As the ribs elevate, the body of the sternum swings outward at the sternal angle, and the anterior to posterior dimensions of the thorax increase. The action of the bucket handle demonstrates how the hinge action of the sternum at the sternal angle increases the anterior-posterior dimensions. The handle is farthest from the bucket when it is horizontal; as the handle is brought down, it gets closer to the bucket; thus as the rib cage descends, the sternum swings inward (anterior-posterior dimension is reduced); as the rib cage elevates, the sternum swings outward and the anterior-posterior dimension increases. The overall effect of increasing these dimensions is to increase the thoracic volume and lower the pressure within (inspiration). The elasticity of the lungs (recoil) and the action of certain parts of the *internal intercostal muscles* (acting to pull the ribs downward) creates a decreased thoracic volume and increased pressure (expiration).

at expiration

at inspiration

PLATE 78
see also 79

DIGESTIVE SYSTEM
SCHEME OF THE SYSTEM*
CN ?

1. Begin coloring with the oral cavity. When you get to the stomach, color it in its entirety (including areas t + d, w + d). When coloring the liver, color it in its entirety, noting the areas of overlap (t + d, etc.). These areas should be colored with both colors.

ALIMENTARY CANAL.
ORAL CAVITY a
PHARYNX b
ESOPHAGUS c
STOMACH d
SMALL INTESTINE: *
DUODENUM e
JEJUNUM f
ILEUM g
LARGE INTESTINE: *
CECUM h
VERMIFORM APPENDIX h'
ASCENDING COLON i
TRANSVERSE COLON j
DESCENDING COLON k
SIGMOID COLON L
RECTUM m
ANAL CANAL n

ACCESSORY ORGANS.
TEETH o
TONGUE p
SALIVARY GLANDS: *
SUBLINGUAL q
SUBMANDIBULAR r
PAROTID s
LIVER t
GALL BLADDER u /CYSTIC DUCT u'
COMMON BILE v /HEPATIC DUCT v'
PANCREAS w
SPLEEN x

The digestive system consists of an *alimentary canal* with *accessory organs*. The canal starts with the *oral cavity* and continues to the *anal canal*. The major glands (*liver, pancreas*) have ducts opening into the alimentary canal. The principal function of this canal and associated organs is to prepare ingested food for absorption by the lining cells and the capillaries—both blood and lymphatic. In the mouth, *teeth* and *tongue* pulverize the food with the aid of *salivary gland* secretions and the secretions of thousands of tiny mucous glands embedded in the lining (mucosa) of the oral and pharyngeal cavities. The next site of chemical and mechanical digestion occurs in the *stomach* and continues through the *small intestine*. Only water, minerals, and certain vitamins are absorbed by the *large intestine*. Once absorbed, the nutrients are transported to the liver by the hepatic portal system where many of them are altered, stored, or metered out into the circulation via the hepatic veins. Nutrients are retrieved by the body's cells in the capillary circulation or by diffusion. Note that the canal—from mouth to anus—is not truly a part of the internal environment but is simply a convoluted tube running from the outside at the mouth to the outside at the anus. Like a hole in a doughnut, the canal is continuous with the outer surface of the body. Note that a segment of structure j is not shown.

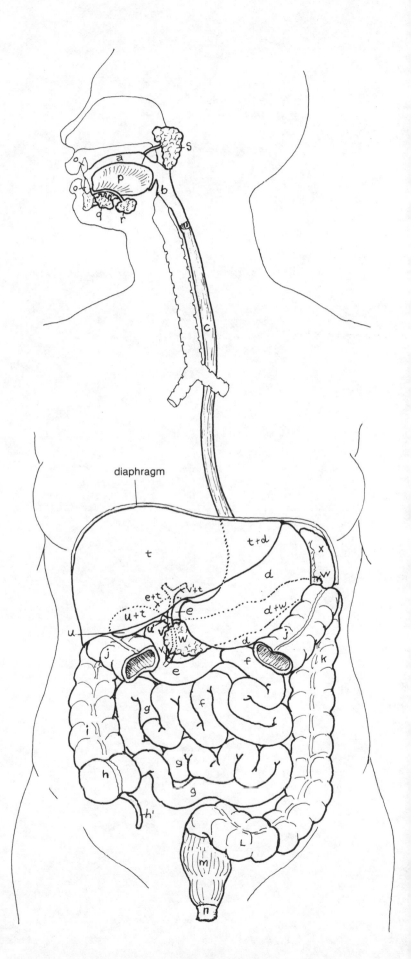

diaphragm

PLATE 79
see also 11, 12, 25, 142

DIGESTIVE SYSTEM
THE MOUTH*
THE TONGUE*

CN ?

1. Use the same colors for the salivary glands below (a–c) as they received on Plate 78 (with different identification letters).

2. It is not necessary to color all of the papillae of q and r. Do not color the teeth.

FRENULUM OF LIP a
GINGIVA (GUM) b
HARD PALATE c
SOFT PALATE d
UVULA e
PALATOGLOSSAL ARCH f
ORAL PHARYNX g
PALATOPHARYNG-EAL ARCH h
TONSILLAR FOSSA i
PALATINE TONSIL j
TONGUE k
BUCCINATOR M. l
BUCCAL FAT m

EPIGLOTTIS n
LINGUAL TONSILS o
PAPILLAE :*
  CIRCUMVALLATE P. p
  FILIFORM P. q
  FUNGIFORM P. r
BITTER s
SOUR t
SALT u
SWEET v

The digestive process begins with the oral cavity (*mouth*). Here ingested food is pulverized by the molars and ripped/torn by the canines and incisors. The muscles of mastication operate the mandible so that chewing can take place. The food is wetted down by thousands of mucous glands embedded in the mucous membrane lining of the mouth and by *salivary glands* (see below) whose ducts open into the mouth as shown. The *tongue*, a muscular organ lined with mucosa, is operated by a number of muscles that arise away from the tongue and from within the tongue itself. The *papillae* on the surface of the tongue provide an abrasive instrument in the initial breakdown of food. Sensory receptors of taste (taste buds) are arranged in the clefts among the papillae. These are actually chemical receptors that transmit stimuli from dissolved substances. The stimuli are interpreted by the brain as *bitter, sour, salty,* or *sweet* according to the general pattern shown at right. It is believed that there are other areas of chemical sensitivity that do not include taste buds.

Unlike the *hard palate,* which is supported by bone, the *soft palate* is supported by skeletal muscle and plays an important role in the swallowing (deglutition) process. The *palatine* and *lingual tonsils,* along with the pharyngeal tonsils (not shown), encircle the opening into the *pharynx.* These masses of lymphatic tissue may play a role in the development of body defense processes (immune response) during the first 10 to 12 years of life. However, the palatine tonsils may enlarge/become infected to such an extent that they require removal (tonsillectomy).

SALIVARY GLANDS*
SUBLINGUAL GLAND a
SUBMANDIBULAR GLAND b
PAROTID GLAND c

The salivary glands seem to have a minimal digestive (enzymatic) effect, but these pairs of glands are quite active in supplying mucus and serous fluid to the mouth during eating. All are innervated by autonomic nerves. The *sublingual glands* lie just deep to the floor of the mouth, into which open their several ducts. The *submandibular glands* lie just below the midmandible and can be felt. Their ducts open at the bases of the frenulum of the tongue (not shown) in the floor of the mouth. The *parotid glands* lie just deep to the skin. Their ducts open to the oral cavity—each orifice can be felt with the tip of the tongue opposite the upper 2nd molar. Viral infection of one or both of these ducts/glands is called mumps.

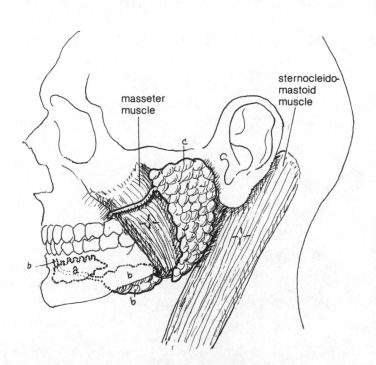
masseter muscle
sternocleido-mastoid muscle

PLATE 80
see also 11, 12, 79

DIGESTIVE SYSTEM
TEETH.

CN ?

1. Use yellow for nerve (f), red for artery (g), and blue for vein (h).
2. Note the vertical arrows to the left of the upper drawing. The one labeled *neck* should be left blank. It is an area of questionable length where the root of the tooth (buried) meets the crown (exposed).
3. Color all the teeth in the mandible and the palate in the illustrations below.
4. Color j, u–y the same as Plate 79, although they had different identification letters.

ENAMEL a
DENTIN b
CEMENTUM c
PULP CAVITY d
PULP e
  NERVE f ARTERY g VEIN h
ROOT CANAL i
GINGIVA j
PERIODONTAL MEMBRANE k
ALVEOLAR BONE L

A *tooth* is a hollow core of sensitive *dentin* filled with *pulp*, capped with insensitive *enamel* projecting above the *gingiva*, buried within a bony socket (*alveolus*) of the mandible/maxilla and secured to that *periodontal*-lined bone by *cementum*. Dentin (dentine) is a bonelike, yellow material, 70% mineral by weight. It is secreted in tubular form by cells lining the pulp cavity adjacent to the dentin. Enamel, the hardest substance in the body, covers the crown of the tooth and is thickest (about 1.5 mm) at the chewing surface. 99% mineral, enamel consists of circular rods arranged in a wave pattern and stuffed with mineral crystals like those seen in bone. The cells that secrete the organic enamel (it mineralizes later) are worn off the enamel surface when the tooth erupts and becomes exposed. The pulp cavity is filled with an embryonic connective tissue supporting *nerves/vessels* supplying the tooth. At the root foramen, the pulp is continuous with the periodontal membrane, a very dense connective tissue similar to periosteum. Cementum is basically bone with a high concentration of fibers, serving as an intermediate tissue between dentin and the periodontal membrane. The gingiva, part of the mucous membrane of the mouth, is firmly anchored to the periosteum of the underlying alveolar bone.

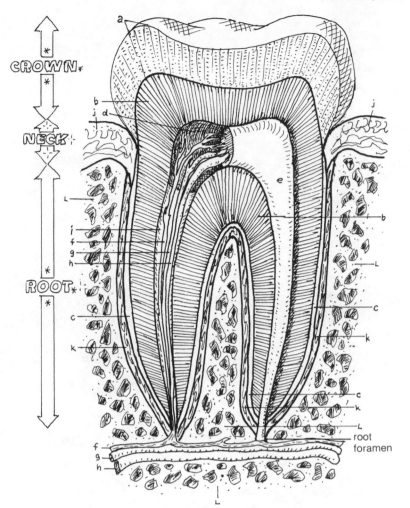

CENTRAL INCISOR m
LATERAL INCISOR n
CANINE o
FIRST PREMOLAR p
SECOND PREMOLAR q
FIRST MOLAR r
SECOND MOLAR s
THIRD MOLAR (WISDOM) t
HARD PALATE u
SOFT PALATE v
UVULA w
PALATOGLOSSAL ARCH x
PALATOPHARYNGEAL ARCH y

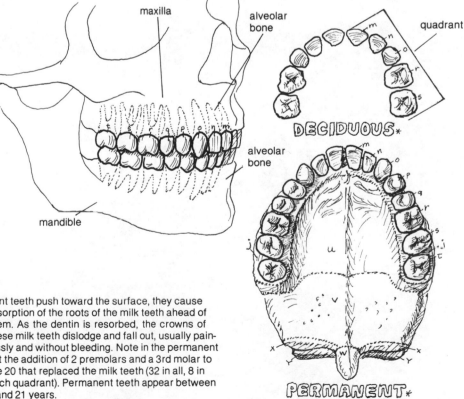

Two sets of teeth (dentition) develop within a lifetime. The first, the *deciduous* (milk) teeth, erupt between 6 and 36 months: 10 in the lower jaw and 10 in the upper. Each tooth type develops on both sides, thus in the milk set there are 5 different types of teeth: 2 *incisors*, 1 *canine*, 2 *molars*. Deep in the bone of both jaws, the *permanent* dentition develops, with an additional 12 teeth that had no deciduous predecessors. As these permanent teeth push toward the surface, they cause resorption of the roots of the milk teeth ahead of them. As the dentin is resorbed, the crowns of these milk teeth dislodge and fall out, usually painlessly and without bleeding. Note in the permanent set the addition of 2 premolars and a 3rd molar to the 20 that replaced the milk teeth (32 in all, 8 in each quadrant). Permanent teeth appear between 6 and 21 years.

PLATE 81
see also 26, 73, 78, 79

DIGESTIVE SYSTEM
PHARYNX & ESOPHAGUS*
CN 20

1. Color the three lower illustrations simultaneously.
2. The regions of the pharynx (d, g, and j) in the lower central illustration are to be colored to provide a clearer picture of the relationship of these arbitrary descriptive divisions to the actual muscular structures.
3. Use a dark gray for the bolus of food (t), and follow the text below carefully when coloring these descriptions of the swallowing process.

WALL OF PHARYNX *
SUPERIOR CONSTRICTOR a
MIDDLE CONSTR. b
INFERIOR CONSTR. c
INTERIOR OF PHARYNX *
NASOPHARYNX d
SOFT PALATE e
UVULA f
OROPHARYNX g
PALATINE TONSIL h
LARYNGOPHARYNX i
ESOPHAGUS j
RELATED STRUCTURES *
TONGUE k
HYOID BONE L
THYROID CARTILAGE m
CRICOID CARTILAGE n & M. n'
TRACHEA o
NASAL CAVITY p
EPIGLOTTIS q
LARYNX r

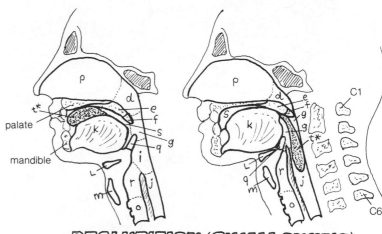

DEGLUTITION (SWALLOWING)*
ORAL CAVITY s
BOLUS OF FOOD t*

The *pharynx* is a complex, mucosa-lined, fibromuscular sac attached above to the base of the skull by fascia, to the upper six cervical vertebrae, open to the nasal cavity above, the oral cavity in front, and the larynx and esophagus below. It is a thoroughfare for both food and air, and it is of critical importance that food find the right tube. One crumb of food attempting entrance to the larynx will set off a violent gale of coughing to blow that indiscreet crumb out of the respiratory passage. Swallowing (*deglutition*) can be divided into three rapidly successive phases: moving of food from oral cavity into the *oropharynx,* movement of food from oropharynx past the larynx, and movement of food into the *esophagus.* In the first phase, the *tongue* is raised against the palate, the palatoglossal arches close together, and the food is forced back into the oropharynx. Almost simultaneously, the second phase occurs: elevation of the *soft palate* and contraction of the *superior constrictor* muscles closing off the nasopharynx, closure of the laryngeal entrance by elevation of the *hyoid bone* and *thyroid cartilage,* and closure of the lateral folds of the upper larynx. In the third phase, the food is forced down behind and alongside the *larynx.* Shortening of the pharynx and contraction of the inferior constrictor muscle commits the food to the esophagus.

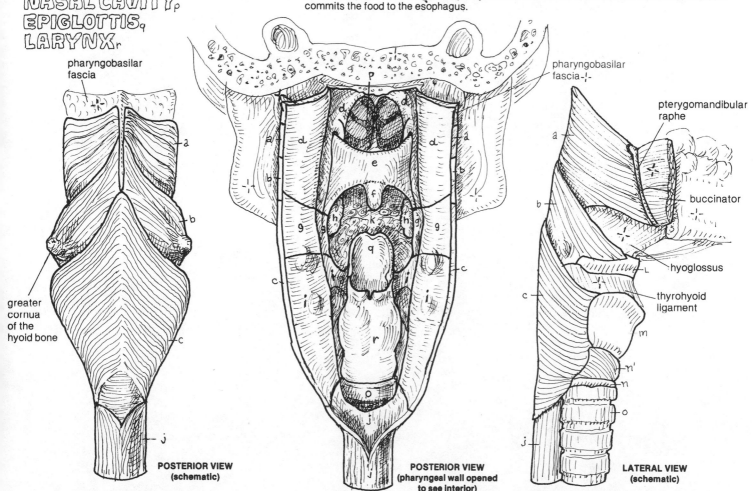

POSTERIOR VIEW
(schematic)

POSTERIOR VIEW
(pharyngeal wall opened
to see interior)

LATERAL VIEW
(schematic)

PLATE 82
see also 49, 75, 78

DIGESTIVE SYSTEM PERITONEUM *

CN 14

1. Start coloring with the illustration on the left, and move to the right. Note that the digestive organs are to be left uncolored in the three upper illustrations even though they are actually covered by visceral peritoneum. A light color is recommended for the parietal peritoneum (a).
2. In the illustration on the right, the dotted areas should be left uncolored.
3. In the illustration below, the digestive organs (d, e, f, j, L, t, w) should be colored the same as on Plate 78 (the letters for these organs are the same on both plates). The thin layers of visceral peritoneum enveloping these organs should

receive the same color as the organs themselves. Note that these visceral peritoneal layers are continuous with parietal peritoneum (a) or mesenteries/omenta.
4. The omentul bursa (*') should be drawn a darker gray than that used for the peritoneal cavity (*). The bursa should not extend beyond the dotted line.
5. Color the aorta and its branching vessel red in the lower illustration.

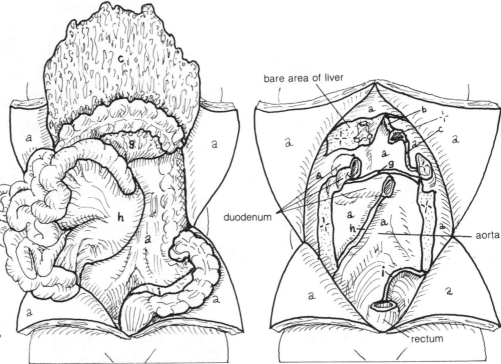

bare area of liver

duodenum

aorta

rectum

The stomach is suspended by the *lesser omentum* and has considerable mobility. The *greater omentum,* connecting stomach to transverse colon (as well as to the spleen and diaphragm, not shown), lies over the abdominal viscera like an apron.

Here the greater omentum and stomach have been lifted upward to expose the *transverse mesocolon* (mesentery suspending the transverse colon) and the *common mesentery* (suspending the major share of the small intestine) as well as the *sigmoid mesocolon* (suspending the sigmoid colon). The rest of the small/large intestine lies behind the *parietal peritoneum.*

Here all structure seen previously has been cut away to show the parietal peritoneum lying over the duodenum, abdominal aorta, etc. This peritoneum also covers the ascending/descending colons, which have been removed to show the areas (dotted) behind them that are not covered with peritoneum. The roots of the mesenteries (cut) are also shown (b, c, g, h, i).

PARIETAL PERITONEUM a
LESSER OMENTUM b
GREATER OMENTUM c
TRANSVERSE MESOCOLON g
MESENTERY h
SIGMOID MESOCOLON i

Similar in character to the pericardial and pleural sacs, which you may have already drawn, the peritoneum is a closed and virtually empty sac lining the abdominal wall, diaphragm, and lying over the pelvic viscera (*parietal peritoneum*). Turning inward, the peritoneum encompasses a number of visceral organs (*visceral peritoneum*), suspending them from the body wall by a fold of peritoneum (*mesentery*) in certain cases (see g and h). In other cases an organ may be suspended by a fold of peritoneum from another organ (*omentum, ligament*) as in cases b and c. In other cases, the organ may be pressed against the posterior body wall by a layer of parietal peritoneum (see structures e and w in the lower drawing). Such structures are said to be *retroperitoneal.* A layer of parietal or visceral peritoneum consists of a single row of squamous or cuboidal secretory epithelial cells reinforced by a thin layer of connective tissue. Necessarily, mesenteries and omenta/ligaments are two layers thick. In the lower drawing, note that the greater omentum is actually four layers thick as its cavity does not exist.

Peritoneum is a serous membrane secreting a fluid that allows the many viscera of the abdominal cavity to slip past one another in their often contorted movements. The viscera are tightly packed within the abdominal cavity, and twisted/trapped organs could mean strangulation of their blood supply and very serious trouble. Happily, this is rarely the case except in occasional newborns and in those who have adhesions (viscera stuck together) following abdominal surgery. The vessels and nerves to the abdominal viscera arise from their sources on the posterior abdominal wall, pass into the mesenteries (between layers, as shown schematically in the lower drawing) and omenta to reach the organ they supply. The layers of peritoneum are inviolate; nothing goes through them—only between or behind them. Note the large cavity or recess behind the stomach in the lower drawing—this is the *omental bursa* or sac created by the rotation of the stomach during fetal life. It is open on the right side just behind the lesser omentum (opening not shown). When one is lying supine, fluids that diffuse from the vessels into the peritoneal cavity (in certain disease states) often collect there.

PERITONEAL CAVITY *
OMENTAL BURSA *'
KIDNEY k

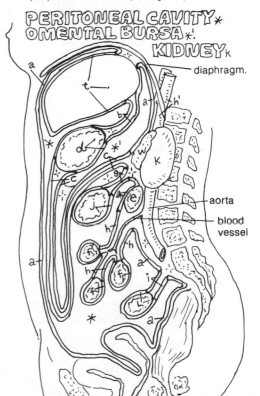

diaphragm

aorta

blood vessel

PLATE 83
see also 58, 64, 78, 82

DIGESTIVE SYSTEM
THE STOMACH *
FUNDUS a
BODY b
PYLORUS c
PYLORIC SPHINCTER d
LESSER CURVATURE e
GREATER CURVATURE f
RUGAE g

STOMACH MUCOSA.
EPITHELIAL LAYER *
   SURFACE & MUCOUS CELLS g¹
   PARIETAL CELLS h
   CHIEF CELLS i
   GASTRIC PIT j
LAMINA PROPRIA k
MUSCULARIS MUCOSAE l

SUBMUCOSA m
OBLIQUE MUSCLE n
CIRCULAR M. o
LONGITUDINAL M. p
SEROSA q

GASTROEPIPLOIC A. r & V. s
GASTRIC A. r' & V. s'
DIAPHRAGM t
ESOPHAGUS u
DUODENUM v

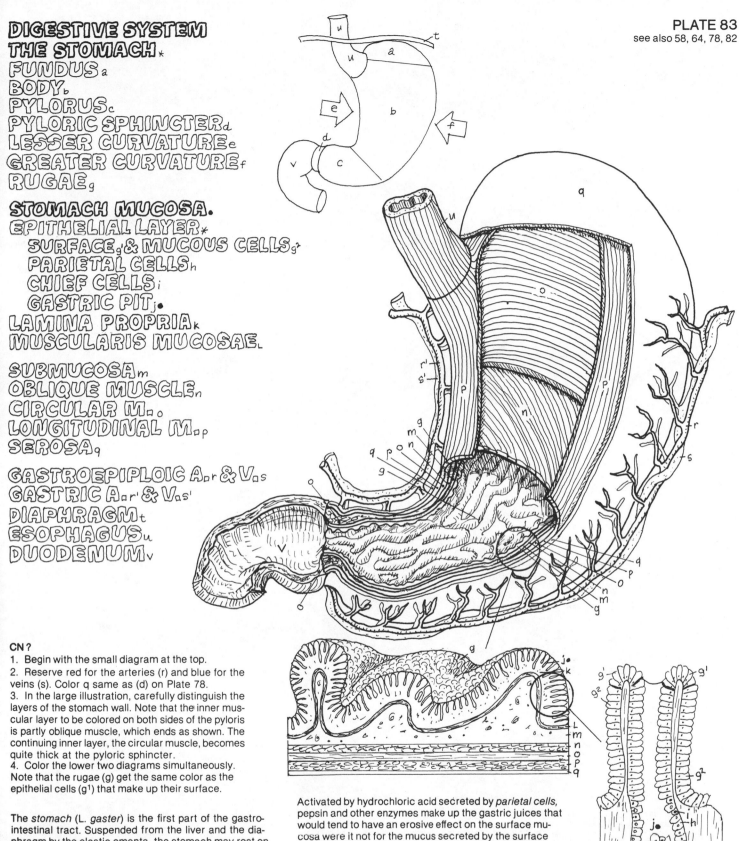

CN?

1. Begin with the small diagram at the top.
2. Reserve red for the arteries (r) and blue for the veins (s). Color q same as (d) on Plate 78.
3. In the large illustration, carefully distinguish the layers of the stomach wall. Note that the inner muscular layer to be colored on both sides of the pyloris is partly oblique muscle, which ends as shown. The continuing inner layer, the circular muscle, becomes quite thick at the pyloric sphincter.
4. Color the lower two diagrams simultaneously. Note that the rugae (g) get the same color as the epithelial cells (g¹) that make up their surface.

The *stomach* (L. *gaster*) is the first part of the gastrointestinal tract. Suspended from the liver and the diaphragm by the elastic omenta, the stomach may rest on the bladder or uterus following a full meal. It stores ingested food and prepares it for eventual treatment by the small intestine. As the *pyloric sphincter* relaxes, churned food is squirted into the *duodenum*. Digestion (breakdown of food) occurs mechanically and enzymatically. Waves of contraction among smooth muscle (peristalsis) In the *muscularis mucosa* and *outer muscular layers* (where the fibers are oriented in 3 directions) create an agitator action in the *gastric pits* and among the *rugae* similar to that in a washing machine. As a result, long-chain molecules are broken down into smaller components. Protein is specifically broken down into smaller units by the enzyme pepsin secreted by *chief cells* in the form of pepsinogen.

Activated by hydrochloric acid secreted by *parietal cells,* pepsin and other enzymes make up the gastric juices that would tend to have an erosive effect on the surface mucosa were it not for the mucus secreted by the surface *epithelial* and neck *mucous cells.* Very little absorption of foodstuffs goes on at the stomach level except readily dissolvable, relatively short-chain compounds. The stomach also secretes a sugar–protein compound (intrinsic factor), which influences the absorption of vitamin B_{12} from the small intestine. Vitamin B_{12} is vital for proper development of red blood corpuscles. Stomach activity is influenced by gastrointestinal hormones and by the vagus (cranial X) nerves.

Note that rugae are the layers of mucosa thrown into wrinkled folds. The mucosa is the lining of the tract directly involved in digestive activity (epithelial layer, lamina propria and muscularis mucosae).

DIGESTIVE SYSTEM
SMALL INTESTINE: DUODENUM, JEJUNUM, ILEUM

see also 58, 64, 78, 82, 83

CN 13

1. The colors red, blue, and green are recommended for the artery (L), vein (m), and lymphatic vessel (k).
2. Color the titles duodenum, jejunum, and ileum; the vertical dimensions (at far right); and the diagram of these structures at lower right with the colors they received on P. 78.
3. The dimensions cited are considered an average among reports of 2–9 meters of small intestine length (1m = 3' 4").
4. Color (b–e) same as Plate 83 where they had different identification letters. Color (f) the same color as you used for jejunum.

DUODENUM
10"
25 cm

JEJUNUM
6'
1.8m

ILEUM
9'
2.7 m

INTESTINAL WALL *
CIRCULAR FOLDS, WITH VILLI a
MUSCULARIS MUCOSAE b
SUBMUCOSA c
CIRCULAR MUSCLE d
LONGITUDINAL M. e
SEROSA f
LYMPHATIC NODULE g

MUCOSA (VILLI) a'
ABSORPTIVE CELLS a²
GOBLET CELLS h
CRYPTS (INTESTINAL GLANDS) i
LAMINA PROPRIA j
LYMPHATIC VESSEL k
ARTERY L VEIN m

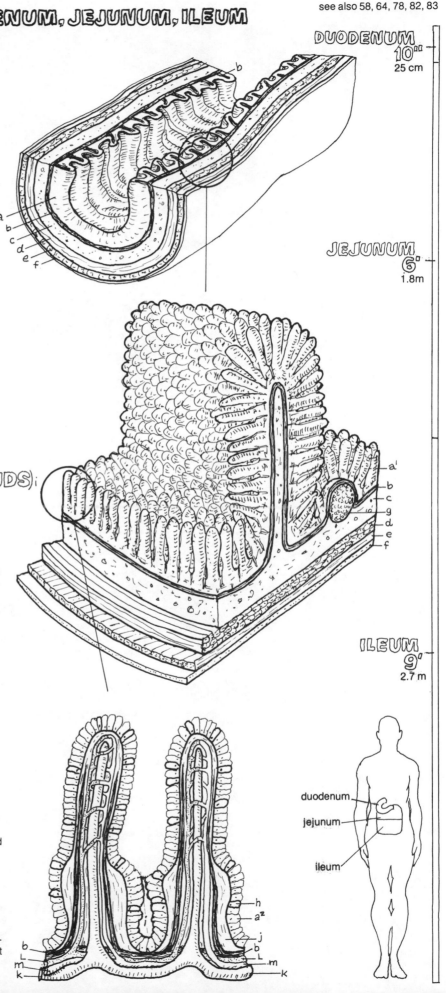

The highly convoluted *small intestine* begins after the pyloric end of the stomach and terminates at the cecum of the large intestine. It is elastically hinged by the common mesentery proper (except for the duodenum) and fills the abdominal cavity within the frame of the large intestine. The *duodenum*, the shortest and most fixed part, is a C-shaped structure just below the liver on the right side and receives the head of the pancreas in its concavity behind the parietal peritoneum (retroperitoneal). Basically all parts of the small intestine are structurally similar. The *villi* decrease in frequency in the ileum and are not frequently seen in the most distal segments of the small intestine. The small intestine receives partially digested food (chyme) from the stomach and breaks it down further by mechanical and enzymatic digestion with the aid of secretions from the pancreas and liver (via the gall bladder). Essentially all digestion of nutrients, including vitamins, occurs here; in addition, the nutrients of molecular dimensions are absorbed by the *lymphatic* and *blood capillaries* in and about the villi (cross section seen in lower drawing) and carted off to the liver, directly (tributaries of hepatic portal system) or indirectly (via the cysterna chyli, thoracic duct, venous system, recirculation to liver). The *circular folds* and the villi serve to increase the surface area of absorption; they are in constant motion during digestion, a movement created by the action of the *muscularis mucosa* and its contributions to the villi and the *larger muscular layers* deep to the *submucosa*.

In various places throughout the small intestine, *nodules of lymphatic tissue* can be found—often in groups or patches in the distal ileum. These are organized condensations of the reticular fibers/cells and lymphocytes that can be seen throughout the *lamina propria* of the gastrointestinal and respiratory mucosa. They represent a center for the development of antibodies against invasion of certain microorganisms.

duodenum
jejunum
ileum

PLATE 85
See also 58, 64, 78, 82, 83, 84

DIGESTIVE SYSTEM
LARGE INTESTINE*

CN ?

1. Color the elements of the uppermost diagram (except arrows e and g) in the same colors used on Plate 78, where they had different identification letters. Note that b and c will receive a single color.
2. Color illustrations from the top down.
3. Note the ileocecal valve (a') in the middle drawing as it opens into the uppermost part of the cecum. Note also that haustra (d') receives the same color as ascending colon.
4. Color serosa (L) the same as (h) from which a section is taken.
5. Color m–o the same as in Plate 84 where they had different letter identifications.

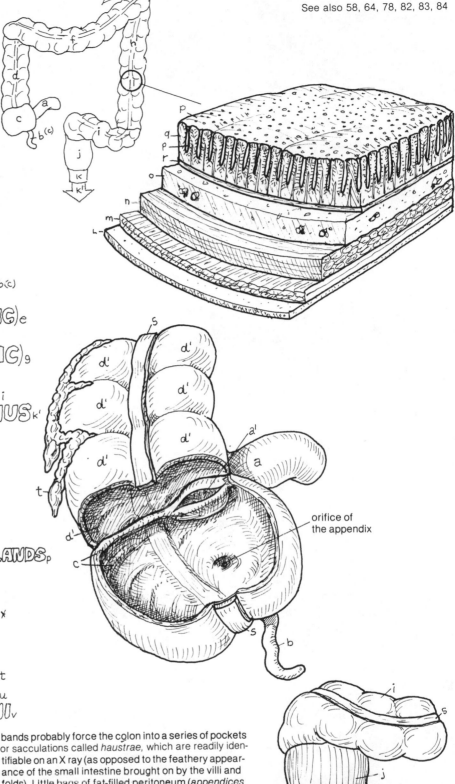

orifice of
the appendix

rectal
transverse
folds

ILEUM a ILEOCECAL VALVE a'

LARGE INTESTINE:*
CECUM c
VERMIFORM APPENDIX b(c)
ASCENDING COLON d
R. COLIC FLEXURE (HEPATIC) e
TRANSVERSE COLON f
L. COLIC FLEXURE (SPLENIC) g
DESCENDING COLON h
SIGMOID (PELVIC) COLON i
RECTUM j ANAL CANAL k ANUS k'

INTESTINAL WALL:*
SEROSA L(h)
LONGITUDINAL M. m
CIRCULAR M. n
SUBMUCOSA o
MUCOSA *
EPITHELIUM/INTESTINAL GLANDS p
LAMINA PROPRIA q
MUSCULARIS MUCOSAE r

INTESTINAL STRUCTURES: *
TAENIA COLI s
HAUSTRA d'
APPENDICES EPIPLOICA t
INTERNAL SPHINCTER ANI u
EXTERNAL SPHINCTER ANI v

The *large intestine*, 1–2 m in length, consists of the *cecum; ascending, transverse, descending,* and *sigmoid colons; rectum* and *anal canal*. By referring to the previous plate, you can see that the large intestine is usually larger and always shorter than the small intestine. It is more regularly arranged (fixed) within the abdominal cavity, for only the transverse and sigmoid colon have mesenteries. It has no villi or folds. The large intestine does not produce digestive enzymes (the intestinal glands of the colon are mucus-secreting) and is therefore not involved in the chemical digestion of chyme. It does, however, absorb water, vitamins, and minerals, thus creating feces (semisolid) from the more fluidlike chyme coming in through the muscular ileocecal valve. Absorbed material passes to the liver via the portal vein. Peristaltic movements of the colon arise from contractions of the *muscularis mucosa* and the two *outer muscular layers*. The outer *longitudinal layers* form 3 rather well-defined bands on the outside of the colon (*taenia coli*), which seem to arise at the appendix and terminate in the sigmoid colon. These bands probably force the colon into a series of pockets or sacculations called *haustrae*, which are readily identifiable on an X ray (as opposed to the feathery appearance of the small intestine brought on by the villi and folds). Little bags of fat-filled peritoneum (*appendices epiploica*) are also associated with the colon. These may communicate with the mucosa of the colon and become inflamed just as the appendix of the cecum may for the same reason (diverticulitis, appendicitis).

The rectum is characterized by a series of transverse folds, the middle of which seems to prevent stored feces from descending to the lower rectum and anal canal until the time of elimination (defecation). Fecal storage may occur well into the sigmoid colon. Relaxation of the *internal* and *external anal sphincters* in association with peristalsis of the colon bring on defecation. In the 4-cm long anal canal, the epithelial lining changes from a simple columnar type to the more protective stratified squamous. No significant absorption occurs in the rectum or anal canal.

DIGESTIVE SYSTEM
THE LIVER*

1. Reserve red for the arteries (L, L[1]), blue for the veins (K–k[3], o, p), and green for the bile ducts (m, m[1]).
2. Color both views of the liver simultaneously. The lower view is exposed by lifting up the inferior border of the liver while the superior border is hinged to the diaphragm by the coronary ligaments.
3. The porta of the liver in the central drawing (surrounded by lesser omentum, e[2]) is to be colored gray.
4. In the lower right drawing, the arrows indicate direction of blood or bile flow. Note bile flows in opposite direction relative to portal vein and hepatic artery blood.

see also 58, 64, 66, 78, 82

LOBES
RIGHT LOBE a
LEFT LOBE b
QUADRATE LOBE c
CAUDATE LOBE d

LIGAMENTS
CORONARY LIG. e
TRIANGULAR LIG. e'
LESSER OMENTUM e[2] & ITS
   LIG. VENOSUM e[3]
FALCIFORM LIG. e[4] & ITS
   LIG. TERES (ROUND LIG.) e[5]

VISCERAL IMPRESSIONS
RENAL (R. KIDNEY) f
COLIC (TRANSVERSE COLON) g
GASTRIC (STOMACH) h
ESOPHAGEAL i
DUODENAL j

PORTA*
PORTAL VEIN k
HEPATIC ARTERY L
BILE DUCTS m

The *liver* (L. *hepar*), weighing about 1.5 kg, occupies the upper right and part of the upper left quadrants of the abdominal cavity. As you can see, it is rounded above and tapers to a thin inferior border, below which the *gall bladder* peeks out. The inferior or visceral surface (underside) of the liver slants upward and backward from its inferior to superior borders. The liver is largely invested in peritoneum. Where it is not, it is called a *bare area* (a'). Superiorly, the *coronary ligaments* reflect to become the parietal peritoneum of the diaphragm. Anteriorly, the coronary ligaments merge to become the *falciform ligament,* which (in its lowest border) conducts the old umbilical vein (*ligamentum teres*) to the umbilicus. On the underside, the posterior layers of the coronary ligaments form the *lesser omentum* (suspending the stomach), which encircles the porta of the liver and its contents. Deep within the lesser omentum lies the old ductus venosus (*ligamentum venosum*), which conducted blood from the portal vein to the hepatic vein or inferior vena cava in the fetus. The *triangular ligaments* are simply the corners of the coronary ligaments. Due to its extensive surface area, several parts of the liver come in contact with other abdominal organs. Try to visualize these relationships (see visceral impressions).

A microscopic description: from the outer capsule, delicate fibrous tissue turns inward to divide the liver into *lobules,* the functional units. *Portal blood* brings nutrient-laden blood to the *cells of the lobules,* which glean the nutrients from the *sinusoidal* blood. The "filtered" blood enters the *central veins* which are tributaries of the *hepatic veins.* These join the *inferior vena cava* just below the diaphragm. Hepatic cells disburse their products into the sinusoids except for bile, which is absorbed by tiny bile canals. These merge to form the *bile ducts.*

The four apparent lobes of the liver relate only to the surface. The *hepatic artery* divides into left and right hepatic arteries, and the hepatic bile duct is formed from right and left bile ducts; thus the liver is essentially two (*left and right*) lobes.

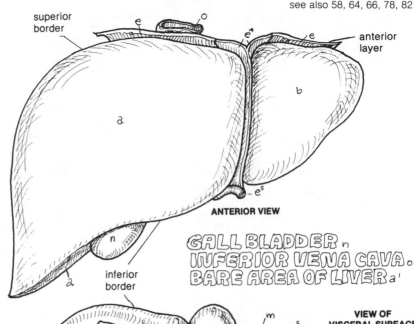

superior border

anterior layer

ANTERIOR VIEW

inferior border

GALL BLADDER n
INFERIOR VENA CAVA o
BARE AREA OF LIVER a'

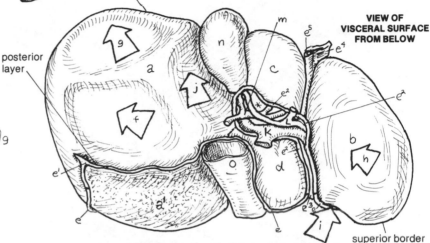

VIEW OF VISCERAL SURFACE FROM BELOW

posterior layer

superior border

BRANCH OF PORTAL VEIN k'
BRANCH OF HEPATIC A. L' } TRIAD*
BILE DUCT m'
SINUSOIDS p
HEPATIC CELLS q
CENTRAL VEIN k[2]
HEPATIC VEIN k[3]

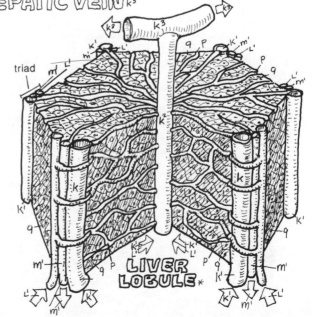

triad

LIVER LOBULE*

PLATE 87
see also 57, 58, 62, 64, 78, 86

DIGESTIVE SYSTEM
GALL BLADDER, PANCREAS, SPLEEN
CN 9

1. Reserve red for the arteries (j), blue for the veins (k), and a different shade of blue for the inferior vena cava (L). Use the same colors for gall bladder, pancreas, and spleen as they received on Plate 78 where they had different identification letters.
2. Do not color the duodenum.

fundus

liver

body

a

gastric
impression

renal
impression

hilus

c

neck

b

body

h tail

colic
impression

duodenum

i

head

uncinate process

neck

b neck

h

R. & L. HEPATIC DUCT d
COMMON HEPATIC DUCT e
CYSTIC DUCT f
COMMON BILE DUCT g
PANCREATIC DUCT h
DUODENAL PAPILLA i
ABDOMINAL AORTA j
CELIAC TRUNK j'
SPLENIC A. j²
COMMON HEPATIC j³
SUP. MESENTERIC A. j⁴
PORTAL VEIN k
SUP. MESENTERIC V. k'
SPLENIC V. k²
INFERIOR VENA CAVA L

The 50-ml capacity *gall bladder* is tucked away against the visceral surface of the liver with its *cystic duct* merging with the *common hepatic* duct to form the *common bile duct*. Its lining is fairly typical for the digestive tract except that its mucosa is thrown into complex folds and ridges creating a honeycomb appearance. Its many microvilli suggest an absorptive function. The gall bladder stores bile. The bile is produced in the liver and ducted directly (common bile duct) to the duodenum. When the sphincter muscle at the *duodenal papilla* is constricted, bile is forced back into the cystic duct and gall bladder. There the bile is stored, concentrated, and acidified (bile is 97% water, 1% bile pigments/salts, 2% mineral salts and fatty acids). At meal time, the sphincter relaxes, the gall bladder contracts in response to gastrointestinal hormones and the vagus nerves, and bile is directed to the duodenum. The yellowish bile (a color due to the presence of pigments) renders the ingested fats more soluble in water where the digestive enzymes can function. Bile salts accomplish this by breaking up masses of fat into small globules (emulsion), thus increasing their overall surface area. Water soluble lipases (enzymes) then have a better grasp on the fat structure and can break it down into units that can be absorbed by the lining cells of the small intestine.

The *pancreas* is a retroperitoneal structure whose head lies in the crook of the duodenum and whose tail touches the spleen. In the cadaver, it lies just deep to the stomach. The pancreas has two kinds of glands, most of which have ducts that join the extensive *pancreatic duct* which enters the duodenal papilla often in company with the common bile duct. These exocrine glands secrete an alkaline mixture of enzymes that pour into the duodenum at an approximate rate of 2000 ml every 24 hours and aid in the digestion (breakdown) of proteins, fats, and carbohydrates for absorption by the lining cells of the small intestine. Pancreatic secretion is regulated by hormones and vagus nerves. The endocrine portion of the pancreas will be considered on Plate 111.

The *spleen* is a purple, concave, delicate structure tucked under the diaphragm on the left side adjacent to the 10th rib. It is an organ of the lymphatic system consisting of organized masses of encapsulated lymphatic tissue intimately associated with blood sinusoids and other vessels. In effect, the spleen filters blood. The spleen manufactures lymphocytes and monocytes for export and is very active in immune response to the presence of antigens (microorganisms, etc.). Its macrophages remove debris from the blood and specifically break down aged red blood corpuscles. The heme portion of the hemoglobin molecule is converted indirectly into bilirubin, which is conducted to the liver by way of the hepatic portal vein and incorporated into the manufacture of bile. In fact, it is largely responsible for the yellow color of bile. Accumulation of bilirubin in the blood is *jaundice* and is generally indicative of liver or gall bladder disease. The storage function of red blood corpuscles in the spleen is generally considered to be minimal.

URINARY SYSTEM
THE URINARY TRACT*

PLATE 88
see also 89, 93, 96

CN 13
1. Color the urinary tract in the lower drawings first, then in the central drawing.
2. Color the various areas of the kidney that contact neighboring visceral structures.
3. Only the male urethra is divided into 3 sections.

KIDNEY a
URETER b
URINARY BLADDER c
URETHRA d
  PROSTATIC d'
  MEMBRANOUS d²
  SPONGY d³

RELATIONS OF KIDNEYS*
RIGHT KIDNEY
  SUPRARENAL AREA e
  LIVER f
  DUODENAL g
  COLIC h
LEFT KIDNEY
  SUPRARENAL AREA e'
  SPLENIC i
  GASTRIC j
  PANCREATIC k
  JEJUNAL L
  COLIC h'

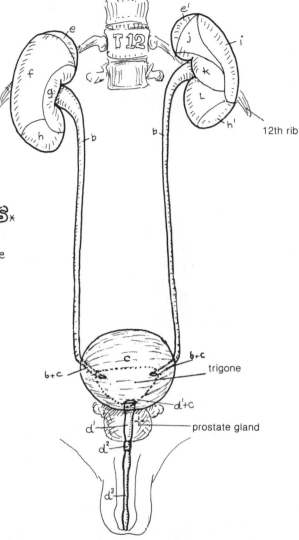

12th rib
trigone
prostate gland

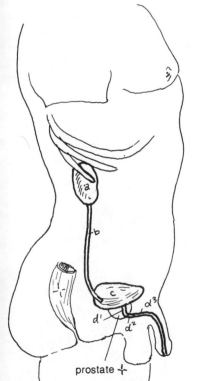

prostate +

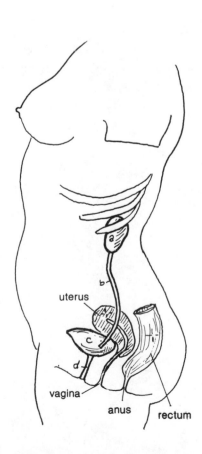

uterus
vagina
anus
rectum

The *urinary tract* represents a pathway for the elimination of metabolic by-products and unessential chemicals dissolved in water. Of the structures making up the tract, perhaps the *kidneys* are most interesting in that they process the blood plasma and enter into a series of exchanges between their tubules, the blood, and the interstitial (tissue) fluid to achieve a constant acid-base balance and to preserve body water volume. The kidneys, then, are not merely instruments of excretion, but are essential organs involved in conserving metabolic products, working to maintain electrical, chemical, and concentration balances and the integrity of body water compartments. The process is dynamic, and what is excreted as waste in one moment may be retained as precious the next. The *ureters* are epithelial-lined, fibromuscular tubes conveying urine to the holding tank, the *urinary bladder*. The *urethra* drains the bladder and is considerably longer in males (20 cm) than in females (4 cm). The trigone of the bladder is a triangular area at the base of the bladder into whose corners fit the two ureters and urethra.

When drawing the relations of the kidneys, try to visualize these various organs collectively making contact with the kidneys. Your understanding of the rather tight "fit" of the abdominal viscera will be considerably enhanced. Note that the right kidney is lower than the left. This is so simply because the liver is in the way.

PLATE 89
see also 29, 88

URINARY SYSTEM
KIDNEYS & VESSELS IN ABDOMINAL CAVITY.

CN 21

1. Note that the urinary tract (a-a²) receives one color (a bright or very dark one).
2. Reserve red for L–L² and blue for i–i².

KIDNEY a
URETER a'
URINARY BLADDER a²
DIAPHRAGM b
QUADRATUS LUMBORUM M. c
TRANSVERSUS ABDOMINIS M. d
ILIACUS M. e
PSOAS M. f
HEPATIC Vs g
ESOPHAGUS h
INFERIOR VENA CAVA i
RENAL V. j
SUPRARENAL V. k
COMMON ILIAC V. i'
EXT. & INT. ILIAC V. i²
ABDOMINAL AORTA L
COMMON ILIAC A. L'
EXT. & INTERNAL ILIAC A. L²
SUPRARENAL GLAND m
SUPRARENAL A. n
CELIAC A. & BRANCHES o
SUPERIOR MESENTERIC A. p
TESTICULAR A. q / V. q'
INFERIOR MESENTERIC A r
RENAL A. s
RECTUM t
DUCTUS DEFERENS u

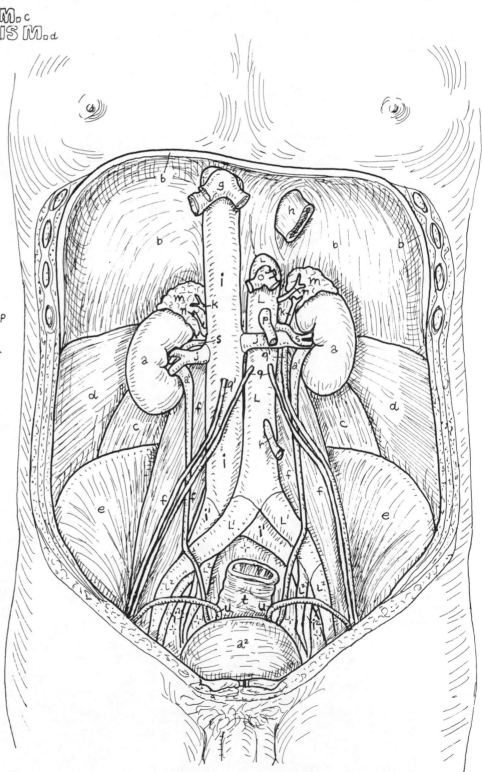

The *paired kidneys* and *ureters* lie behind the parietal peritoneum on the posterior abdominal wall. Thus they are crossed by a variety of vessels some of which are also retroperitoneal and some of which are packed in their mesentery along with their related organs. These relationships are extremely important to the surgeon doing a retroperitoneal dissection. To reduce the complexity of the illustration, a number of nerves, ganglia, lymph nodes, vessels, mesenteries, parietal peritoneum, and intestinal viscera have not been shown. The intestines, their mesenteries, and their vessels/nerves/lymphatics all cross anterior to the kidneys and ureters. The ureters are subject to constriction at three places along their route: at the origin of the ureter where the renal pelvis narrows to become the ureter; where the ureter crosses over the pelvic brim and the iliac vessels; where the ureters enter the *urinary bladder*. At these narrow areas, developing stones often get hung up and block the lumen (channel) of the ureter. Near the bladder, note the *ductus deferens* passing over and in front of the ureters on both sides en route to the inguinal canal.

PLATE 90
see also 88, 91

URINARY SYSTEM
KIDNEY, CORONAL SECTION.

CN 11

1. Reserve red for the artery (i) and blue for the vein (j).
2. Use the same color for renal capsule (a) as was used for kidney on Plate 88. Color ureter (h) the same as on that plate.
3. Note the cross sections of minor calyces (e, out of the plane of this section) which open into the major calyces (f).

RENAL CAPSULE a
CORTEX b
PYRAMID (MEDULLA) c
PAPILLA d
MINOR CALYX e
MAJOR CALYX f
RENAL PELVIS g
URETER h
RENAL ARTERY i
RENAL VEIN j
RENAL SINUS k

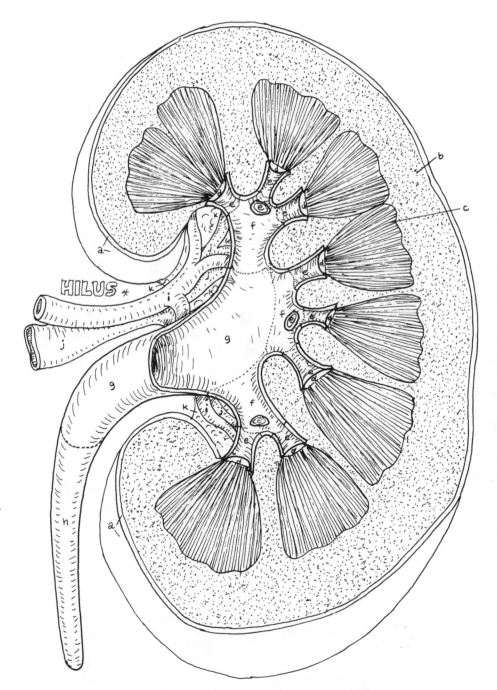

HILUS *

The kidney might be described as having a central part and a peripheral part: the outer, peripheral part consists of the cortex and the medullary pyramids; the inner, central part consists of a group of tubes growing out of the ureter. The *medulla* and *cortex* are made up of the uriniferous tubules (the nephrons and collecting ducts), a part of which processes the blood plasma and a part of which adds to/subtracts from the filtrate resulting in the formation of urine. The tubes (calyces, pelvis) conduct urine passively to the ureter. The cortex is somewhat darker than the medulla and contains the renal corpuscles and convoluted tubules for the most part. Depending on the way the kidney is sectioned, the cortex may appear to have groups of striations coursing through it (from the medulla), a multitude of pinholes throughout, or a combination of both. The medulla contains the straight tubules (largely collecting ducts) and is therefore striated. The collecting ducts converge onto the apex of each of the kidney's 8 to 18 pyramids and open into the *minor calyx* via the papilla. A similar number of funnel-shaped minor calyces merge to form about 3 *major calyces*, which open into the *renal pelvis*. The renal pelvis and its branching calyces fit within the *renal sinus*, packed in loose connective tissue and sharing space with the *renal vessels*. The sinus is a cavity that is an inward extension of the hilus. At the hilus the renal pelvis narrows to become the *ureter*. The kidney is encapsulated by a thin but strong sheath of dense fibrous tissue.

PLATE 91
see also 88, 90

URINARY SYSTEM
THE URINIFEROUS TUBULE *

CN 16

1. When coloring the kidney cross section to the right, you may use the colors from the preceding plate. Note that the external borders of the wedge of kidney below receive the corresponding colors of the part of the cross section to which it refers.

2. In drawing the glomerular capsule at far right, though j^1, j^2, and j^3 receive the same color, you might wish to lighten j^3 to distinguish the cavity from the other layers.

3. The directional arrows receive the color of the structures to which they refer.

4. Color interlobular artery (q) bright red.

NEPHRON *
RENAL CORPUSCLE *
GLOMERULUS i
GLOMERULAR CAPSULE j
PARIETAL LAYER j^1
VISCERAL LAYER j^2
(PODOCYTES) j^2
CAPSULAR SPACE j^3
PROXIMAL TUBULE k
CONVOLUTED PART k^1
STRAIGHT PART k^2
LOOP OF HENLE L
DISTAL TUBULE m
STRAIGHT PART m^1
CONVOLUTED PART m^2

COLLECTING DUCT n

The functional unit of the kidney is the *nephron,* of which there are about one million per kidney. Each nephron and a collecting duct form a *uriniferous tubule.* In association with the myriad blood vessels, these tubules fill up the medulla and cortex of the kidney. The plasma of the blood is filtered in the *glomerulus* of capillaries, which show multiple small pores superimposed by the cells of the *visceral layer of the capsule.* These cells (podocytes) have cytoplasmic processes that encircle the porous capillaries like a fine weave separated by thin slits. It is through these pores and slits that all but the cells and the largest elements (proteins) of the plasma pass into the *capsular space* (lumen) and into the *proximal tubules* at a rate of about 125 ml/minute/kidney. The pyramid-shaped cells of the proximal tubule are responsible for absorption from the filtrate of 85% of the sodium chloride and water, all of the glucose, small proteins, amino acids, and certain vitamins. Relatively little secretion from the cells into the filtrate occurs here. Undesired filtered products of metabolism remain in the lumen of the tubule and continue the trek to the calyces. The *loop of Henle* creates a mechanism for increasing the concentration of the urine particles (solutes) by drawing water into the tissues between the tubules. Conservation of water by the kidneys is one of its most critical functions, and by the time the filtrate reaches the distal tubules, about 80% of the original amount has been reabsorbed by the tubular cells. Strongly influenced by hormones, the *distal convoluted tubules* and *collecting ducts* absorb most of the water remaining so that 99% of the original filtrate has been returned to the tissues and 1% passes into the minor calyces. The various ions found in the urine (that part of the filtrate excreted into the calyces) are the leftovers of a complex exchange and trading of ions between the tubular cells, the tubular lumen, the neighboring capillaries, and the surrounding extracellular fluid.

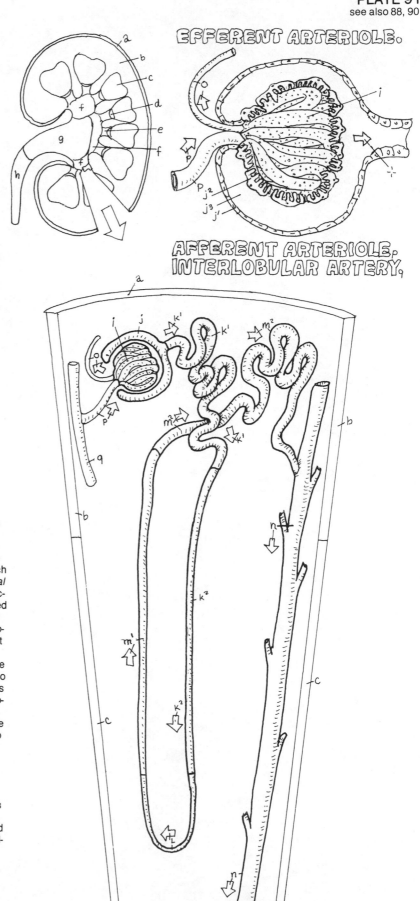

EFFERENT ARTERIOLE o

AFFERENT ARTERIOLE p
INTERLOBULAR ARTERY q

PLATE 92
see also 88, 91, 90

URINARY SYSTEM CIRCULATORY PATTERN OF THE KIDNEY*

CN 8
1. Color the arteries and veins in the top drawing. The veins are all dotted structures and should be colored blue.
2. Use bright red for the interlobular artery (d) in both illustrations, so you can see the relationship between the two drawings.
3. In the sectional drawing below, it is suggested that the glomerular capsule and space as well as the tubules/collecting ducts be left blank to better appreciate the capillary network around the tubules/ducts. The veins (dotted structures) should all be colored blue as above.
4. Color d–g the colors they received on Plate 91, where they had different identification letters.

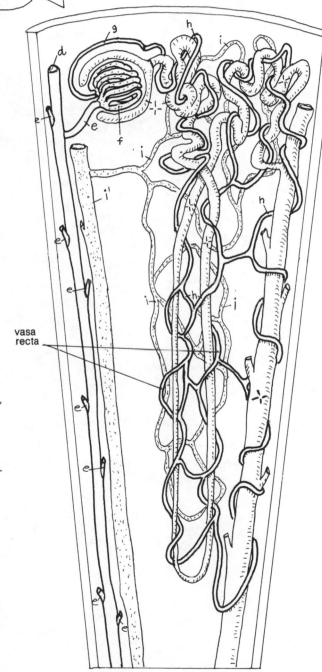

vasa
recta

RENAL A. a
  SEGMENTAL A. a'
INTERLOBAR A. b
ARCUATE A. c
INTERLOBULAR A. d
AFFERENT ARTERIOLE e
GLOMERULUS f
EFFERENT ARTERIOLE g
PERITUBULAR CAPILLARIES h

PERITUBULAR V. i
INTERLOBULAR V. i'
ARCUATE V. i²
INTERLOBAR V. i³
SEGMENTAL V. i⁴
RENAL V. i⁵

The *renal artery* breaks up into five anterior and one posterior *segmental arteries*, each of which supplies one segment of the kidney as shown above. Collateral circulation (anastomoses) among these segments is considered inadequate for normal function; obstruction of one such artery may mean loss of an entire segment, a matter of some concern to the surgeon. Within the renal sinus, the segmental vessels branch into *interlobar arteries,* which pass up between (inter-) the lobes or pyramids. An *arcuate artery* springs from these, arcing over the medulla. *Interlobular arteries* project up into the cortex to give off the *afferent arterioles* that feed the *glomerulus.* The blood leaves the glomerulus via the *efferent arterioles,* which open into a network of *capillaries* entwined about the convoluted and straight tubules as well as the collecting ducts. The capillaries about the straight tubules/ducts in the medulla form a series of interconnecting loops (vasa recta or straight vessels). Veins draining these peritubular networks join the *interlobular veins,* and venous blood proceeds toward the hilus in the same pattern as the arteries. Much of the filtrate reabsorbed by the tubular/duct cells diffuses into these capillaries to be returned to the tissues or recirculated. The relationship of the vasa recta to the loops of Henle is a critical factor in the success of water reabsorption. In the untreated diabetic, the blood glucose level is well above normal (hyperglycemia) in part because the cells of the proximal tubules are so efficient at reabsorbing the glucose from the filtrate and secreting it to the peritubular capillaries. These capillaries may secrete unwanted ions into the surrounding extracellular fluid from which the tubular cells may reabsorb them and secrete them into the tubular lumen. Thus the circulatory pattern among the nephrons and collecting ducts is a vital feature in the preservation of body water and the maintenance of chemical equilibrium throughout the body.

PLATE 93
see also 88, 89, 30, 28, 59

REPRODUCTIVE SYSTEM
THE MALE REPRODUCTIVE SYSTEM*

CN 14

1. Color both lower views simultaneously. In the front view note that part of the ductus deferens (d) and seminal vesicles (e) are located behind the bladder. These portions should be colored lightly to give the proper effect.

2. Color the drawing to the right. The coverings of the spermatic cord (one of which is the cremaster muscle) and testis are actually composed of several layers. Use red for (m), blue for (n) and (n').

SCROTUM a
TESTIS b
EPIDIDYMIS c
DUCTUS DEFERENS d
SEMINAL VESICLE e
EJACULATORY DUCT f
URETHRA g
BULBOURETHRAL GLAND h
PROSTATE GLAND i
PENIS j
UROGENITAL DIAPHRAGM k

SPERMATIC CORD.
COVERINGS L
CONSTITUENTS*
DUCTUS DEFERENS d
TESTICULAR ARTERY m
TESTICULAR VEIN n
(PAMPINFORM PLEXUS) n'

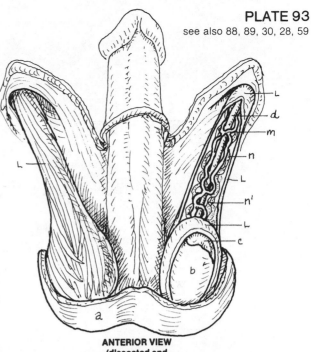

ANTERIOR VIEW
(dissected and
penis elevated)

As the ductus deferens passes through the abdominal wall (inguinal canal), from inside to outside, it picks up a *testicular artery* and *vein(s)*, some nerves and lymphatics as companion structures. The collection of these make up the *constituents* of the spermatic cord. Passing through the inguinal canal, they become invested by a representative layer from the abdominal wall layers ('less rectus'); these are the *coverings of the spermatic cord* and testes. In the drawing above, all coverings are shown as one; on the left side, coverings are dissected to view the constituents. In a vasectomy procedure, the ductus deferens is identified within the cord and it alone is cut, tied, and the cut segments are separated.

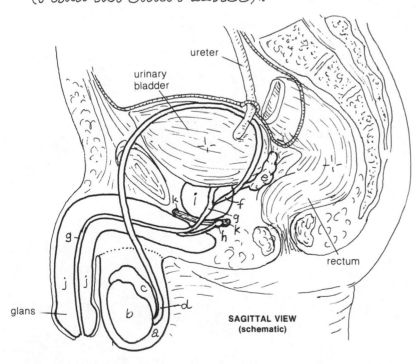

ureter
urinary bladder
glans
rectum
SAGITTAL VIEW
(schematic)

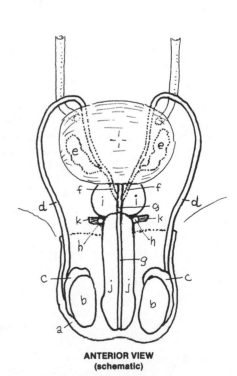

ANTERIOR VIEW
(schematic)

The *male reproductive system* consists of the primary organs, the *testes*, suspended within a sac of skin, the *scrotum;* a series of ducts; and a number of glands. Development of the male germinating cells (sperm) in the testes requires a temperature of about 35 degrees Celsius (95° F), and this is achieved by their presence in the scrotum some distance away from the warmer body cavities. The temperature within the scrotum can be adjusted slightly by action of smooth muscle in its walls, which can close the scrotal wall about the testes (contraction) or relax the walls to fall away loosely, allowing the heat to dissipate within. Following storage in the *epididymis,* sperm cells move through the *ductus (vas) deferens,* passing through the abdominal wall and pelvic cavity to enter the prostatic

urethra via the pencil-point shaped *ejaculatory duct.* Here the nutrient-rich secretions of the *prostate* gland and seminal vesicles are added to the population of sperm, forming semen. Prior to the release of the semen (ejaculation), the *bulbourethral glands* secrete, apparently lubricating the already mucous-gland-lined urethra. The urethra passes through three distinct structures: the prostate gland, a fibromuscular shelf (*urogenital diaphragm*) dividing part of the perineum (region below the prostate) into two spaces, and the spongy body of the *penis*. In general, the penis and scrotum constitute the external genital organs (L. *genitalis* = belonging to birth).

REPRODUCTIVE SYSTEM
THE TESTES*

CN ?

1. When coloring the seminiferous tubules (b) in the sagittal section of the testis at the top of the page, do not color in the background connective tissue in which each tubule is coiled.
2. Similarly, leave out the background tissue when coloring the spermatogenic and interstitial cells.
3. Color (a) the color of the testis on Plate 93. Color (e) and (f) the same colors as on that plate, where they had different identification letters.
4. A spermatozoon (singular), one of the spermatazoa (k) shown in the middle drawing, has been enlarged to show its detailed structure.

PLATE 94
see also 93

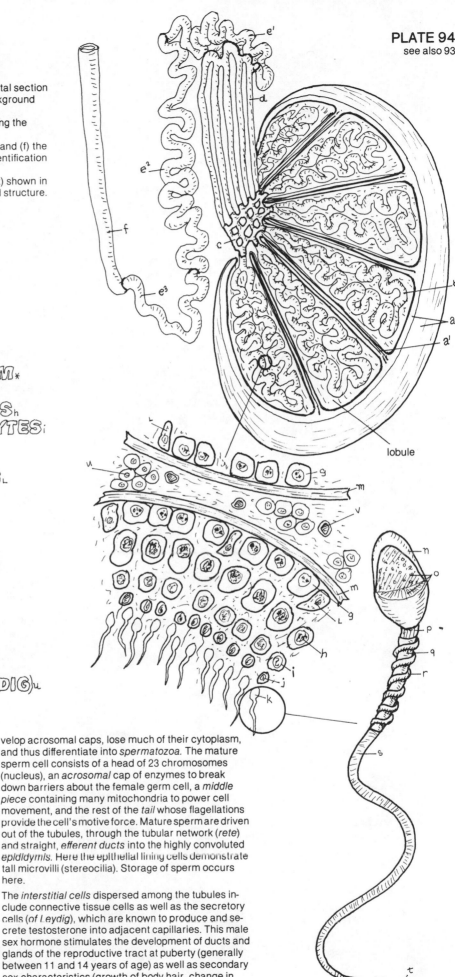

lobule

TUNICA ALBUGINEA a
  SEPTUM a'
SEMINIFEROUS TUBULE b
RETE TESTIS c
EFFERENT DUCTS d
EPIDIDYMIS e
  HEAD e' BODY e² TAIL e³
DUCTUS DEFERENS f

SPERMATOGENIC EPITHELIUM *
  SPERMATOGONIA g
  PRIMARY SPERMATOCYTES h
  SECONDARY SPERMATOCYTES i
  SPERMATIDS j
  SPERMATOZOA k
SERTOLI (SUPPORTING) CELLS L
BASEMENT MEMBRANE m
SPERMATOZOON k
  HEAD *
    ACROSOME n
    NUCLEUS o
  TAIL *
    NECK p
    MIDDLE PIECE q
      MITOCHONDRIA r
    PRINCIPAL PIECE s
    END PIECE t
INTERSTITIAL CELLS (OF LEYDIG) u
BLOOD VESSELS v

The *testes* are glands that arise on the posterior abdominal wall during fetal development. As the developing body lengthens, these organs seem to "descend" (actually they do not) into outpocketings of the abdominal wall (scrotum). The testes have two functions: development and excretion of male germ cells (sperm, spermatozoa) and the secretion of testosterone, the male sex hormone.

The *seminiferous tubules,* highly coiled within each of the lobules partitioned by *septa* of connective tissue from the dense capsule *tunica albuginea,* are lined with organized masses of cells, the *spermatogenic epithelia* and *supporting (Sertoli) cells.* The most primitive of these sperm-developing cells, *spermatogonia,* divide perhaps several times, following which several daughter cells are pushed out toward the lumen of the tubule. These change character (differentiate) to become *primary spermatocytes,* the largest of the developing germ cells. These undergo division to become *secondary spermatocytes,* at which time the number of chromosomes is reduced from 46 to 23 (meiosis). Each pair of newly formed secondary spermatocytes rapidly divides again to form four *spermatids.* These small cells develop tails, condense their nuclei, de-

velop acrosomal caps, lose much of their cytoplasm, and thus differentiate into *spermatozoa.* The mature sperm cell consists of a head of 23 chromosomes (nucleus), an *acrosomal* cap of enzymes to break down barriers about the female germ cell, a *middle piece* containing many mitochondria to power cell movement, and the rest of the *tail* whose flagellations provide the cell's motive force. Mature sperm are driven out of the tubules, through the tubular network (*rete*) and straight, *efferent ducts* into the highly convoluted *epididymis.* Here the epithelial lining cells demonstrate tall microvilli (stereocilia). Storage of sperm occurs here.

The *interstitial cells* dispersed among the tubules include connective tissue cells as well as the secretory cells (*of Leydig*), which are known to produce and secrete testosterone into adjacent capillaries. This male sex hormone stimulates the development of ducts and glands of the reproductive tract at puberty (generally between 11 and 14 years of age) as well as secondary sex characteristics (growth of body hair, change in voice due to change in larynx structure, increased skeletal growth, etc.). Secretion of testosterone is influenced by hormones of the pituitary gland.

PLATE 95
see also 93, 30, 94, 88

REPRODUCTIVE SYSTEM
URETHRA, PENIS &
UROGENITAL REGION*
CN 17

1. Reserve the colors blue for the vein (i), red for the artery (j), and yellow for the nerve (k), all located in the cross section of the penis below.
2. Color the top and middle illustrations simultaneously. The urogenital diaphragm is enlarged in the upper two drawings to better visualize and color its structure.

URETHRA*
PROSTATIC URETHRA a
MEMBRANOUS U. b
PENILE U. c

PENIS*
CORPUS CAVERNOSUM d
CRUS OF PENIS d'
BULB OF PENIS e
CORPUS SPONGIOSUM e'
GLANS e²
PREPUCE (FORESKIN) f

RELATED STRUCTURES*
SUPERFICIAL FASCIA g
DEEP FASCIA h
VEIN i ARTERY j
NERVE k
SUSPENSORY LIGAMENT l
LEVATOR ANI m
   (PELVIC DIAPHRAGM) m
UROGENITAL DIAPHRAGM n
BULBOURETHRAL GLAND o

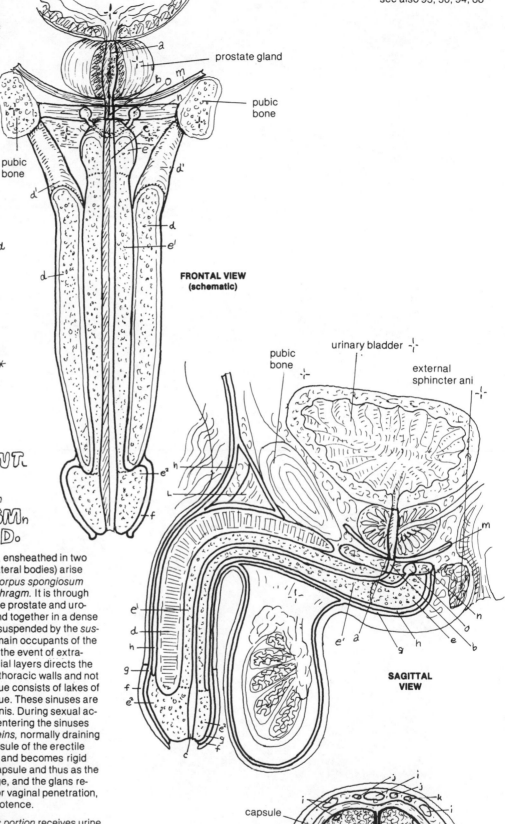

FRONTAL VIEW (schematic)

SAGITTAL VIEW

CROSS SECTION

The *penis* consists of three bodies of erectile tissue, ensheathed in two layers of fasciae. The *corpora cavernosa* (the two lateral bodies) arise from the underside of the pubic bones; the central *corpus spongiosum* arises as a *bulb* suspended from the *urogenital diaphragm*. It is through the *bulb of the penis* that the urethra passes from the prostate and urogenital diaphragm above. The three bodies are bound together in a dense stocking of *deep perineal fascia* and hang as a unit suspended by the *suspensory ligament*. These roots of the penis are the main occupants of the urogenital portion of the perineum (see Plate 30). In the event of extravasation (leakage) of urine, the arrangement of fascial layers directs the accumulation of fluid in the anterior abdominal and thoracic walls and not in the buttocks, thighs, or scrotum. The erectile tissue consists of lakes of veins (cavernous sinuses) bound by fibroelastic tissue. These sinuses are fed by small branches of the deep arteries to the penis. During sexual activity, these *arteries* dilate and the volume of blood entering the sinuses increases, expanding them. As a result, the *small veins,* normally draining the cavernous sinuses, are pressed against the capsule of the erectile bodies and blood cannot drain. The penis enlarges and becomes rigid (erection). The glans does not incorporate a thick capsule and thus as the arterial input increases, so does the venous drainage, and the glans remains nonrigid. A rigid penis is generally required for vaginal penetration, thus an inability to achieve erection constitutes impotence.

The *urethra* in the male has three parts. The *prostatic portion* receives urine from the urinary bladder, sperm from the ejaculatory ducts, and secretions from the prostate via several ducts. A complex neuromuscular mechanism prevents voiding of urine during the formation of semen. The urethra, filled with mucus-secreting glands in its mucosa, continues through the pelvic diaphragm and into the thin urogenital diaphragm, a fibromuscular sphincter containing the bulbourethral glands. This is the *membranous urethra*. Leaving the diaphragm, the urethra immediately enters the bulb of the penis to pass on through the corpus spongiosum (*spongy or penile urethra*) and open to the outside at the glans.

PLATE 96
see also 93, 88, 30

REPRODUCTIVE SYSTEM
THE FEMALE REPRODUCTIVE SYSTEM *

CN 18

1. Color the two (upper) views of the internal reproductive structures simultaneously. In the sagittal view, color the double line (✳) representing the peritoneum in gray.
2. In the lower drawing, color the vestibule gray after coloring the other structures located in that area (L–p).
3. Color the vagina (d) and its orifice (o) the same color.
4. Note that structures (f–h) are shown in both main drawings.

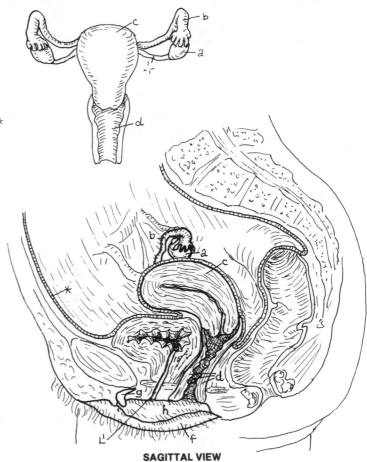

INTERNAL REPRODUCTIVE ORGANS *
OVARY a
UTERINE (FALLOPIAN) TUBE b
UTERUS c
VAGINA d

The *female reproductive system* consists of internal and external parts. The primary organ of this system is the *ovary*, which produces the female germ cells (ova) and secretes the hormones estrogen and progesterone. Estrogen is the principal female sex hormone, and among other things is responsible for the development of secondary sexual characteristics (breast development, broadening of hips, growth of pubic hair, etc.) as well as the development of glands and ducts of the reproductive tract at puberty. The ovary, like the testis, arises on the posterior abdominal wall (adjacent to the kidneys) during early fetal development. It also descends along that wall, like the testis, but is interrupted early in its journey by a pair of ligaments to the ovary and uterus and is retained in the pelvis. The *uterus* serves as a site for implantation and nourishment of the new embryo; the *uterine tubes* as a vehicle for the conduct of the freshly fertilized or unfertilized ovum to the uterus. The *vagina*, a fibromuscular sheath, receives the semen from the penis and transmits it to the uterus and acts as a birth canal from the uterus to the outside for the newborn child. Although the ovaries and testes share a common origin, as do the male/female external genital structures, the uterus, its tubes, and the upper two-thirds of the vagina arise from a duct system quite distinct from that in the male.

SAGITTAL VIEW

EXTERNAL GENITAL STRUCTURES *
MONS PUBIS e
LABIA MAJORA f
CLITORIS g
LABIA MINORA h
PREPUCE OF CLITORIS i
FRENULUM OF CLITORIS j
FOURCHETTE k
VESTIBULE *
ORIFICE OF URETHRA / URETHRA l
PARAURETHRAL GLANDS m
HYMEN n
VAGINAL ORIFICE o
VESTIBULAR GLANDS p
PERINEAL BODY q
ANUS r

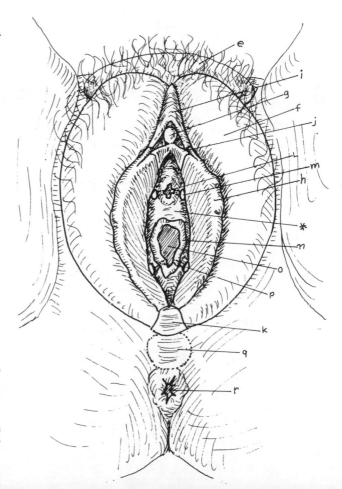

The *mons pubis* and *labia majora* share a common structure: adipose and fibrous tissue. The smaller, more pigmented *labia minora* contribute to the cloaks of the *clitoris* anteriorly and merge with the labia majora posteriorly as the *fourchette*. The cleft between the labia minora is the *vestibule* and receives the orifices of the short *urethra*, the *vagina*, and the small ducts of four *glands*. The orifices of the urethra and vagina are opened here; they are normally closed/collapsed. The *hymen* is a layer of mucosa that completely/incompletely covers the vaginal orifice in the sexually uninitiated. Remnants of it (as shown) are often retained in the sexually active. The *perineal body*, deep to the skin at the site indicated, is a fibromuscular mass serving as a central tendon of a number of perineal muscles, all of which help stabilize and support perineal structures and the uterus.

PLATE 97
see also 96

REPRODUCTIVE SYSTEM
THE OVARY*

CN 18

1. Reserve the colors red for all vessels marked (c), blue for (p--p¹), and yellow for the corpus luteum (n–n¹) and leave the corpus albicans (n²) white. Color (a) and (s) the same as (a) and (b), respectively, in Plate 96.
2. The connective tissue surface of the ovary should be colored light gray.
3. Color all the oocytes and ova the same color (e) even though the surrounding follicles/antrum receive different colors. Note the degenerating (atretic) follicle (k), which is not in the series of progressive follicular development.

4. Note that the corpus hemorrhagicum (m) receives the color red in its interior to suggest clotting blood.
5. The suspensory ligament of the ovary (o) is shown as if transparent, so color the ligament over the colored blood vessels passing through it.

EPITHELIUM a
TUNICA ALBUGINEA b
CAPILLARIES IN OVARY c
CONNECTIVE TISSUE STROMA d*
OOGENIC EPITHELIUM e
 OOCYTE/OVUM e
 PRIMORDIAL FOLLICLE f
 PRIMARY FOLL. g
 SECONDARY FOLL. h
 MATURING FOLL. i
 MATURE (GRAAFIAN) FOLL. j
 ATRETIC FOLL. k
 RUPTURED FOLL. L
 DISCHARGED OVUM L'
CORPUS HEMORRHAGICUM m/c'
YOUNG CORPUS LUTEUM n
MATURE CORPUS LUTEUM n'
CORPUS ALBICANS n²÷

RELATED STRUCTURES *
SUSPENSORY LIG. OF OVARY o
 OVARIAN A. c²& V. p
UTERINE A. c³ & V. p'
OVARIAN LIGAMENT q
MESOVARIUM r
UTERINE TUBE s
 FIMBRIAE t

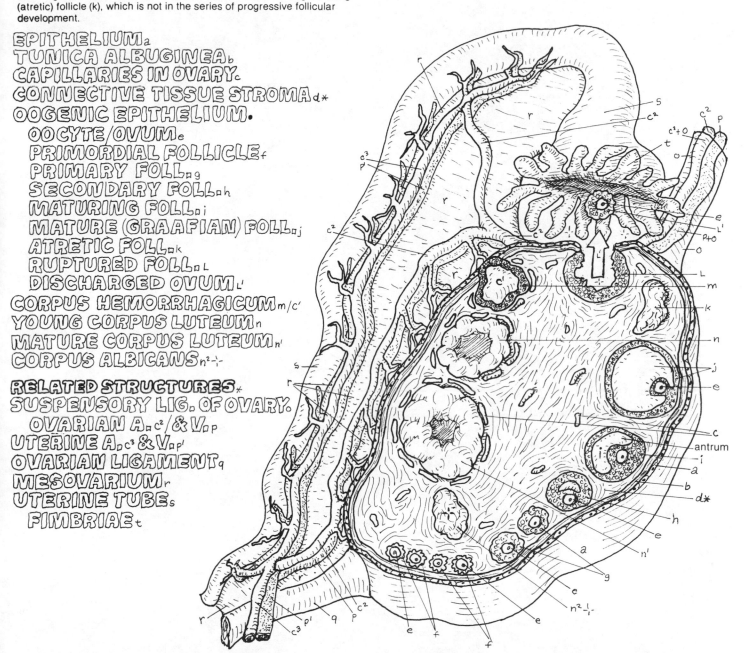

Development of female germ cells and the secretion of the hormones estrogen and progesterone are the functions of the *ovary*. Its location and relationship to the uterus/uterine tubes may be seen in the next plate. Confined by the thin but dense *epithelial-lined tunica albuginea,* many ovarian follicles in various stages of development can be seen here. A follicle consists of an immature epithelial germ cell (*oocyte*) surrounded by one or more layers of nongerminating cells. These germ cells were seeded in the ovary early in development—over 400,000 of them. Of these, only 500 or so will mature, the rest stopping short in their development and degenerating with their follicular cells (atretic follicles). Development of an *ovum* starts with the *primordial follicle*—an oocyte with one layer of follicular cells. The oocyte increases in size and maturity as the follicle cells increase in number. In the *secondary follicular stage,* a small lake (antrum) appears filled with follicular fluid. This antrum continues to increase/expand at the expense of the follicle cells, which are pushed away from the oocyte except for a layer of cells (*mature follicle*). Those cells in the outer-

most part of the follicle secrete estrogen during the proliferative phase of the reproductive cycle. (See Plate 99.) On about the 14th day of that cycle, the ovum (surrounded by a sugar-protein coat, the zona pellucida, and some follicular cells) bursts from the follicle into the waiting fingers (*fimbriae*) of the *uterine tube.* The *ruptured follicle* involutes, and some bleeding and clotting goes on (*corpus hemorrhagicum*) as the follicle cells transition, characterized by accumulating large amounts of lipid. This newly formed structure (*corpus luteum*) secretes estrogen and progesterone during the secretory phase of the cycle, and in the event of pregnancy, will support the developing embryo/fetus for up to 3 months with these secretions. Should pregnancy not ensue, the corpus luteum will involute and degenerate as the *corpus albicans*. Structures relating to 2 or 3 different but sequential cycles can be seen in the ovary at one time (primordial follicle of one, corpus luteum of another, and corpus albicans of yet another).

REPRODUCTIVE SYSTEM
THE UTERUS & UTERINE TUBES*

CN 17

1. The uterus, its tubes, the ovary and related ligaments are blanketed by peritoneum: the broad ligament (i). Color each part of the uterus (a, b, c), its tubes (f, g, h), the ovary and its ligament (o, k, L), and the round ligament (j). Then, on the left side of the uterus, color the broad ligament (i) a light gray over the previously colored structures. In this way, you have color-coded the various structures and also their peritoneal covering (a + i, b + i, c + i, f + i, g + i, h + i, j + i, k + i, L + i, and o + i). Note that the *cut edge* of the peritoneum over the uterus receives only the color of the peritoneum (i).

2. In coloring the fundus (a), body (b), and cervix (c), note that you are only coloring the exterior surface of these structures. Internally, you are coloring structure (c¹, d, e) common to all parts of the uterus.

3. Now color the diagram at lower right: the ovary, the ovum, and its directional arrows the same color as the ovary in the central illustration; and the sperm and its directional arrows the same color as the

vagina in which it is deposited by the penis. The sperm is greatly exaggerated in size in this diagram.

4. Use red for the ovarian artery (m), blue for the ovarian vein (n).

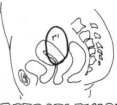

ANTEFLEXION, RETROFLEXION,

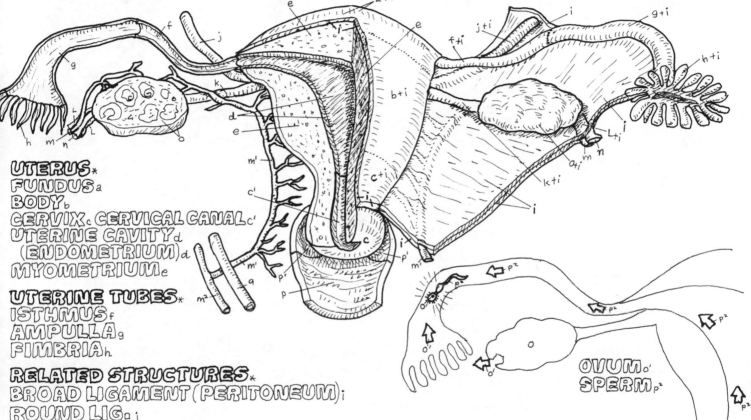

UTERUS*
FUNDUS a
BODY b
CERVIX c **CERVICAL CANAL** c'
UTERINE CAVITY d
   (ENDOMETRIUM) d
MYOMETRIUM e

UTERINE TUBES*
ISTHMUS f
AMPULLA g
FIMBRIA h

RELATED STRUCTURES*
BROAD LIGAMENT (PERITONEUM) i
ROUND LIG. j
OVARIAN LIG. k
SUSPENSORY LIG. OF OVARY L
   OVARIAN VESSELS (A m **& V** n **)**
OVARY o
VAGINA p **FORNIX OF VAGINA** p'
UTERINE ARTERY m'
SUPERIOR VESICAL A. m²
URETER q

OVUM o'
SPERM p²

The ovaries, uterus and its tubes, and the vagina make up the internal organs of reproduction in the female. The ovaries lie on the posterior-lateral wall of the pelvis, supported by the *suspensory ligament of the ovary* (which transmits its vessels), the *ovarian ligament,* and an extension of the *broad ligament.* In this view, the ovaries have been brought to the horizontal to better clarify their relationship to the uterine tubes. While coloring the ovary, refer to the previous plate on the ovarian cycle for more detail. The *uterine tubes* are lateral extensions of the uterus, lined with ciliated columnar epithelium supported by connective tissue and smooth muscle. The rhythmic contractions of this muscle aid the *ovum* in its trek to the *uterine cavity,* and the lining cells support it nutritionally. The tube shows three rather distinct parts: the *fimbria,* which encloses the anterior and superior surfaces of the ovary, "catches" the discharged ovum, and whisks it into its interior; the *ampulla* or widest part of the tube; and the *isthmus* whose lumen narrows as it en-

ters the uterine wall and cavity. The *uterus* is a pear-shaped structure whose neck (*cervix*) fits into the upper part of the vagina and whose *body/fundus* is bent (*anteflexed*) and tilted (*anteverted*) anteriorly over the bladder. Backward bending/tilting (*retroflexion/*retroversion) of the uterus is not uncommon, particularly in women who have given birth. The latter position of the uterus ("tipped"), if significant, may induce a variety of complaints from pain to infertility. The situation also predisposes to mild slipping of the uterus into the vagina (prolapse) since the uterus is more or less in the axis of the cervix/vagina. The wall of the uterus, you can see, is largely smooth muscle (*myometrium*) lined with a glandular layer of variable thickness (*endometrium*) that is extremely sensitive to the hormones estrogen/progesterone. (When coloring the endometrium, you might wish to refer to the following plate on the reproductive cycle). Where the cervix fits into the *vagina,* a circular moat or trough is formed around it (*fornix*). This fibroelastic area expands considerably during intercourse. Just lateral to the cervix/body of the uterus, the *ureter,* en route to the bladder, passes close by the *uterine artery* (a relationship of no small significance to the gynecologic surgeon). Because of the potentially precarious position of the uterus, the ligamentous support of that structure is crucial. The broad ligament, a blanketlike layer of peritoneum lying over the uterus, its tubes, and the ovaries, plays a central supportive role, in association with others not shown here.

PLATE 98
see also 96, 97

PLATE 99
see also 97, 98, 108

REPRODUCTIVE SYSTEM
THE REPRODUCTIVE CYCLE*

CN 10

1. Color the curves for FSH and LH from day 1 to 28. Since these hormones influence the ovarian cycle, color the ovarian follicles (a–a³), the ovulating follicle (a⁴), the corpora lutea (b–b¹), and the developing corpus albicans (c).

2. Color the curves for estrogen and progesterone from day 1 to 28. Since these hormones influence the uterine endometrial cycle, color the horizontal bar below the endometrium in the proliferative and secretory phases (i & j) from day 4 to day 28. Then color the horizontal bar below the deteriorating endometrium (h) from day 28 to day 4 in red (note areas to be col-

ored are at both ends of the chart). Then color structures (k¹–L) noting how they develop in the endometrium until the onset of menstruation. Structure (L) should be colored red; note degenerating epithelium and glands (k¹ and k²) overlap their colors with broken spiral arteries (L) in the menstruum (L¹ and k²).

3. The days marked on this plate are averages. Timing varies from person to person and cycle to cycle. The curves of the hormonal cycle reflect relative hormone levels in the blood plasma. These curves are significant primarily as they relate to one another and not as indicating absolute amounts.

OVARIAN CYCLE*
PRIMORDIAL FOLL. a
PRIMARY FOLL. a¹
SECONDARY FOLL. a²
MATURE FOLL. a³
OVULATION. a⁴
CORPUS LUTEUM b,b¹
CORPUS ALBICANS c

HORMONAL CYCLE*
FSH d
ESTROGEN e
LH f
PROGESTERONE g

MENSTRUAL CYCLE*
MENSTRUATION h
PROLIFERATIVE PHASE i
SECRETORY PHASE j
ENDOMETRIUM k *
EPITHELIUM k¹
GLANDS k²
SPIRAL ARTERIES L
MENSTRUUM k²+L

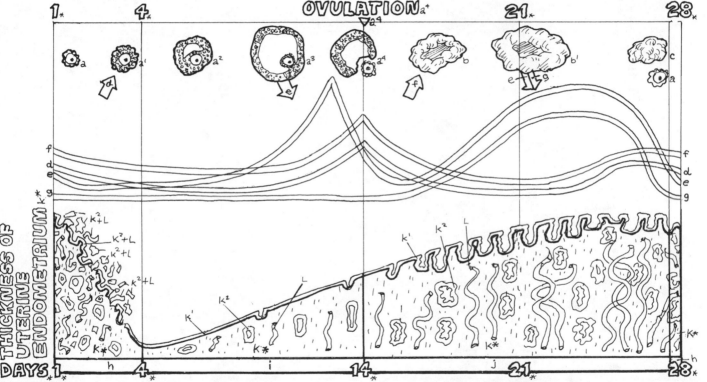

The 28-day, human *female reproductive cycle,* initiated and maintained by *hormones,* involving significant alterations in *ovarian* (follicular) and *uterine* (endometrial) structure, and characterized by a period of "bleeding" (*menstruation*), begins at about 12 years of age (menarche) and ends at about 45 years of age (menopause). The progressive changes that occur in the ovary and uterus during each cycle serve to develop and release the female germ cell for possible fertilization by the male germ cell and to prepare the endometrium for implantation of the fertilized ovum, respectively.

The first day of menstruation is considered the first day of the cycle, and menstruation is generally completed by the 5th day. At this time, endometrial growth resumes under the influence of *estrogen* and progresses through the 14th day (*proliferative phase*) and on to about day 28. From day 14 to 28 the *endometrium* also shows signs of increased gland growth and secretion (*secretory phase*) due largely to the influence of *progesterone.* On about day 26, in the absence of fertilization, the estrogen/progesterone levels drop, and the endometrium begins to break down (menstruation) on about day 28. If fertilization occurs (on about day 16), the estrogen/progesterone levels remain elevated, and the endometrium remains in the proper nutrient condition to accept the fertilized ovum. Let's leave the uterus for a moment.

Back about day 26, after it was apparent to the hypophysis that fertilization had not and would not occur, that gland began to secrete follicle stimulating hormone (*FSH*), which stimulated the ovary to develop a new follicle

(ovum) *for the next cycle.* By day 28 and the next few days of the new cycle (while menstruation is going on in the uterus), the ovary is well on its way toward developing a new ovum. By day 6 the new follicle is producing estrogen, which acts on the uterus to stimulate continued regrowth of the endometrium. By day 14 the ovum has matured sufficiently to burst out of the ovary (ovulation), a complex phenomenon requiring relatively high levels of FSH, LH, and estrogen. The ruptured follicle then transforms into a lipid-rich *corpus luteum,* under the influence of luteinizing hormone (*LH*). This body, in turn, produces relatively high levels of estrogen/progesterone, stimulating continued growth and glandular secretion in the endometrium. Should fertilization occur, the corpus luteum continues to secrete its hormones for the next 90 days. Should fertilization not occur, the corpus luteum begins to involute on about day 26, ceases to secrete its hormones, and slowly degenerates as a corpus albicans. Lacking hormonal stimulation, the endometrium's rate of glandular secretion is overtaken by the rate of fluid absorption by the local veins, and the tissues collapse. *Spiral arteries* are induced to constrict or are bent to the breaking point by the breakdown. Glands, arteries, veins, epithelial and connective tissues are torn. The vessels rapidly constrict but the damage is done. Menstruation is a reality. The broken tissue (menstruum: mostly glandular tissue and secretions, and a small amount of blood, not to mention one unfertilized ovum) is sloughed and gravitates toward the vagina. By day 5, only about 1 mm (in height) of endometrium is left for regeneration. Meanwhile, back at the ovary . . .

PLATE 100
see also 33, 69, 108

REPRODUCTIVE SYSTEM
THE BREAST (MAMMARY GLAND) *

CN 16

1. A light color for the superficial fascia (e) is recommended.
2. Color the pectoralis major (c) in both drawings. In the central (upper) drawing, overlap the color for deep fascia (d) with the color for pectoralis major (c).

RIB a CLAVICLE a'
INTERCOSTAL MUSCLES b
PECTORALIS MAJOR M. c
DEEP FASCIA OF PECT. MAJ. d
SUPERFICIAL FASCIA (FAT) e
SUSPENSORY LIGAMENT f
GLANDULAR LOBE g
LACTIFEROUS DUCT h
LACTIFEROUS SINUS i
NIPPLE j
AREOLA k

LYMPHATIC DRAINAGE *
AXILLARY NODES L
AXILLARY/APICAL N. L'
PARASTERNAL N. L2
TO OPPOSITE BREAST L3
TO RECTUS SHEATH L4

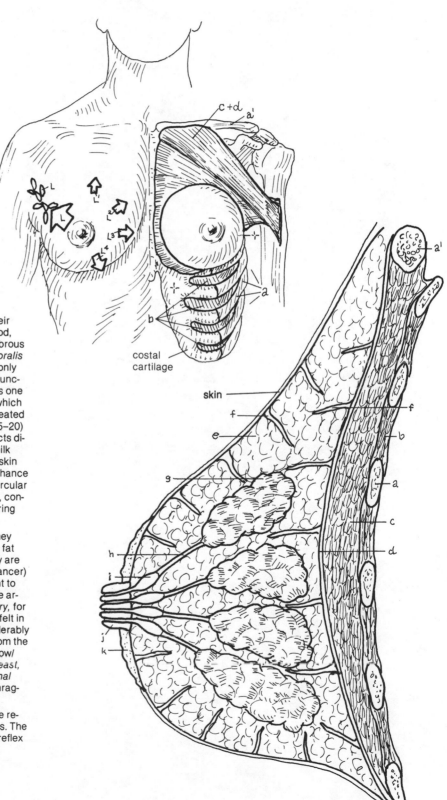

costal
cartilage

skin

The *breast* consists of exocrine tubulo-alveolar glands and their ducts packed in fatty *superficial fascia* along with nerves, blood, and lymphatic vessels; covered with skin, and supported by fibrous *suspensory ligaments* borrowed from the *deep fascia of pectoralis major.* Breasts are characteristic of both sexes, but they are only developed in the adult (postpubescent) female. The simplest functional unit of the breast is the lobule, which may be as small as one gland and its duct. A collection of lobules constitute a *lobe,* of which there are 15–20 in each breast. The ducts of these lobes—created by the merging lobular ducts—are called *lactiferous ducts* (15–20) and converge on the nipple. Just short of the nipple, these ducts dilate to form *lactiferous sinuses,* which probably function as milk reservoirs during lactation. The *nipple* consists of pigmented skin with some smooth muscle fibers (erection of the nipple may enhance flow of milk through the ducts) set in connective tissue. The circular *areola,* also pigmented more highly than the surrounding skin, contains sebaceous glands that may act as a skin lubricant during suckling by the newborn.

The *lymphatic* vessels are an important part of the breast: they drain the fat portion of the milk produced during lactation (the fat molecules are generally too big to get into the veins), and they are a vehicle for the transfer of infected material or neoplastic (cancer) cells from the breast to more distant parts. Thus it is important to consider the lymph nodes filtering the lymph of the breast (see arrows). The most important set of nodes perhaps are the *axillary,* for they receive the bulk of the lymph stream and they are easily felt in the axilla along the thoracic wall. These nodes enlarge considerably in response to infection or the presence of neoplastic cells from the breast (or any part of the upper limb). Other routes of lymph flow/ neoplastic cell migration (metastasis) include the *opposite breast,* the neck (via the *apical group),* the thorax (via the *parasternal nodes),* and the abdomen (via the *rectus sheath* and the diaphragmatic nodes).

Milk production, occurring after delivery of the newborn, is the result of the action of many hormones influencing the gland cells. The letdown and excretion of milk results from a neuroendocrine reflex mechanism that is initiated by the suckling baby at the nipple.

PLATE 101
see also 3, 97, 98, 99

REPRODUCTIVE SYSTEM
DEVELOPMENT OF THE EMBRYO* (PART 1)

CN 9
1. This plate should be colored as the first of a 3-plate sequence; labels and colors will be the same for the 3 plates. The text on each plate may require that you refer to the other 2 plates (preferably colored in) as you read.
2. After coloring each stage of development below, color its appropriate location in the uterine tube.

FERTILIZATION (A, B)*
FEMALE PRONUCLEUS a
HEAD OF SPERM b
MALE PRONUCLEUS b'
ZONA PELLUCIDA c

CLEAVAGE (C, D, E)*
2-BLASTOMERE STAGE d
4-BLASTOMERE STAGE e
MORULA f

EARLY STAGE BLASTOCYST (F) g*
TROPHOBLASTS h
INNER CELL MASS i
BLASTOCOELE j

IMPLANTATION k*

Penetration of the female germ cell (A, ovum) by one and only one male germ cell (sperm) constitutes *fertilization*. This new cell with 2 *pronuclei* of 23 chromosomes each is called the zygote (B), and its formation is the first of many steps in the development of a new individual. Fertilization occurs in the outer half of the uterine tube within 24–36 hours after ovulation. Once the sperm breaks through the *zona pellucida* and cell membrane of the ovum (an accomplishment due in part to enzymes in the acrosome of the sperm), it loses its tail to become the male pronucleus (b'). The membranes of the 2 pronuclei soon fuse and then disappear (not shown), and the zygote undergoes normal cell division. Two daughter cells are formed (*blastomeres*) each of which has a nucleus containing 46 chromosomes—the number found in all cells of the body except germ cells (ova and sperm). Progressive division (*cleavage*) of these (C) and subsequent blastomeres (D, etc.) soon creates a mass of cells (E, *morula*) packed within the zona pellucida and slowly rolling toward the uterus.

By 7 days post-fertilization, the growing morula has developed into a *blastocyst* (F): a ball of cells with a fluid-filled cavity (*blastocoele*) in which lies an *inner cell mass*. The blastocyst has lost its zona pellucida. On about day 7 it will imbed in the lining of the uterus. The outer cells of the blastocyst are called *trophoblasts*. After coloring the next plate (Part 2), you will see that the trophoblast cells will form a protective membrane (chorion) about the developing embryo. From this layer a mass of fingerlike projections (chorionic villi) will grow out and spearhead the implantation of the blastocyst into the uterine endometrium. A layer of cells (mesoderm) will peel off from the trophoblast cells and form a part of the chorion and villi, the amnion, and the yolk sac. This *extraembryonic* mesoderm (it does not contribute to the formation of the embryo itself) also forms a *connecting stalk*, which attaches the embryo to the chorion. The blastocoele is also extraembryonic and will be taken up by the expanding amnion (see structures G through J). The inner cell mass will form the embryonic disc (see structure H), the amnion membrane and its cavity (in which the embryo will be enveloped), and the yolk sac.

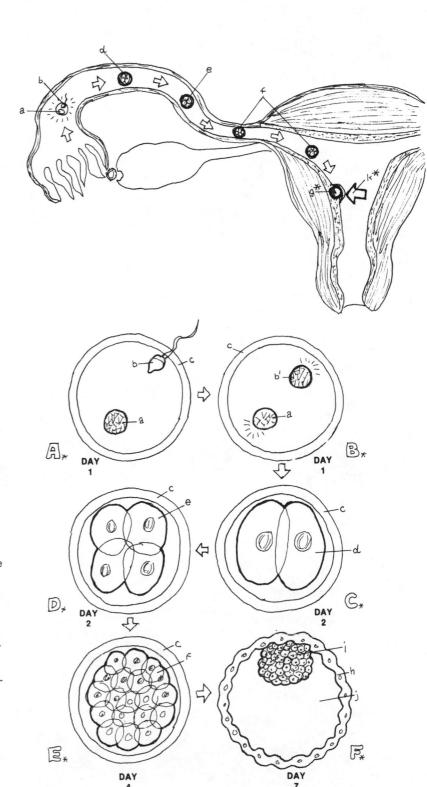

PLATE 102
see also 97–99, 101

REPRODUCTIVE SYSTEM
DEVELOPMENT OF THE EMBRYO (2)

CN 4

1. In figure G, cells of the embryonic ectoderm and entoderm (disc, n) are not to be colored.
2. Color the mesoderm (h^1) and the connecting stalk (h^2) the same color as the trophoblast (h). In figures I and J, the trophoblast (h) and underlying mesoderm (h^1) form the chorion and villi (h^3, h^4), and they should all be the same color. In figure J, the lower portion of the yolk sac is now the cavity above the entodermal part (p) of the embryo and should not be colored. Note how the extraembryonic mesodern of the amnion and yolk sac is continuous with the embryonic mesoderm of the developing heart in figure J.
3. The yolk sac (m) and the allantois (m^1) should be the same color.
4. The title of the umbilical cord (s), pointing to a group of structures making up the cord, should receive a separate color, which will be used for the cord on the next plate.

BLASTOCYST (F, G, H)
TROPHOBLAST h
MESODERM h¹/CONNECTING STALK h²
BLASTOCOELE j
AMNION L /AMNIOTIC CAVITY L¹
YOLK SAC m
EMBRYONIC DISC n⁻⁺⁻

EMBRYO (I, J)
ECTODERMAL o/MESODERMAL p PART o/p⁻⁺⁻
ENTODERMAL PART q⁻⁺⁻

CHORION h³ CHORIONIC VILLI h⁴
ALLANTOIS m¹

In this plate you will see that the trophoblast layer contributes to the membranes enveloping the embryo and that the inner cell mass (seen in the previous plate) forms the embryo, its amnion membrane, and its yolk sac. In figures G through J, follow the fate of the structures discussed below.

The *trophoblast* (h) and its underlying *mesoderm* (h^1) become the *chorion* (h^3) and *chorionic villi* (h^4). In the more advanced stage of embryonic development, most of the villi disappear except for the part that first penetrated the uterine lining, and this part (h^4) represents the fetal contribution to the placenta. Note how the extraembryonic mesoderm (h^1) not only forms part of the chorion but becomes part of the amnion and yolk sac as well. The *amniotic cavity* (L^1) forms within the inner cell mass, separating the formative embryo from the *amnion*. The amniotic cavity expands at the expense of the blastocoele (G–J) which gets used up as the spreading amnion and growing embryo force the yolk sac, allantois, and connecting stalk to form a single structure (the *umbilical cord,* shown in figure J). About day 14, the primitive *yolk sac* decreases in size and is replaced by a secondary yolk sac (process not shown). Its entoderm produces the future germ cells of the ovary/testes. It is insignificant as a source of nutrition and is ultimately choked off by the expanding embryo and amnion. The constricted part (yolk stalk) is incorporated into the umbilical cord while the sac may remain intact until birth. The roof of the yolk sac contributes embryonic entoderm to the formative embryo. The *allantois* (m^1) (figures I and J) is an outpocketing of the yolk sac. It is not functionally significant in humans, however, the mesoderm surrounding it (figure J) develops the umbilical vessels that will conduct maternal blood from the placenta to the fetus and fetal blood back to the placenta. The *embryo* develops within the inner cell mass as a two-layered disc of epiblast (embryonic ectoderm and potential mesoderm) and entoderm seen in figure G. Between day 14 and 21, some of the primitive ectodermal cells migrate in between the ectoderm and the entoderm layers (not shown in these views). These migrating cells are called *embryonic* mesoderm. The embryo now consists of three primary germ layers, and from these all structures of the human body develop. In drawings A through J, we have shown and you have colored the development of the three-layered embryo, its umbilical cord, and its principal membranes, the chorion and amnion.

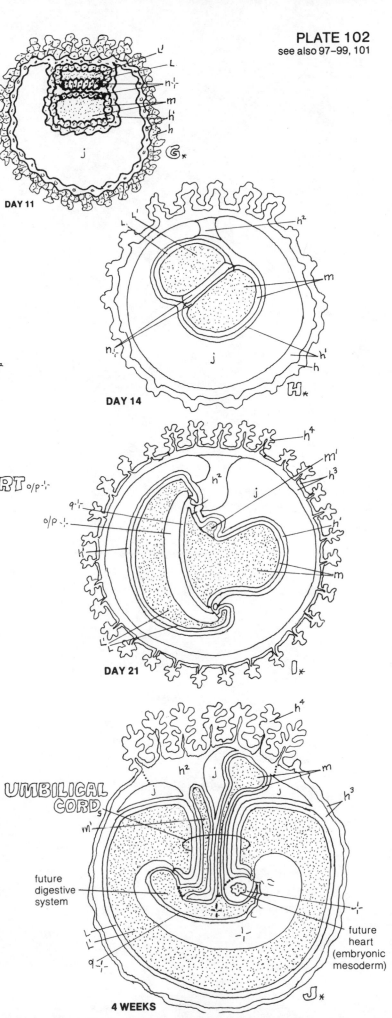

DAY 11

G

DAY 14

H

DAY 21

I

UMBILICAL CORD

future digestive system

future heart (embryonic mesoderm)

4 WEEKS

J

REPRODUCTIVE SYSTEM
EMBRYO/FETUS*
FETAL/MATERNAL COVERINGS*
PLACENTA*

PLATE 103
see also 97–99, 101, 102, 82, 66

CN 11

1. In the lower drawing, the amniotic fluid fills in the spaces around the placental origin of the umbilical cord. Also note that the decidua parietalis and myometrium have been combined as one layer, the uterine wall (1.), due to space limitations.
2. Light colors for (t) and (v) are recommended to contrast with the dark uterine cavity (y•).

EMBRYO r₊ FETUS r₊
UMBILICAL CORD s
AMNION + CAVITY l
YOLK SAC m
CHORION h/ VILLI h⁺
DECIDUA p *
   D. CAPSULARIS t
   D. BASALIS u
   D. PARIETALIS v
MYOMETRIUM w₊
MUCUS PLUG x
UTERINE CAVITY y•
CERVIX z

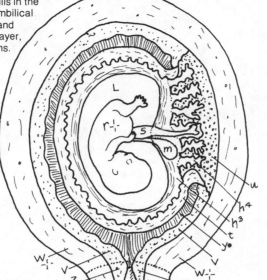

8-WEEK-OLD EMBRYO

The developing embryo (called the fetus after 8 weeks of development) lies within and is supported, nurtured, and protected by membranes and sacs. These coverings have both maternal and blastocyst (fetal) origins. Those of fetal origin include the *amnion* and *chorion,* the *umbilical cord,* and the *yolk sac* and *allantois.* Those of maternal origin are thickened, fairly distinct layers of the uterine endometrium in which the blastocyst implanted. These layers, the *decidua,* will be discarded with the fetal membranes following birth of the newborn.

The deepest layer of the decidua is the *parietalis* which lies adjacent to the *myometrium.* Only the deepest part of this layer will be retained after discharge of the "afterbirth," and it is from this layer that the new endometrium will be generated. The decidua *basalis* is that region of the endometrium that receives the first burrowing trophoblastic villi of the blastocyst. It is the maternal contribution to the placenta. It consists of glandular and vascular tissue surrounding the chorionic villi, which represent the fetal contribution to the placenta. Here, in the *placenta,* maternal (uterine) vessels of the basalis open into spaces among the vascular villi. Oxygen, nutrients, and fetal wastes are exchanged here. The vessels of the villi converge at the umbilical cord to become umbilical vessels (not shown). The most superficial decidua *capsularis* is immediately adjacent to the chorion and is the only maternal covering to surround the fetus and its amnion and chorion. As the fetus and amnion expand to fill the *uterine cavity,* the capsularis is pressed against the parietalis on the opposite side of the uterus. As this happens, it degenerates and disappears.

Of the fetal membranes, only the chorion and amnion envelop the embryo/fetus. In later development, the chorion loses most of its villi except at the implantation site where the villi are an integral part of the placenta. The fetus develops within the fluid-filled amniotic cavity, surrounded by the amnion. As early as 4 weeks post-fertilization, the amnion balloons against the chorion. The plasmalike amniotic fluid gives freedom to the embryo to develop its form without mechanical pressure. It also acts as a water cushion absorbing shock forces. Just prior to birth (parturition), the chorion/amnion membranes surrounding the fetus break and a half liter or more amniotic fluid pushes the *cervical mucus plug* out and floods out the *vagina* ("breaking the bag of waters"). Parturition generally occurs 280 days after fertilization. In the lower drawing, note how compression of abdominal organs, urinary bladder, and rectum occurs in the later stages of pregnancy. Immobilization of the diaphragm is common, putting the responsibility of inspiration on the intercostal muscles.

PLACENTA*
CHORIONIC VILLI h⁺
DECIDUA BASALIS u
UTERINE WALL 1.
VAGINA 2.

The structural organization of the *embryo/fetus* is derived from the three primary germ layers: ectoderm, mesoderm and entoderm. *Embryonic ectoderm* develops into the epidermis of the skin and related appendages (hair, glands, sense receptors, etc.), the nervous system, and certain other epithelial linings and glands. *Embryonic entoderm* develops into the epithelial linings of the digestive and respiratory tracts as well as certain other epithelial linings and glands. *Embryonic mesoderm* (as contrasted with the extraembryonic mesoderm of the chorion, amnion, and umbilical cord) develops into the muscles of the body including the heart, blood vessels, lymphatic vessels/organs, much of the urinary system, and all other tissues not arising from ectoderm or entoderm.

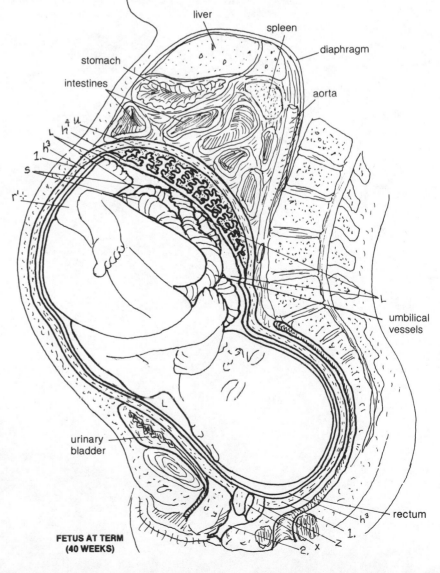

liver
spleen
diaphragm
stomach
intestines
aorta
umbilical vessels
urinary bladder
rectum

FETUS AT TERM (40 WEEKS)

PLATE 104
see also 8, 4, 5

INTEGUMENT (SKIN) ORGANIZATION*

CN 18

1. Reserve yellow for the nerve (g), red for the artery (h), blue for the vein (dotted vessel labeled i), and a light color for the lymphatic vessels (j). Note the vessels cut in cross section in the dermis and at the papilla of the hair follicle.
2. Color both drawings simultaneously. Note that the stratum lucidum (b) is shown only in the lower drawing.

EPIDERMIS*
STRATUM CORNEUM a
STRATUM LUCIDUM b
STRATUM GRANULOSUM c
STRATUM SPINOSUM d
STRATUM BASALE e
(GERMINATING LAYER) e

DERMIS*
CONNECTIVE TISSUE f
PAPILLAE f'
NERVE g
ARTERY h VEIN i
LYMPHATIC VESSEL j
HAIR*
SHAFT k
FOLLICLE l
BULB OF FOLLICLE m MATRIX m'
DERMAL PAPILLA n
ARRECTOR PILI MUSCLE o
SEBACEOUS GLAND p
SWEAT GLAND q

SUPERFICIAL FASCIA r

The *integument* (cutaneous layer), variably thick, highly sensitized and vascular, covering the body consists of two layers: the multilayered epithelial epidermis and the fibrous dermis. The dermis is continuous below with the fatty, fibrous superficial fascia (subcutaneous tissue), an intermediate layer of variable thickness between skin and the deeper structure (fascia-lined skeletal muscle or periosteum-lined bone). The *epidermis* consists of layers of cells most of which arise from the frequently dividing *germinating* cells of the *stratum basale.* The daughter cells are pushed up to form another layer characterized by flattened cells with short spines/processes (*stratum spinosum*). The older cells of the next layer (*stratum granulosum*) have granules that relate to the protein keratin. The next outer layer of cells, seen only in thick skin, consists of flattened cells that form a bright layer (*stratum lucidum*) immediately adjacent to the outer, thick *stratum corneum.* This outer layer consists of flattened ghosts of cells in which the cytoplasm and nucleus have been replaced by keratin (densely packed filaments embedded in a dense structureless medium). It is largely variations in thickness in this layer that account for differences in skin thickness. Cells of the epidermis that do not arise from germinating cells are the pigment cells found in the basal and dermal layers. These cells secrete melanin pigment into the lower epidermal layers and the hair follicles.

The *dermis* consists of thick bundles of fibrous tissue among which are found many *blood* and *lymphatic vessels* oriented in networks, sweat glands,

hair follicles and the related sebaceous glands and arrector pili muscles. The avascular epidermis gets its nutrition from vessels reaching up through the *papillae of connective tissue. Sweat glands* found throughout almost all skin help to stabilize body temperature by excreting in response to excessive heat. The subsequent evaporation of the excreted fluid is a cooling process. *Sebaceous glands* excrete an oily material (sebum), which helps to protect the skin from dehydration. *Hair* is an outgrowth of epidermal cells that pushed down into the dermis to form the *hair follicle* during early fetal development. Within the follicle *bulb,* concentric layers of keratinized, pigmented cells (originating from the *matrix*) form the hair *shaft* that grows out beyond the surface of the skin. The *dermal papilla,* like the papillae under the epidermis, supply the hair shaft with nutrition from the tuft of vessels. Loss of the papillae means loss of the hair. The *arrector pili muscle,* attached to the hair follicle, elevates the hair shaft and aids excretion of sebum. Skin and all its appendages protect the body against injurious invasion by microorganisms, chemicals, and ultraviolet radiation; play an important role in body temperature regulation; and act as a sensor informing the person of the state of his or her environment (see the next plate).

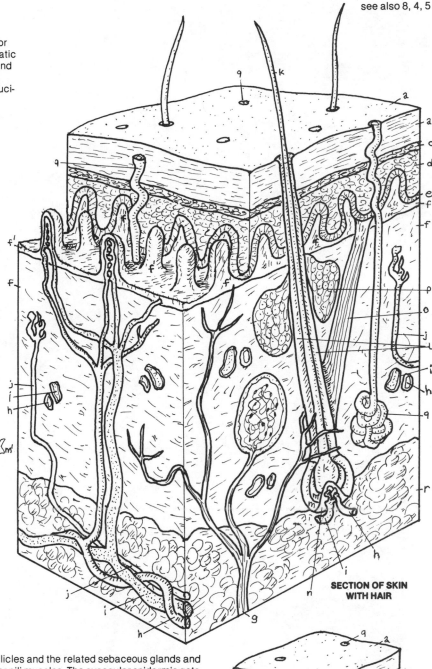

SECTION OF SKIN WITH HAIR

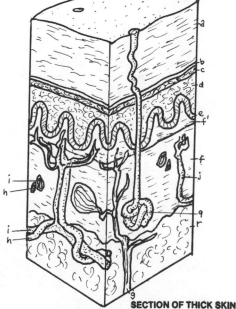

SECTION OF THICK SKIN FROM SOLE OF FOOT

PLATE 105
see also 104, 114

INTEGUMENT (SKIN)
SENSORY RECEPTORS OF THE SKIN∗

EPIDERMIS 1∴
DERMIS 2∗
SUPERFICIAL FASCIA 3∴

CN 6

1. To visually separate the superficial fascia from the dermis from the epidermis, color the dermis light gray and note that it includes the papilla.
2. After coloring the nerve endings (a–e), color the network of sensory axons (f) yellow.

Sensory receptors make up a vast network of body-wide sensors that inform the central nervous system about the environment both within and outside the body. Such receptors are the terminals or endings of sensory nerve cells. In response to one of a variety of stimulations by energy states or forces (light waves, different degrees of mechanical contact, muscle stretch, certain chemical concentrations, etc.), a receptor will initiate an electrochemical reaction (impulse), which rapidly passes down the axon of a sensory nerve cell to the central nervous system. In response to this impulse, a quick reflex movement or a thoughtful, decisive move may be made, or possibly no reaction will be observed at all. Here you are coloring those receptors found in or near the skin—receptors that make you aware of changes in the external environment (and which are constantly advising the central nervous system of the state of things even though you may not be aware of it). Test these receptors on yourself as you color.

PAIN a
FREE NERVE ENDINGS a

One of two types of nerve endings that reach into the epidermis, free nerve endings are generally believed to fire in response to strong and *painful* stimulation. These endings are also found throughout the connective tissues of the body.

TOUCH b
MERKEL'S DISCS b
MEISSNER'S CORPUSCLES b¹
ROOT HAIR PLEXUSES b²

These receptors have a very low threshold of sensitivity and will therefore fire with the faintest *touch*, as you can test on yourself. The hair follicle is invested with free endings as well as the encapsulated discs of Merkel, which reach up into the epidermal layers. Meissner's corpuscles consist of a core of nerve fibers and cells surrounded by other cell layers.

PRESSURE c
PACINIAN CORPUSCLES c

The Pacinian corpuscle consists of a nerve ending surrounded by many layers of flattened cells. Deformation of these capsules in the superficial fascia (and elsewhere) cause the nerve terminal to fire, resulting in an awareness of *pressure* above a certain threshold. They are also sensitive to vibration.

COLD d
KRAUSE CORPUSCLES d
HEAT e
RUFFINI CORPUSCLES e

These receptors of *temperature* are generally bulb-shaped and consist of nerve endings surrounded by several layers of flattened satellite cells. Experimental evidence for their cold/hot sensing function is scanty.

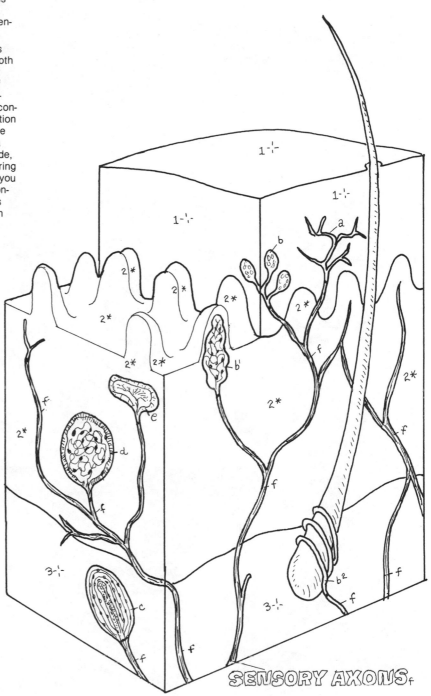

SENSORY AXONS f

PLATE 106
see also 4

ENDOCRINE SYSTEM
LOCATION OF ENDOCRINE GLANDS *

CN 9

1. Use a light color for the thyroid gland (c) so that the four smaller parathyroid glands stand out when drawn with a darker color. These 4 glands are located on the *posterior* capsule of the thyroid; though not visible from this anterior view, they are shown here for identification purposes. Their exact location can be seen on Plate 109.

HYPOPHYSIS (PITUITARY) a
PINEAL b
THYROID c
PARATHYROIDS d
THYMUS e
ADRENALS f
PANCREAS g
OVARIES h
TESTES i

Endocrine glands consist of masses of secretory cells and neighboring capillaries supported by connective tissue. They may occur as microscopic "islands" of endocrine tissue within a larger non-endocrine structure (islets within the *pancreas*, interstitial cells of Leydig within the *testis,* follicular/lutein cells within the *ovary,* etc.), or they may form a single organ easily seen without visual aid (*hypophysis, thyroid, parathyroids, adrenals*, etc.). Characteristically, endocrine glands are without ducts, secreting their product (hormones) directly into the capillaries or tissue fluids. Hormones are chemical agents usually effective among cells some distance from their source. In concert with the nervous system, they integrate the activities of varied and sometimes seemingly unrelated structures through facilitation and inhibition of organ function resulting in growth, reproductive cycles/activity, and metabolic stability. Such harmony of the internal environment is called homeostasis.

The endocrine glands shown here are the traditional ones, and some of these are in question as to endocrine classification (thymus and pineal). Several groups of cells known to produce "factors" or "humors" (generally accepted as hormones) but not included *on this plate* are certain hypothalamic cells (neurosecretory cells), certain cells of the kidney, the gastrointestinal tract, and the placenta. Discussions of ovarian and testicular hormones may be found on Plates 94, 96, and 99, and the pineal on Plate 123.

The *thymus,* a member of the lymphatic system, is located in the anterior/superior mediastinum (just above and in front of the heart). It is known to play a critical role in the seeding of the lymphatic organs (lymph nodes, diffuse lymphatic tissue, etc.) with potential "T" lymphocytes, which secrete a substance that attacks the protein of certain tumor cells, foreign cells, and microorganisms (cellular immunity). There is evidence that the thymus produces a hormone (thymosin) that enhances the development of "T" lymphocytes. Activity of the thymus wanes significantly after puberty; it ultimately atrophies to be replaced with fibrous tissue.

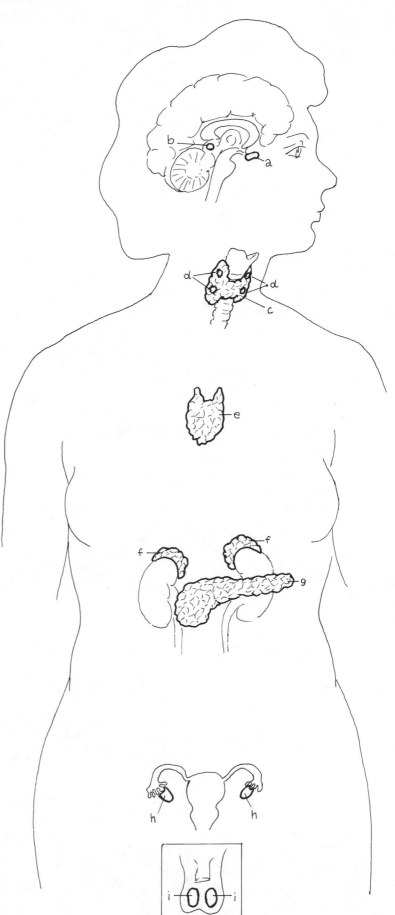

PLATE 107
see also 106, 108

ENDOCRINE SYSTEM
HYPOPHYSIS (PITUITARY GLAND)
& HYPOTHALAMUS ✳

CN 14

1. Save light blue for the portal system (h), dark blue for the hypophyseal veins (j), red for the hypophyseal arteries (g and L), purple for the capillary network (m), and yellow for the nerve tracts (k).
2. The intermediate lobe cannot be seen in the illustration to the right; color it in the middle illustration.

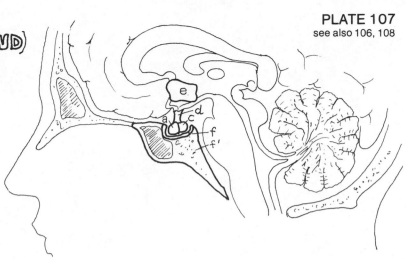

HYPOPHYSIS ✳
ANTERIOR LOBE ₐ
INTERMEDIATE LOBE ᵦ
POSTERIOR LOBE ₍
HYPOPHYSEAL STALK ₔ
HYPOTHALAMUS ₑ
SELLA TURCICA ᵩ OF SPHENOID BONE ᵩ'

The pituitary gland (hypophysis) basically consists of two lobes: anterior (including the intermediate lobe) and posterior. The hypothalamus, a part of the brain, is intimately related to the hypophysis: to the anterior lobe by a portal system of vessels; to the posterior lobe by a bundle of secretory neurons. The hypothalamus and hypophysis greatly influence the activity of certain other endocrine glands as well as a number of specific metabolic functions.

ANTERIOR LOBE (ADENOHYPOPHYSIS) ₐ
SUPERIOR HYPOPHYSEAL ARTERY ₉
PORTAL SYSTEM ₕ
CAPILLARIES ₕ' VENULE ₕ² SINUSOIDS ₕ³
SECRETORY CELLS ᵢ
HYPOPHYSEAL VEIN ⱼ

Hormones released from *secretory neurons* in the *hypothalamus* enter local capillaries, pass through *portal venules/veins* into the *sinusoids* of the *anterior lobe*. There they stimulate certain secretory, *nonneural* cells whose hormones enter the sinusoids drained by *hypophyseal veins*. Two, possibly three, cell types secrete the 7 hormones of the anterior/intermediate lobes: FSH, LH, TSH, growth hormone, MSH, ACTH, and prolactin. These may be studied in the following plate. Note that many of these hormones stimulate other glands to secrete their products. E.g., follicle stimulating and luteinizing hormones act on ovarian follicles/corpora lutea to secrete estrogen/progesterone; in the male, FSH stimulates spermatogenesis and LH stimulates testosterone secretion. Pituitary overactivity/underactivity often creates dramatic changes in body shape and function, such as gigantism and dwarfism. *The intermediate lobe* in humans may very well not be functional.

POSTERIOR LOBE (NEUROHYPOPHYSIS) ₍
NERVE TRACTS ₖ
INFERIOR HYPOPHYSEAL ARTERY ₗ
CAPILLARY NETWORK ₘ
VEIN ⱼ
HYPOTHALAMUS ₑ
SUPRAOPTIC NUCLEI ₑ'
PARAVENTRICULAR NUCLEI ₑ²

The *posterior lobe* has no secretory cells of its own. Secretory neurons of the *supraoptic* and *paraventricular nuclei* (centers in the hypothalamus) extend down through the *hypophyseal stalk* to *capillary networks* in the posterior lobe. There these neurons release oxytocin and antidiuretic hormones into the circulation. See the following plate for the action of these hormones.

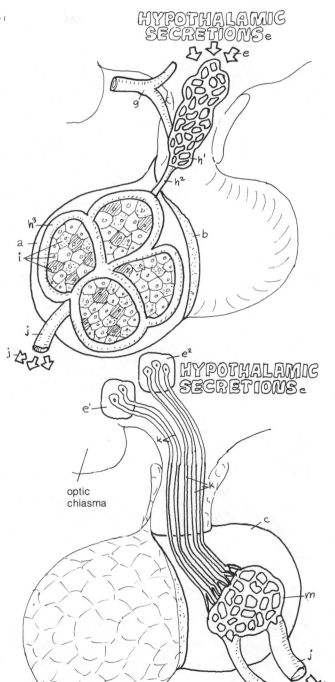

HYPOTHALAMIC SECRETIONS ₑ

HYPOTHALAMIC SECRETIONS ₑ

optic chiasma

PLATE 108
see also 107, 99, 100

ENDOCRINE SYSTEM
HYPOPHYSIS & ITS TARGET ORGANS∗

CN 16

1. To get the most from this plate, pay close attention to the color identifications. Look now to the bottom of the page and note the colors of the 5 target organ hormones (j–p) and the colors representing growth, pigmentation, milk ejection and water conservation. These hormones/effects are repeated above the hypothalamus indicating their negative feedback effect on the secretory neurons.

HYPOPHYSEAL HORMONES∗
FOLLICLE STIMULATING H./FSH$_a$
LUTEINIZING H./LH$_b$
THYROTROPIN/TSH$_c$
GROWTH H./SOMATOTROPIN/STH$_d$
MELANOCYTE STIMULATING H./MSH$_e$
ADRENOCORTICOTROPIN/ACTH$_f$
PROLACTIN$_g$
OXYTOCIN$_h$
ANTIDIURETIC H./ADH/VASOPRESSIN$_i$

In the previous plate we showed that the hypophysis is intimately related to the hypothalamus. In this plate we see the *hormones of the hypophysis,* the structures to which they are specifically directed ("*target organs*"), and the hormones of the "target organs." These two plates demonstrate one of the most fundamental operating principles of the life process: self-regulation by feedback. Consider: adrenocorticotropic hormone (*ACTH*) stimulates the adrenal cortex to secrete *adrenal cortical hormones,* many of which act back on the hypothalamus to regulate ACTH secretion; thyroid stimulating hormone (*TSH*) stimulates the thyroid gland to secrete thyroxine (thyroid hormone), which acts back on the hypothalamus (via the blood) to control TSH secretion. In these cases, the hypothalamus releases hormones that stimulate the anterior lobe to release its hormones. The same is true for *FSH* and *LH.* Consider the breast: the newborn suckling at the breast stimulates sensory nerves whose impulses reach the hypothalamus via the spinal cord. In response, all other prerequisites being met, the hypothalamic secretory neurons release *oxytocin* at the posterior lobe. Oxytocin enters the circulation to stimulate musclelike cells about mammary gland cells to let down milk (*ejection*). Completion of suckling removes the stimulus, and secretion of oxytocin stops. Consider the kidney: loss of body water (due to sweating, for example) creates a minute change in osmotic pressure of the blood. Receptors in the hypothalamus, sensitive to this change, induce sensory neurons to secrete antidiuretic hormone (*ADH*) into the circulation at the posterior lobe. ADH increases the permeability of the distal/collecting tubules of the kidney to water, resulting in increased reabsorption of water and concentration of urine. Subsequent restoration of fluid levels decreases the osmotic pressure and removes the stimulus for hypothalamic secretion of ADH. On a larger scale, feedback operates in the cases of *prolactin, growth hormone,* and *MSH.* Prolactin stimulates the secretion (not ejection) of milk after delivery (previously *inhibited* by hypothalamic hormone). Growth hormone stimulates body growth and metabolism. MSH increases pigmentation in the skin, an activity often associated with ACTH.

TARGET ORGAN
HORMONES/EFFECTS∗
ESTROGEN$_j$
PROGESTERONE$_k$
TESTOSTERONE$_L$
THYROXIN$_m$
GROWTH$_n$
SKIN PIGMENTATION$_o$
ADRENAL CORTICAL H.$_p$

MILK EJECTION/SUCKLING$_q$
WATER CONSERVATION$_r$

HYPOTHALAMIC HORMONES∗

j OVARY k TESTIS L THYROID m BONE n SKIN o ADRENAL p BREAST q KIDNEY r

PLATE 109
see also 53, 61, 62, 106, 108, 73, 53

ENDOCRINE SYSTEM
THYROID GLAND & *
PARATHYROID GLANDS *

CN 12

1. Use a light color for the thyroid gland (e), and a dark color for the parathyroids (i).
2. Reserve red for the arterial vessels (g) and blue for the veins (h). In both cases, if possible, color the major vessels lightly, using full color intensity for the thyroid arteries and veins. If feasible, color structures (a–d) and (f) with the same colors used on Plate 73 (where they had different identifying letters).

HYOID BONE a
THYRO-HYOID MEMBRANE b
THYROID CARTILAGE c
CRICOID CARTILAGE d
CRICOTHYROID MEM. d' & MUSC. d²
THYROID GLAND: *
　LATERAL LOBE e
　ISTHMUS e'
TRACHEA f
MAJOR ARTERIAL VESSELS g
INFERIOR THYROID A. g'
SUPERIOR THYROID A. g²
MAJOR VENOUS VESSELS h
SUPERIOR THYROID V. h'
MIDDLE THYROID V. h²
INFERIOR THYROID V. h³
PARATHYROID GLANDS: *
　SUPERIOR PARATHYROIDS i
　INFERIOR PARATHYROIDS i'
PHARYNX j
ESOPHAGUS k

The *thyroid gland,* covering the 2nd to 4th *tracheal rings* anteriorly at a vertebral level of about C6, is bound by a fibrous capsule whose posterior layer encloses the four parathyroid glands. The thyroid gland consists of right and left lobes connected by an isthmus. It is here that thyroxine is produced under stimulation by thyroid stimulating hormone from the anterior lobe of the pituitary gland. Thyroxine increases oxygen consumption in practically all tissues. Oxygen is the fuel for metabolic activity, thus thyroxine maintains the metabolic rate. Thyroxine is involved at many levels in growth, development, proper nervous activity, as well as metabolism of carbohydrates and fats. Excessive secretion of thyroxine results in one or more of the following: weight loss, extreme nervousness, tremors, protruding eyeballs, an elevated basal metabolic rate, and an enlarged thyroid or goiter (thyrotoxicosis). Thyroid insufficiency in children is generally manifested by dwarfism and mental retardation (cretinism); in adults, the skin is yellowish, mental activity is diminished, the voice changes, and accumulation of mucous material in the skin and fascia gives a puffy appearance (myxedema).

The *parathyroids* consist of small buttons of highly vascular tissue containing two cell types, one of which secretes parathormone. Parathormone maintains proper calcium ion levels in the blood/ tissues by stimulating disintegration and resorption of bone tissue, resulting in release of calcium ions. Normal skeletal and cardiac muscle activity as well as blood clotting depend on normal calcium levels in the plasma. Insufficiency of parathyroid function causes tetany (stiffness, cramps, spasms, and convulsions), due to muscle instability brought on by reduced available calcium. Overactivity of the parathyroids is often associated with kidney disease (deposition of calcium, formation of stones, etc.), bone disease (demineralization and resorption), and excessive calcium levels in the blood (muscular weakness, etc.).

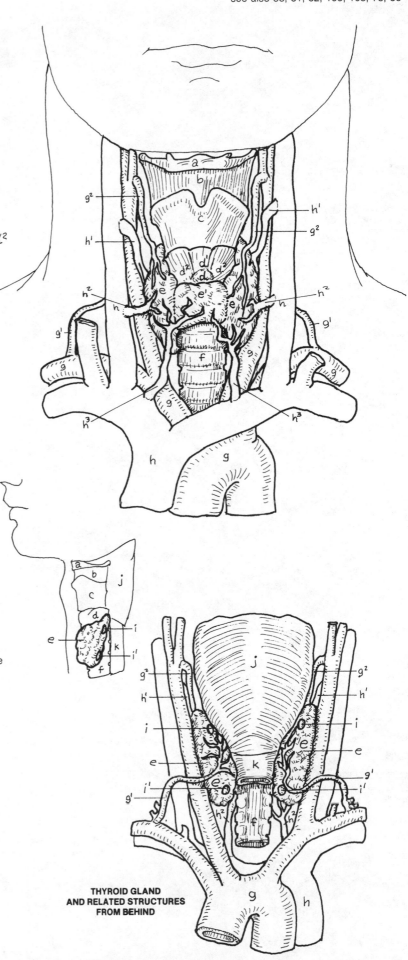

THYROID GLAND
AND RELATED STRUCTURES
FROM BEHIND

PLATE 110
see also 106, 108, 88, 89, 57

ENDOCRINE SYSTEM
ADRENALS (SUPRARENAL GLANDS)*
CN 15

1. Reserve red for the arterial vessels b and c. Color b's lightly; color c's more strongly.
2. Reserve blue for the veins d and e. Color d's lightly; color e's more strongly.
3. Reserve yellow for the autonomic nerves/plexus (f, f1).
4. In the lower drawing at right, note the title *skin* can be left without color, as the skin would lose a degree of color (regardless of the amount of pigmentation) in shock/fear.

ADRENAL GLANDS a
ABDOMINAL AORTA & BRANCHES b
  MIDDLE SUPRARENAL A. c
  RENAL A. b'
    INFERIOR SUPRARENAL c'
  INFERIOR PHRENIC A. b²
    SUPERIOR SUPRARENAL A. c²
INFERIOR VENA CAVA d
  R. SUPRARENAL V. e
  RENAL V. d'
    L. SUPRARENAL V. e'
GREATER SPLANCHNIC N. f
  CELIAC PLEXUS f'

CAPSULE a
CORTEX:*
  ZONA GLOMERULOSA g
  ZONA FASCICULATA h
  ZONA RETICULARIS i
MEDULLA j
  ARTERIES b VEINS d

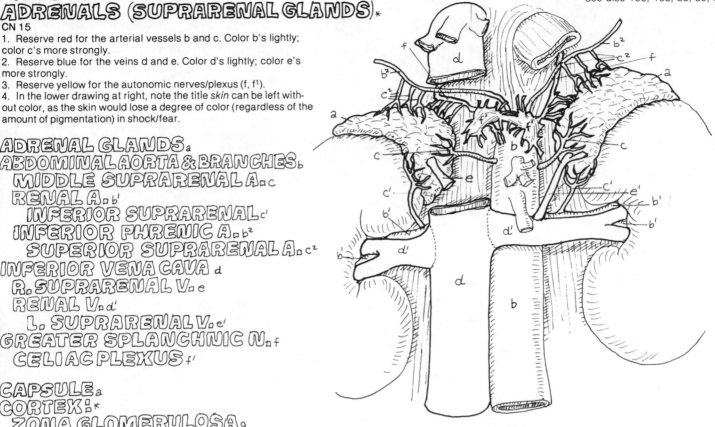

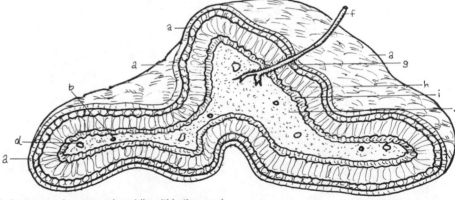

The *adrenal glands* (*ad*, near + *ren*, kidney; properly called suprarenals; *supra,* above) lie within the renal fascia on the superior and medial aspects of each kidney. As with other endocrine glands, the adrenals are abundantly vascularized. Like the kidneys, they are retroperitoneal. The adrenals are two different glands encapsulated as one: the *cortex* and the *medulla*. The medulla consists of cords of secretory and nerve (ganglion) cells. Fibers of the greater splanchnic nerve (sympathetic division of the autonomic nervous system) stimulate the secretory cells to release epinephrine. This hormone stimulates the metabolic rate and the breakdown/mobilization of starch (glycogen) and lipids (fatty acids), resulting in more available energy. They elicit the "fight or flight" reaction in response to life-threatening situations: increased nervous system activity, dilated pupils, increased blood supply to skeletal muscle, blood shunted away from skin and gastrointestinal tract to more critical areas, increased respiration rate, and increased heart rate and force of contraction.

The adrenal cortex is organized into three regions: the *zona glomerulosa* (secreting hormones dealing with fluid/electrolyte balance, such as aldosterone and other mineralocorticoids); and the *zona fasciculata* and *reticularis* (secreting hormones influencing carbohydrate metabolism, such as cortisol and other glucocorticoids; and low levels of sex hormones). ACTH from the anterior lobe of the pituitary stimulates secretion of the glucocorticoids. Aldosterone is secreted in response to certain enzymes in the blood (renin—angiotensin system). All these hormones play roles involving all aspects of protein, carbohydrate, electrolyte, and water metabolism; thus the adrenal cortex is necessary for life. Insufficiency of adrenocortical function results in Addison's disease (characterized by an inability to withstand stress, no appetite, weakness, and many other symptoms). Overactivity of the adrenal cortex involving sex hormones causes masculinization of females and precocious development of secondary sex characteristics in prepubescent males. Excessive secretion of glucocorticoids causes Cushing's syndrome (characterized by poor wound healing, increased deposition of fat, moon face, and serious metabolic deficiencies).

THE ADRENAL MEDULLA j
BRAIN k PUPILS l
MUSCLES m SKIN +/-
LUNGS n HEART o
STOMACH p INTESTINES q

PLATE 111
see also 106,
108, 87

ENDOCRINE SYSTEM
GASTROINTESTINAL HORMONES &*
PANCREATIC SECRETIONS*

CN 8
1. In the central illustration, use a bright, light color for the glandular acini (d) and the arrows indicating the flow of enzymes along the pancreatic duct. Color the five glandular acini at right (representing the exocrine glands that largely make up the pancreas).
2. Color each of the three gastrointestinal hormones and their arrows.
3. Color the alpha and beta cells in the pancreas and in the magnified view to the right. These cells make up the islets of the pancreas.
4. Color the splenic vein (g) blue.
5. Color the title, bile, and its directional arrows gray.

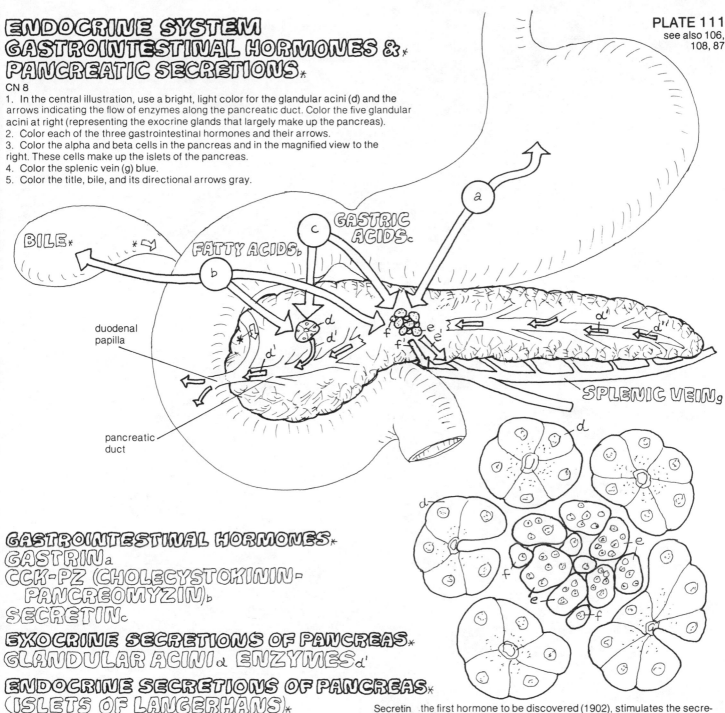

GASTROINTESTINAL HORMONES*
GASTRIN a
CCK-PZ (CHOLECYSTOKININ-
PANCREOMYZIN) b
SECRETIN c

EXOCRINE SECRETIONS OF PANCREAS*
GLANDULAR ACINI d ENZYMES d'

ENDOCRINE SECRETIONS OF PANCREAS*
(ISLETS OF LANGERHANS)*
BETA CELLS e / INSULIN e'
ALPHA CELLS f / GLUCAGON f'

Gastrointestinal hormones are a group of small proteins (polypeptides) secreted by certain cells of the gastrointestinal mucosa, which stimulate or inhibit the secretory activity of the gall bladder, stomach, duodenum, and pancreas (and possibly other digestive organs to a lesser degree). These hormones work in concert with autonomic nerves and other hormones to regulate the secretory activity of the digestive tract. The three hormones whose identity and function have been clearly established are gastrin, CCK-PZ, and secretin. These and other proposed gastrointestinal hormones have a variety of physiologic actions (often synergistic/antagonistic) of which only the principal ones are mentioned here.

Gastrin secreted by the gastric mucosa, stimulates gastric (hydrochloric) acid secretion in response to eating, as well as stimulation by the vagus (autonomic) nerve. It also stimulates secretion of pepsin and the release of insulin from the pancreas.

CCK–PZ secreted by the duodenal mucosa, stimulates contractions of the gall bladder and the flow of bile to the duodenum, release of pancreatic enzymes from the glandular acini (lobules with a grape or acinous shape), and the secretion of insulin. Once thought to be two hormones (cholecystokinin and pancreomyzin), CCK-PZ is now considered a single agent influencing both gall bladder and pancreas.

Secretin the first hormone to be discovered (1902), stimulates the secretion of water and bicarbonate ions in the pancreatic juices, which tends to reduce the acidity of the duodenal environment. Secretin, like the other gastrointestinal hormones, stimulates the secretion of insulin.

Insulin is a protein secreted by *beta cells* of the *islets* (of Langerhans) in the pancreas. It is required for life. Insulin is secreted in response to increased levels of blood glucose, increased activity of the vagus nerve, and the presence of glucose (simple sugar) in the stomach and duodenum. In the latter case, orally administered glucose triggers release of gastrointestinal hormones which, via the blood, stimulates the beta cells to secrete insulin. It is the level of glucose in the blood, however, that *regulates* the secretion of insulin. The uptake of sugar by most tissues (except intestines, brain, liver) is dependent upon insulin, and failure of this sugar to be absorbed (insulin deficiency) creates a critical metabolic dilemma that ultimately involves carbohydrate, fat, protein, mineral and water metabolism (diabetes mellitus). The disease is characterized by sustained high blood sugar, sugar in the urine, weight loss in the face of increased appetite, etc. Excessive secretion of insulin reduces the blood sugar, creating a collection of signs/symptoms resulting from glucose insufficiency (hypoglycemia). The *alpha cells* of the islets secrete *glucagon* (polypeptide), which acts on the liver to break down its sugar stores (glycogen) thus increasing the sugar concentration of the blood. Its secretion is stimulated by stress factors (infection, exercise, fear, etc.) and inhibited by the presence of glucose in the plasma and other factors. Glucagon also affects lipid metabolism (lipid breakdown) and protein metabolism (conversion of amino acids to glucose).

PLATE 112

NERVOUS SYSTEM
STRUCTURAL CLASSIFICATION OF
NEURONS.
AXON COVERINGS.

CN 12

1. Color the elements of each neuron before going on to the next.
2. In the illustration of the multipolar neuron, the axon is shown covered with neurilemma. The dissected view of the coverings is shown to its right.

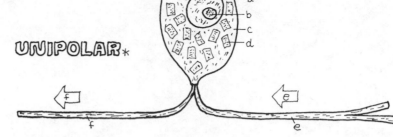

UNIPOLAR*

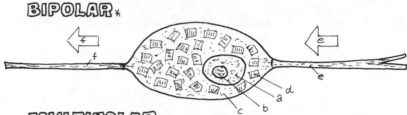

BIPOLAR*

NEURON.
CELL BODY*
NUCLEUS a
NUCLEOLUS b
CYTOPLASM c
NISSL BODIES d

PROCESSES*
PERIPHERAL PROCESS e
CENTRAL PROCESS f
DENDRITE g
AXON h

MULTIPOLAR*

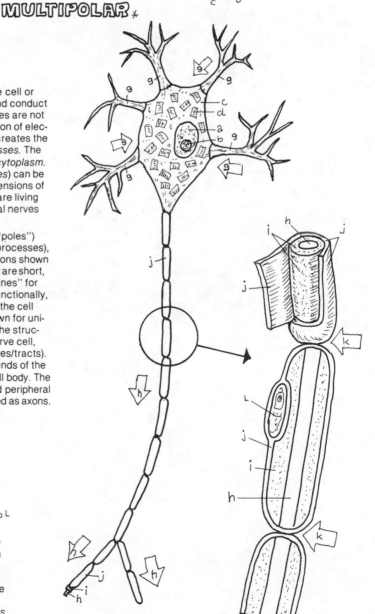

The fundamental functional unit of the nervous system is the nerve cell or *neuron.* Nerve cells are characterized by their ability to generate and conduct electrochemical energy forms called nerve impulses. Nerve impulses are not electrons, yet they are associated with electricity, for it is the diffusion of electrically charged atoms (ions) across the nerve cell membrane that creates the impulse. A nerve cell consists of a *cell body* and one or more *processes.* The cell body consists of the *nucleus* of the cell and some surrounding *cytoplasm.* Relatively large clumps of rough endoplasmic reticulum (*Nissl bodies*) can be seen in the cytoplasm of most nerve cell bodies. Processes are extensions of the cell body and consist of membrane-lined cytoplasm. Thus they are living structures. Under proper conditions, certain processes in peripheral nerves can regenerate after being cut.

Neurons are structurally classified by the number of processes ("poles") associated with each cell body: *unipolar* (one process), *bipolar* (two processes), and *multipolar* (two or more processes). The three basic configurations shown summarize the many varied shapes of neurons. Those processes that are short, highly branched and treelike, without coverings, and often with "spines" for synapses (connections with other neurons) are called *dendrites.* Functionally, dendrites are defined as those processes that conduct impulses to the cell body. This is fine in multipolar neurons, but the definition breaks down for unipolar and bipolar neurons, where the functional dendrites have all the structural characteristics of axons. *Axons,* restricted to one per each nerve cell, are long thin processes that tend to travel together in bundles (nerves/tracts). They are often ensheathed by coverings and branch mainly at the ends of the processes. Functionally, axons conduct impulses away from the cell body. The processes of unipolar/bipolar neurons are often termed central and peripheral processes; in the context of nerves/tracts, they are usually considered as axons.

AXON COVERINGS*
MYELIN i
NEURILEMMA j
NODE OF RANVIER k
NUCLEUS OF SCHWANN CELL L

Most axons are enveloped in one or two coverings, myelin and/or neurilemma. *Neurilemma* consists of the cell membrane of *Schwann cells* which wraps around larger axons of peripheral nerves to form multilayered myelin sheaths. Myelin sheaths of axons of the central nervous system are formed by certain neuroglial cells. *Myelin,* a phospholipid, insulates axons and increases their rates of impulse conduction. Neurilemma plays a critical role in the regeneration of peripheral nerves. The periodic gaps along a myelinated nerve (*nodes of Ranvier*) represent junctions between successive Schwann cells; they also increase rates of impulse conduction.

PLATE 113
see also 112

NERVOUS SYSTEM
ANATOMY OF A SYNAPSE*

CN 9

1. Color the entire cell body (c) with a single color; its processes have their own colors.
2. Use dark colors for structures (g) and (j).

PRESYNAPTIC AXONₐ
SYNAPTIC KNOB♭
CELL BODYᵪ
DENDRITE_d
POSTSYNAPTIC AXONₑ

Connections among neurons are called *synapses* (Gr. clasp). Synapses are means by which excitatory (or inhibitory) transmissions can be made from one or more neurons to others. One or two synapses among neurons (as shown below) make possible simple reflex arcs between sensory input and motor output. Multiple synapses (shown in the nerve cell above, receiving many presynaptic axons) greatly increase the available options of nervous activity. The ability to integrate, coordinate, associate, and modify sensory input and memories of previous experiences to achieve a desired motor (muscular) response is directly related to the number of synapses within the brain and spinal cord . . . and that number has been calculated to exceed 10,000,000,000,000. Certain neurons are known to receive more than 5000 synapses per nerve cell.

SYNAPSE*
PRESYNAPTIC AXONₐ
SYNAPTIC KNOB♭
MITOCHONDRIA_f
SYNAPTIC VESICLES_g
PRESYNAPTIC MEMBRANE_h
SYNAPTIC CLEFT_i
NEUROTRANSMITTER_j
POSTSYNAPTIC MEMBRANE_k
POSTSYNAPTIC AXONₑ

TYPES OF SYNAPSE*
AXO♭ AXONICₑ
AXO♭ SOMATICᵪ
AXO♭ DENDRITIC_d

A typical synapse can occur between axon and axon, axon and cell body (soma), or axon and dendrite. A synapse, exposed by electron microscopy, appears to work this way. An electrochemical impulse moves down the cell membrane of the *presynaptic axon*. As the impulse approaches the dilated *synaptic knob*, vesicles of *neurotransmitter* substance move toward the *presynaptic membrane*, merge with it, and the transmitter substance is ejected into the *synaptic cleft*. *Mitochondria* energize the rapid renewed production of the transmitter substance. As you can see, the two neurons engaged in a synapse do not make physical contact. The transmitter substance combines with a specific molecular arrangement in the *post*-synaptic membrane of the receiving neuron (receptor), and the postsynaptic neuron reacts in one of two ways: it becomes chemically excited and, in the face of repeated synaptic transmissions or multiple synapses (facilitation), will reach and surpass the threshold necessary for firing an electrochemical impulse; or it is chemically inhibited from becoming excited and in the face of such repeated transmissions/synapses (inhibition) will *not* reach the threshold necessary for generating an impulse. The sum of neuron activity in the brain and spinal cord is largely reflected in the facilitation and inhibition of stimuli from sensory receptors and of motor output.

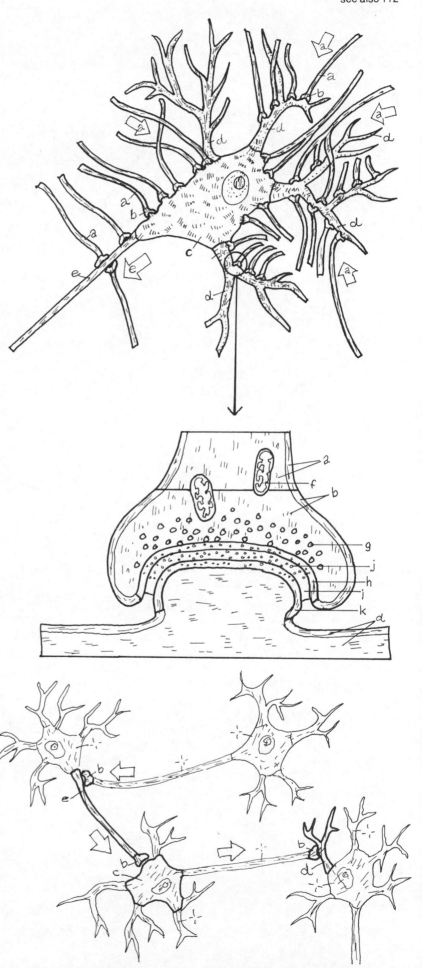

NERVOUS SYSTEM
FUNCTIONAL CLASSIFICATION
OF NEURONS / NERVE ENDINGS *

PLATE 114
see also 112, 113

In general, most neurons of the nervous system basically function in one of three modes: they conduct impulses from the periphery of the body to the central nervous system (afferent neurons); they conduct impulses from the central nervous system to the periphery of the body (efferent neurons); or they form a network of interconnecting neurons between afferent and efferent neurons. If the neurons are going to/coming from the periphery of the body (musculoskeletal structures of the limbs and the body wall or the skin and fascia), the prefix *somatic* is applied (somatic afferent/somatic efferent). If the neurons are going to/coming from structures with hollow cavities (viscera), the prefix *visceral* is applied (visceral afferent/visceral efferent). Not considered here are neurons secreting neurohormones/releasing factors or those specialized receptor neurons (osmoreceptors, and so on) contained entirely within the CNS.

CN 11
1. In the lower two drawings, note that the entire sensory and motor neurons receive one color each. In the upper drawings, their component parts receive different colors.
2. Color b, b¹, and c the colors they received on the preceding 2 plates, where they had different identification letters.

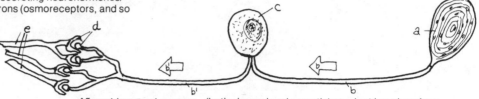

SENSORY NEURON (AFFERENT) *
RECEPTOR a
AXON (PERIPHERAL PROCESS) b
CELL BODY c
AXON (CENTRAL PROCESS) b¹
SYNAPSES d
CENTRAL NERVOUS SYSTEM e

Afferent (sensory) neurons (both visceral and somatic) conduct impulses from sensory receptors to synapses in the central nervous system. The receptors may be sensitive to touch, pressure, pain, position, muscle tension, chemical concentration, light, or other mechanical stimulus. These *receptors* inform a person of his or her external or internal environment and the changes that occur within each. The neurons conducting impulses from these receptors are almost always unipolar neurons. Their *peripheral processes* ("axons") conduct the impulses to the *cell bodies* and the *central processes* conduct the impulses into the brain or spinal cord (*central nervous system*) where they synapse at the same, higher, or lower levels as those levels at which they entered.

SOMATIC MOTOR NEURON (EFFERENT) *
CELL BODY c
AXON b
MOTOR END PLATE f
SKELETAL MUSCLE (EFFECTOR) g

Somatic efferent (motor) neurons conduct impulses from *cell bodies* located in the central nervous system (CNS) through *axons* that terminate by branching near skeletal muscle fibers and becoming incorporated into infoldings of the cell membrane (sarcolemma) of the muscle cell. This integrated unit is called the *motor end plate*. Here the neuron "end feet" release the chemical transmitter that causes chemical changes in the muscle cell membrane inducing the *muscle cell* (effector) to shorten or contract in response.

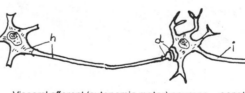

AUTONOMIC MOTOR NEURON (EFFERENT) *
PREGANGLIONIC NEURON h
SYNAPSE d
POST GANGLIONIC NEURON i
SMOOTH MUSCLE (EFFECTOR) j

Visceral efferent (autonomic motor) neurons constitute the autonomic nervous system (ANS). Here two neurons are involved. Their site of synapse is the cell body of the second neuron. Collections of cell bodies outside the CNS are called *ganglia*. The first or *preganglionic* neuron arises in the CNS, and its axon embarks for a ganglion usually located near the CNS. There it *synapses* with the cell body of the *post*ganglionic neuron whose axon proceeds to the effector organ: *smooth muscle, cardiac muscle,* or *glands*. In response to stimulation by this neuron, the smooth or cardiac muscle contracts or the gland secretes. In general, only viscera have smooth muscle or glands, and only ANS neurons innervate them.

ASSOCIATION NEURON (INTERNEURON) *
SENSORY NEURON k
ASSOCIATION NEURON *
MOTOR NEURON L

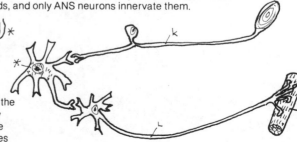

Association neurons are found mostly in the CNS. They make up the bulk of the neurons of the brain and spinal cord. They come in a variety of shapes and sizes. Many of them are directly related to incoming afferent impulses and others to outgoing efferent impulses. Others serve to integrate sensory input with higher centers to effect an appropriate motor output. Cell bodies of these neurons make up much of the gray matter of the CNS, and their myelinated axons make up much of the white matter. In the most simple situation, they connect sensory and motor neurons in a reflex arc, as shown here.

NERVOUS SYSTEM
REFLEX ARCS*

PLATE 115
see also 114

CN 8

1. Color the upper drawing first, beginning where the hammer taps the tendon (where the stretch receptor and sensory axon are located).

2. Complete the diagram of the monosynaptic arc. To simplify matters, each nerve, with its roots and branches (f through i), is shown containing only one of each kind of neuron, and each is greatly magnified so it can be drawn. As you color each of the spinal nerve parts, be aware that there are actually hundreds of neuron processes composing those parts (and hundreds of cell bodies in those ganglia).

3. Color the drawing of the hand withdrawing from the flame. Note that two muscles are involved in this reflex: one extends the wrist and fingers (+) and one flexes the wrist and fingers (–). In this case, the flexors are inhibited (–) from contracting, allowing the extensors to raise the fingers from the source of heat and pain.

4. Do not color the motor neuron cell body (e) and axon (e¹) synapsing with the inhibitory association neuron. Note the –¦– symbols associated with this neuron.

SPINAL CORD ₐ
GRAY MATTER ♭*
WHITE MATTER ꜀ ¦

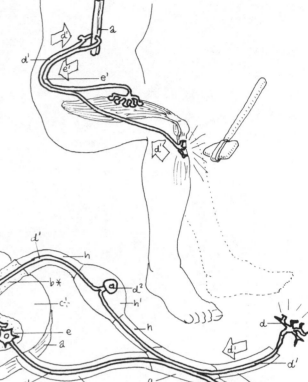

MONOSYNAPTIC ARC *
(2 NEURONS)*

STRETCH RECEPTOR ₔ
SENSORY AXON ₔ'
SENSORY NEURON CELL BODY ₔ²
MOTOR NEURON CELL BODY ₑ
MOTOR AXON ₑ'
MOTOR END PLATE ₑ²
EFFECTOR ₑ³

BRANCHES OF SPINAL N. f
SPINAL N. g
DORSAL ROOT ₕ GANGLION ₕ'
VENTRAL ROOT ᵢ

A reflex represents a basic activity of the nervous system: response to a stimulus without wilful initiation (involuntary). Except for skilled movements, body motions are largely reflexive: heartbeat, respiratory movements, digestive activity, postural adjustments. To various stimuli, the response is always muscular contraction (or glandular secretion). The simplest reflex is the *monosynaptic stretch reflex:* only one synapse is involved. The reflex begins with the tap of a tendon, stimulating many *stretch receptors*. The impulses are conducted by sensory neurons whose *axons* make up part of the *spinal nerve and its branches* (a *nerve* is a collection of sensory and motor axons outside the CNS). As the nerve approaches the spinal cord, its sensory root splits off to enter the spinal cord on its dorsal surface

(hence, sensory root = dorsal root). The *cell bodies* of these sensory unipolar neurons form a discrete swelling in the dorsal root of the spinal nerve, called the *dorsal root ganglion*. The synapses between the central processes ("axons") of the *sensory neurons* and the *motor neurons* occur in the gray matter (cell bodies, dendrites and unmyelinated axons) of the spinal cord. The impulses are then conducted by the *axons* of the motor neurons, which leave the spinal cord via the *ventral (motor) root* of the spinal nerve, join the sensory axons within the spinal nerve, and then branch off to the muscle (*effector*) whose tendon was tapped/stretched. The muscle contracts weakly in response to impulses traveling along this motor nerve route.

POLYSYNAPTIC ARC *
(MULTI-NEURON)*
ASSOCIATION NEURON ᵢ
(INTERNEURON) ᵢ
PAIN RECEPTOR ₔ

Polysynaptic reflexes range from the simple withdrawal reflex shown here to more complex reflexes involving several segments of spinal cord or several centers in the brain. They are much more common than stretch reflexes. Association neurons in the gray matter mediate the transfer of excitation from sensory to motor neurons. In this case, the central process of the sensory neuron splits to synapse

with two association neurons, one of which is inhibitory (–). Impulses generated along this neuron inhibit the motor neuron from firing an impulse, and the flexor muscles innervated by such neurons do not contract. Simultaneously, the excitatory association neurons (one shown) facilitate the firing of the motor neurons to the extensor muscles, and these muscles contract in response.

PLATE 116

NERVOUS SYSTEM ORGANIZATION*

CN 6

1. Color both illustrations simultaneously, noting that the cranial nerves do not appear in the standing figure. When coloring the spinal nerves in that figure, note that the branches become lines (due to space limitations). In these cases, simply draw over the lines.

CENTRAL NERVOUS SYSTEM (CNS)*

BRAIN.
CEREBRUM a
BRAINSTEM b
CEREBELLUM c
SPINAL CORD d

The nervous system consists of neurons arranged into a highly integrated central part (*brain* and *spinal cord,* or CNS) and bundles of neuronal processes largely making up the peripheral part. The CNS involves great numbers of multipolar, association, and some upper motor neurons interconnected to form: (1) centers or *nuclei* (generally called gray matter) consisting of cell bodies, dendrites, and unmyelinated axons; and (2) bundles or *tracts* of myelinated axons (generally called white matter). The gray and white matter of the brain forms the following structures: the *cerebrum* (characterized by an outer cortex of gray matter and masses of underlying tracts and nuclei), the *brainstem* (characterized by columns of white matter coursing among discrete and diffuse areas of gray matter), and the *cerebellum* (characterized by a cortex of gray matter and underlying tracts and nuclei). The spinal cord is an extension of the central nervous system, beginning at the foramen magnum of the skull, and passing through the canal of the vertebral column down to the level of the 4th lumbar vertebra. It is arranged into an H-shaped central region of gray matter surrounded by columns of tracts.

PERIPHERAL NERVOUS SYSTEM (PNS)*

CRANIAL NERVES (12 PAIR) e
SPINAL NERVES (31 PAIR) f

The peripheral part (peripheral nervous system or PNS) consists of bundles of sensory and motor axons (collections of which are called nerves) radiating from the brain and spinal cord segmentally and bilaterally and reaching to all parts of the body (visceral and somatic) through a predictable pattern of distribution. Those nerves projecting from the brain are called *cranial nerves;* those projecting from the spinal cord are called *spinal nerves.* Discrete collections of cell bodies of sensory neurons are found in the dorsal roots of spinal nerves (labeled in left illustration). Cell bodies of autonomic (visceral) motor neurons (specifically, the postganglionic neurons) are also located in discrete sites throughout the body. The term *ganglion* (pl. ganglia) is generally reserved for collections of such cell bodies within the PNS and outside the CNS. Cell bodies of somatic motor neurons are located within the gray matter of the spinal cord (for spinal nerves) and brainstem (for cranial nerves) and are therefore more properly called nuclei.

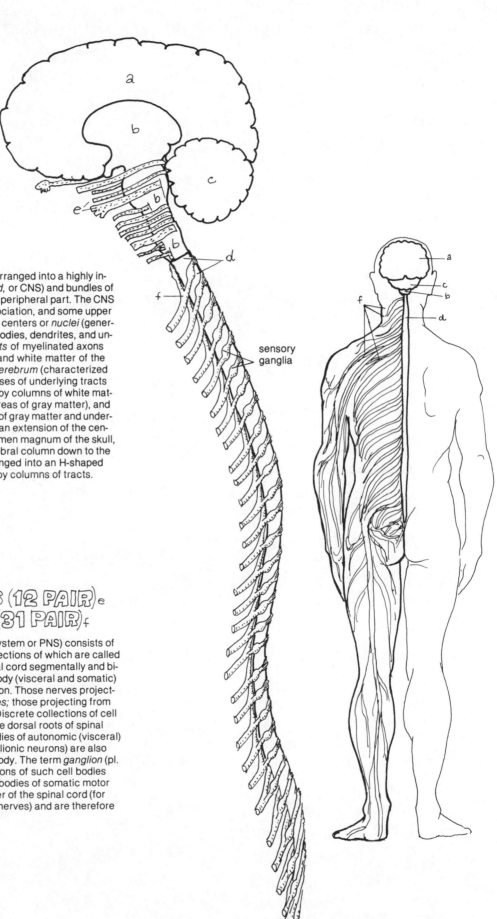

sensory ganglia

PLATE 117

NERVOUS SYSTEM
DEVELOPMENT OF CENTRAL NERVOUS SYSTEM*

CN 15

1. Color each illustration completely before going on to the next. Take careful note of the developmental changes taking place from one stage to the next.

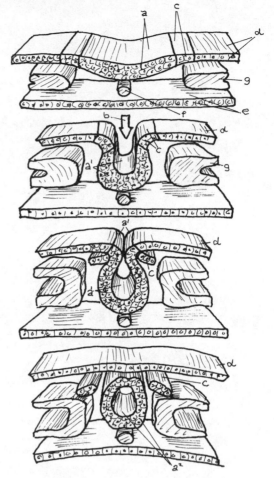

NEURAL PLATE₂/FOLD₂/TUBE₂²
NEURAL GROOVE♭
NEURAL CREST꜀
ECTODERM OF SURFACE (SKIN)d
ENTODERM (GUT)ₑ
NOTOCHORD𝒇
MESODERM𝓰
(SKELETON/MUSCLE)𝓰

The nervous system develops from ectoderm, one of the three primary germ layers of the embryo. The arrangement of these basic layers with respect to the dorsal body wall of a three-week-old embryo can be seen at right in idealized cross sections. The ectodermal layer of the developing skin folds inward along the midline of the back from head to tail. As the tube forms, the ectoderm separates from it. This neural tube will become the brain and the spinal cord. The neural crest cells will develop into certain nerve cells of the peripheral nervous system. The surrounding mesoderm will form the cranium (for the brain) and the vertebral column (surrounding the spinal cord) and related muscles. The notochord (a primitive supporting rod for the embryo) will be absorbed by the developing vertebral column, and remnants of it will remain as the core of the intervertebral discs (nucleus pulposus). The entoderm will contribute to the development of the digestive tract.

FOREBRAINₕ
TELENCEPHALONᵢ
DIENCEPHALONⱼ
MIDBRAINₖ
(MESENCEPHALON)ₖ
HINDBRAINₗ
METENCEPHALONₘ
MYELENCEPHALONₙ
SPINAL CORDₒ

The central nervous system begins as a dorsal, hollow neural tube. The head or cephalic one-third of the tube undergoes significantly greater proliferation than the caudal two-thirds. This cephalic portion will become the brain and the caudal part of the spinal cord. These illustrations concentrate on the changes occurring in the developing brain. By the end of three weeks of embryonic development, three regions of the developing brain are apparent: forebrain, midbrain, and hindbrain. With further growth, the forebrain expands to form the massive telencephalon (endbrain) and the more central diencephalon (in-between brain). The midbrain retains its largely tubular shape as the mesencephalon (midbrain). The hindbrain differentiates into the upper metencephalon (changebrain), characterized by a large dorsal outpocketing, and the lower myelencephalon (spinal brain), which narrows down to become the spinal cord at the level of the foramen magnum of the skull. Thus, five regions form from the basic three. The adult derivatives of these five regions include: cerebral hemispheres or cerebrum (telencephalon); thalamus, hypothalamus, and epithalamus (diencephalon and hidden from view by the expansive hemispheres); the colliculi and cerebral peduncles (mesencephalon and also hidden from view by the hemispheres); pons and cerebellum (metencephalon); medulla oblongata (myelencelpalon).

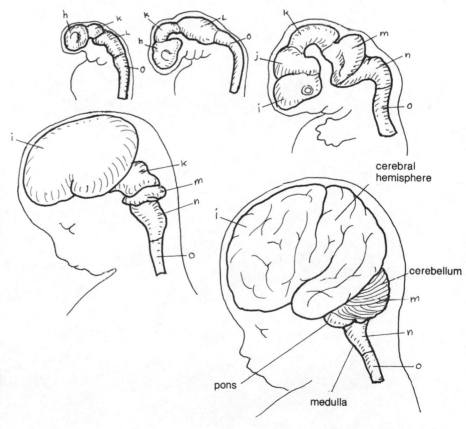

cerebral hemisphere

cerebellum

pons

medulla

PLATE 118
see also 117

NERVOUS SYSTEM
DEVELOPMENT OF THE VENTRICLES *

CN 13

1. The first five titles (h, k, l, o, a²) should receive the same color used for them on the preceding plate.
2. Complete each upper illustration completely before proceeding to the next.
3. Color the two lower views of the ventricles simultaneously.
4. The dotted areas in the middle drawing represent developing brain tissue which is organized as shown in the upper right illustration and on P. 117.

FOREBRAIN_h
MIDBRAIN_k
HINDBRAIN_l
SPINAL CORD_o
NEURAL CAVITY_a²

LATERAL VENTRICLES_b
INTERVENTRICULAR FORAMEN_c
THIRD VENTRICLE_d
CEREBRAL AQUEDUCT_e
FOURTH VENTRICLE_f
CENTRAL CANAL OF SPINAL CORD_o
CHOROID PLEXUS_i

The central nervous system develops from a hollow neural tube in the dorsal half of the embryo. The cavity of that tube is destined to become the ventricles of the brain, and the shapes of these spaces reflect the changes and mechanical pressures experienced by the developing brain regions of which they are a part. First follow the development of the cavity of the *forebrain*. The upper forebrain (telencephalon) undergoes tremendous expansion in several directions, and its cavities (*lateral or first/second ventricles*—one for each side) seem to point in the directions of brain growth. Note the size of the lateral ventricles relative to that of the other cavities. The cavity of the lower part of the forebrain (diencephalon) becomes compressed into a thin slit (*third ventricle*) by the developing hemispheres. The lateral ventricles of those hemispheres communicate with the third ventricle by way of *interventricular foramina*. The thalamus abuts against the third ventricle on each side. The cavity of the *midbrain* (mesencephalon) is only slightly modified during development because the external changes of this region are relatively mild. This cavity retains its tubular shape as the *cerebral aqueduct* connecting third and fourth ventricles. The developing cavity of the *hindbrain* becomes slightly distorted as it is pulled slightly posteriorly (dorsally) and laterally by the developing cerebellar hemispheres. This *fourth ventricle* is shared by both metencephalon and myelencephalon. Below, it dives into the substance of the medulla (myelencephalon) to become the tiny *central canal of the spinal cord*. In each of the ventricles (less the aqueduct), certain portions of its lining cells (ependyma—not shown) become integrated with the highly vascular, innermost covering of the brain (pia mater). This combination of tissues makes up the *choroid plexuses* attached to the roof of each ventricle. The choroid plexus secretes cerebrospinal fluid, which flows through the ventricles and into the subarachnoid space between the brain coverings.

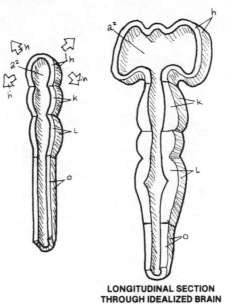
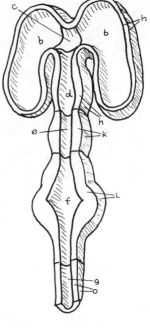

**LONGITUDINAL SECTION
THROUGH IDEALIZED BRAIN
OF DEVELOPING EMBRYO**

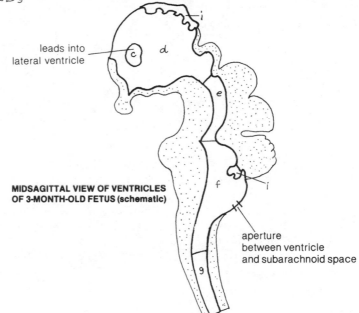

leads into lateral ventricle

**MIDSAGITTAL VIEW OF VENTRICLES
OF 3-MONTH-OLD FETUS (schematic)**

aperture between ventricle and subarachnoid space

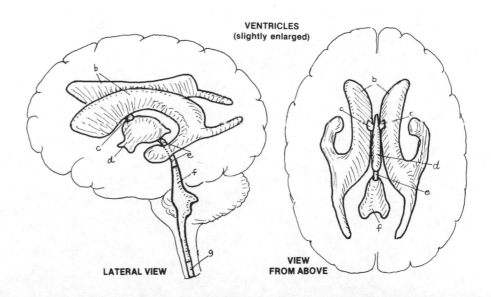

**VENTRICLES
(slightly enlarged)**

LATERAL VIEW

**VIEW
FROM ABOVE**

CN 3

1. Note that the three meninges are shown extending out of the illustration to the right for easy identification.
2. Use 3 colors not used for the lower titles in Plate 118, since all 10 will be used on the next plate.
3. The spinal nerve roots just below the spinal cord (cauda equina) have been cut away for better viewing of the lumbar cistern.
4. Color the dura (a) lining the cranial bones with lighter pressure than used on the falx.

DURA MATER a
FALX CEREBRI a'
TENTORIUM CEREBELLI a²
ARACHNOID b
SUBARACHNOID SPACE b'•
PIA MATER c
FILUM TERMINALE c'

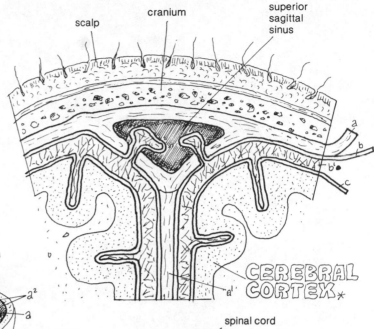

scalp   cranium   superior sagittal sinus

CEREBRAL CORTEX *

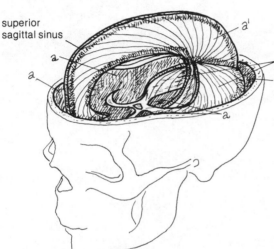

INFOLDINGS (SEPTA)
OF DURA MATER
(brain and skull cap removed)

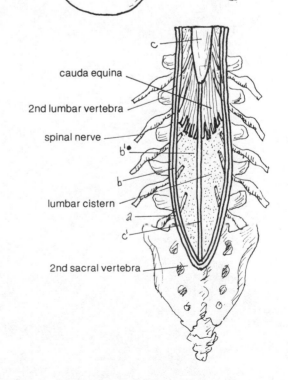

spinal cord

roots of spinal nerve

cauda equina

2nd lumbar vertebra

spinal nerve

lumbar cistern

2nd sacral vertebra

The central nervous system is enveloped by fibrous coverings called *meninges*. The outermost covering (*dura mater*) is the thickest, consisting largely of collagen fibers and fibroblasts. About the brain, the dura is composed of two layers. The outer layer is firmly adherent to the cranial bones as their periosteum. The thinner inner layer turns inward at certain sides to become partitions between areas of the brain. Note the scythe-shaped septum separating the cerebral hemispheres (not shown): this is the *falx cerebri*. Posteriorly, the inner dura forms a tentlike covering over the cerebellum (*tentorium cerebelli*), separating it from the occipital lobes above. These are the principal dural infoldings in whose margins are a number of venous sinuses that drain the brain. Note the superior sagittal sinus in the upper margin of the falx. This large vein has special significance as you shall see. In the canal of the vertebral column, the dura is one layer, as the vertebrae have their own periosteum and shock-absorbing ligaments. The dura, continuing below from the foramen magnum, forms a sheath for the spinal cord down to the level of the 2nd sacral vertebra where it is firmly anchored. The dura forms sleeves about the roots of a short portion of the first parts of the spinal nerves.

The *arachnoid* mater has a spider-web consistency and lines the inner surface of the dura throughout the CNS. Deep to the arachnoid is the very thin *pia mater*, the innermost covering of the brain and spinal cord. This highly vascular membrane is almost adherent to the arachnoid in certain places about the brain (pia-arachnoid). However, in most areas there is considerable space between the two: the *subarachnoid space*. This space is especially large in some locations; note the lumbar cistern between the end point of the spinal cord (2nd lumbar vertebra) and the end of the dural sac (2nd sacral vertebra). This space is normally filled with spinal nerve roots seeking exit from the sac and entry to the body periphery. The *filum terminale* is an extension of pia through the cistern and attached to the dural sac.

PLATE 120
see also 119, 118

NERVOUS SYSTEM
CIRCULATION SCHEME OF
CEREBROSPINAL FLUID (CSF)*

1. Color the meninges (a, b, c) the same color as in the preceding plate.
2. When coloring the subarachnoid space (b²) in black, notice the cisterns (dotted areas representing expanded portions of this space) receive different colors.
3. Color d–h the colors they received in Plate 118, where they had different identification letters. Color the 3rd and 4th ventricles the same color as the lateral ventricle (e¹).

DURA MATER a
SUPERIOR SAGITTAL SINUS a*
ARACHNOID b VILLI (GRANULATIONS) b'
SUBARACHNOID SPACE b²
PIA MATER c

CIRCULATION SCHEME:
CHOROID PLEXUS d
VENTRICLES: e
LATERAL e' 3RD e² 4TH e³
INTERVENTRICULAR FORAMEN f
CEREBRAL AQUEDUCT g
CENTRAL CANAL h
MEDIAN/LATERAL APERTURES i
SUBARACHNOID SPACES: b²
GREAT CISTERN j
SUPERIOR CISTERN k
PONTINE CISTERN l
INTERPEDUNCULAR CISTERN m
LUMBAR CISTERN n CSF n'

The brain and spinal cord are immersed in about 100 ml or more of *cerebrospinal fluid (CSF).* In fact, they float in it, restricted in their movement by the *dura mater.* CSF is an extracellular fluid that plays an important shock-absorbing role. It may also have a metabolic function.

Clear and colorless, CSF is secreted by the *choroid plexus,* which consists of a network of capillaries intertwined with the lining of the ventricles. Although secreted in all four ventricles, most CSF probably arises in the lateral ventricles. CSF flows through the ventricles and aqueduct and drains into the *subarachnoid space* just below the cerebellum (*great cistern*) through three passageways or *apertures.* The fluid also seeps into the tiny *central canal* of the spinal cord. The CSF circulates about the brain and spinal cord within the

subarachnoid space. Due to flexures, projections, and depressions, the CSF pools in certain locations called *cisterns.* The *lumbar cistern* is of particular significance for it is the usual site of CSF sampling for diagnostic purposes (seeking evidence of microorganisms, hemorrhage, increased pressure, and space-occupying masses). In the lumbar puncture procedure, a few milliliters of CSF are withdrawn by needle from the lumbar cistern at the level of the 4th or 5th lumbar vertebra, where there is no danger of striking the spinal cord (which ends at L2) and very little risk of stabbing the spinal roots (which generally move aside as the needle enters the cistern). CSF is ultimately reabsorbed by the *superior sagittal sinus* via tiny, cauliflower-shaped outpocketings of the arachnoid (*villi*). With age, these villi tend to form granulations, suggesting that reabsorption of CSF diminishes with age.

PLATE 121
see also 116, 119, 11, 12

NERVOUS SYSTEM
CEREBRAL HEMISPHERES * (PART 1)

CN 5

1. This and the next plate should be colored together. Understanding of the text will require reference to both plates. Note the corpus callosum (j) on this plate; its title is on part 2 (next plate).

2. Color each of the four lobes in these two views of the cerebral hemispheres. Color the specific areas within the lobes (a¹, a², b¹, c¹, and d¹) a darker shade of the same color.

3. Note that the two hemispheres of the brain have been separated in the illustration for purposes of explanation. When they are joined together, the longitudinal fissure (represented by the arrow, e*) resembles the central sulcus (e¹) and the lateral fissure (e²).

CEREBRAL HEMISPHERES.

CEREBRAL CORTEX *
FRONTAL LOBE a
PRINCIPAL SPEECH AREA a¹
MOTOR AREA (PRE-CENTRAL GYRUS) a²
PARIETAL LOBE b
SENSORY AREA (POST-CENTRAL GYRUS) b¹
TEMPORAL LOBE c
AUDITORY AREA c¹
OCCIPITAL LOBE d
VISUAL AREA d¹
MAJOR FISSURES *
LONGITUDINAL FISSURE e *
CENTRAL SULCUS e¹ *
LATERAL FISSURE e² *

The *cerebral hemispheres,* derivatives of the developing telencephalon, consist of (1) an outer *cerebral cortex* of gray matter characterized by fissures, gyri, and sulci (deep grooves, hills, and furrows, respectively) and functionally divided into lobes; (2) underlying *white matter* consisting of numerous tracts oriented along three general directions; (3) discrete masses of gray matter (*basal nuclei*) that subserve motor areas of the cortex; and (4) the paired *lateral ventricles.* The cerebral cortex is the most highly evolved area of the brain. Roughly 6 mm (¼ inch) thick, a large percentage of its highly convoluted surface is tucked away within the depths of the sulci. Areas of the cortex are generally named in relation to the cranial bones that cover them: frontal, parietal, temporal, occipital. Two other areas of the cortex (insula, limbic) are not shown.

Cortical mapping experiments (based on electrical stimulation) and clinical/pathologic data have been the principal methods by which functions of the cortex have been discovered. All parts of the cortex are concerned with storage of experience (memory), exchange of impulses with other cortical areas (association), and the two way transmission of impulses with subcortical areas (afferent/efferent projection). The *frontal lobe* (a) is concerned with intellectual functions such as reasoning and abstract thinking; aggressive and sexual behavior; olfaction or smell; speech (specifically the area labeled a¹); language and the initiation of movement, both skilled (voluntary) and postural. The area labeled a² (*precentral gyrus*) specifically initiates skilled movement, and impulses from this motor area are conducted down the corticospinal tract directly to motor neurons of the cranial/spinal nerves. The *central sulcus* (e¹) might be considered a kind of general boundary between motor areas anteriorly and sensory areas posteriorly.

The *parietal lobe* (b) is concerned with the recognition of specific sensory stimuli (e.g., observing an object one has seen before and being able to make that connection); the ability to use symbols as a means of commu-

nication (language); and the ability to develop ideas and the necessary motor responses to carry them out. The specific area labeled b¹, the *postcentral gyrus,* receives afferent impulses relating to pain, temperature, touch, pressure, and muscle/position sense from receptors all over the body. It is in this area of the parietal lobe that one largely becomes aware (conscious) of these sensations and is able to discriminate among them. Awareness and discrimination of taste are believed to take place at the lowest point of the postcentral gyrus.

The *temporal lobe* (c) is concerned with olfaction and language (as is the frontal lobe), and emotional behavior with related visceral reactions associated with self-preservation and preservation of the species (including anger, hostility, sexual behavior). The specific area labeled (c¹) receives afferent impulses relating to *hearing;* awareness and discrimination of this sensory mode within a rather narrow auditory spectrum takes place in this area. The *occipital lobe* (d), especially the specific area labeled (d¹), is concerned with receiving *visual* stimuli from the optic tract. Awareness and discrimination of visible structure, within a certain restricted visible spectrum, occurs here.

Functionally speaking, the two hemispheres, especially with respect to the cortex, are not equal; that is, they are not mirror images of one another. One hemisphere tends to be dominant in certain higher functions (mathematical, mechanical, artistic, musical, literary) to one degree or another. Interestingly, most long tracts to and from the cortex (and other areas as well) from sensory and motor neurons, respectively, cross to opposite sides of the CNS enroute. Thus sensory receptors of the left side of the body are generally represented on the right side of the cortex, and motor impulses originating in the right frontal cortex usually generate muscular activity on the left side of the body.

PLATE 122
see also 121

NERVOUS SYSTEM
CEREBRAL HEMISPHERES/CORTEX/TRACTS (2)

CN 6
1. Color the cerebral cortex (f*) gray in all 4 illustrations.
2. Color the corpus callosum (j) in both this and the preceding plate.

CEREBRAL CORTEX f*
SUB CORTICAL AREAS *
LATERAL VENTRICLES₉
BASAL NUCLEI (GANGLIA) *
CAUDATE NUCLEUS h
LENTICULAR NUCLEUS i

The subcortical areas of the cerebral hemispheres include the white matter, the basal nuclei, and the lateral ventricles. The *basal nuclei (ganglia)* are discrete masses of gray matter at the base of the hemispheres on either side of the diencephalon. This relationship can best be appreciated by referring to the next plate. The specific areas of the basal nuclei include the *caudate nucleus* and the *lenticular nucleus*. Both are named according to their shape: the caudate appears to have a head and a progressively narrowing and curving tail, and the lenticular is shaped like a lens with two convex surfaces. Passing between them is the internal capsule, a band of axons distributing impulses between cortex and lower centers of the CNS, and appearing to be part of a capsule of white matter about the lenticular nucleus. The functions of these nuclei can be inferred, in part, from their afferent (input) and efferent (output) connections: the cortex and thalamus send them fibers, and they send fibers to one another, the thalamus, hypothalamus, and midbrain nuclei. Clinical experience with individuals suffering lesions (injuries, destructive tumors, infections) here, i.e., Parkinson's disease and other diseases characterized by tremors, rigidity, spasms, and weakness of skeletal muscle, also provides insights into basal nuclei function. The basal nuclei largely introduce facilitating and inhibitory influences on descending (motor) impulses arising from motor areas of the frontal cortex except the precentral gyrus. They are instrumental in often unconscious "automatic" reflexes that underlie such activities as eating, adjustment of posture, and defensive reactions. Impulses from the basal nuclei generally percolate through networks of brainstem neurons to reach motor neurons of the cranial and spinal nerves.

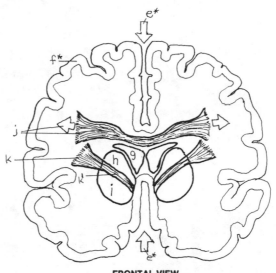

FRONTAL VIEW
(cross section through cerebrum)

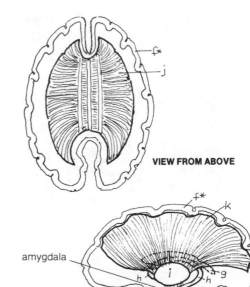

VIEW FROM ABOVE

amygdala

LATERAL VIEW

SUBDIVISIONS OF WHITE MATTER *
COMMISSURES (CORPUS CALLOSUM)ⱼ
PROJECTION TRACTS *
CORONA RADIATA k
INTERNAL CAPSULE k'
ASSOCIATION TRACTS L

The white matter of the hemispheres consists of tracts oriented in three general directions. Tracts connecting left and right hemispheres are called *commissures*, of which the largest is the *corpus callosum* arching above the lateral ventricles. Bundles of white matter (axons) that connect anterior and posterior cortical areas are called *association tracts*. These consist of both long and short bundles. Perhaps the most spectacular mass of white matter is that *projection tract* of myelinated axons radiating to and from all parts of the cortex: the *corona radiata*. It is continuous with the compact *internal capsule* passing between the two basal nuclei. Most communications involving the cerebral cortex travel via these tracts. Of course, impulses can travel across cortical areas through a multiplicity of small neurons with unmyelinated axons and dendrites.

MIDSAGITTAL VIEW
OF CEREBRUM

CN 10

1. Structures h, i, j, and k receive the same colors used on the preceding plate.
2. Note that you are looking at the thalamus (a) in the center drawing through the waters of the III ventricle. A thin wall (septum) prevents you from peering into the right lateral ventricle.

THALAMUS a
HYPOTHALAMUS b
EPITHALAMUS (PINEAL) c
THIRD VENTRICLE d
RELATED STRUCTURES *
CAUDATE NUCLEUS h
LENTICULAR NUCLEUS i
HYPOPHYSIS e
CORPUS CALLOSUM j
LATERAL VENTRICLE g
INTERNAL CAPSULE k

The *diencephalon*, the smaller of the two derivatives of the early forebrain, seems swallowed up within and by the massive cerebral hemispheres. It consists of the central *thalamus,* the more inferior *hypothalamus,* the appendagelike *epithalamus,* and the thin slit of a cavity: the *third ventricle*.

The thalamus consists of several groups of cell bodies and processes that function largely as relay or association centers. A simple concept, but complex structure and even more complex function. The relay nuclei of the thalamus receive ascending input indirectly from most sensory neurons of cranial and spinal nerves. It receives input directly from cranial nerve II (optic), and no input from cranial nerve I (olfactory). The postsynaptic neurons (relay nuclei) project axons to specific sensory or motor areas of the cortex. Association centers of the thalamus project fibers among themselves and to association areas of the cortex. Still other thalamic nuclei connect to other brainstem nuclei including the hypothalamus. Activity among these centers/nuclei and their connections generally results in an integration of sensory experiences resulting in appropriate motor responses; an integration of emotions appropriate to specific sensory input (e.g., crying in response to pain); and regulation and maintenance of the conscious state, subject to facilitating/inhibiting influences from the cerebral cortex. Although sensory systems seem to be the principal concern of the thalamus, thalamic connections to the basal nuclei, hypothalamus, and cerebellum strongly imply the thalamus is in business to influence certain descending (motor) pathways as well.

The hypothalamus is located just below the thalamus on either side of the third ventricle. Consisting of several, tightly packed masses of gray matter interrupted by tracts of white matter, the hypothalamus maintains connections with the frontal and temporal cortices, thalamus, midbrain and lower brainstem, and the neurohypophysis. It is concerned with regulation of the autonomic nervous system, secretory activity of the hypophysis, integration of visceral (autonomic) reflexes and emotional reactions, activation of the drive to eat and the subsequent feeling of satisfaction following fulfillment of that drive, and regulation of body temperature (in part, through the mamillary bodies). In addition, the hypothalamus offers facilitating influences to descending impulses related to both reflexive and skilled movement.

The epithalamus (pineal gland) consists primarily of the pineal body and related nuclei and tracts that have connections with the thalamus, hypothalamus, basal nuclei, and the medial temporal cortex. Precise function of the pineal in humans is unclear, although recent evidence suggests it offers an inhibitory influence on testicular/ovarian activity through the secretion of a hormone (melatonin). Melatonin is also said to have effects on the CNS in response to changes in environmental light, which may relate to natural rhythms or cycles inherent in certain body functions.

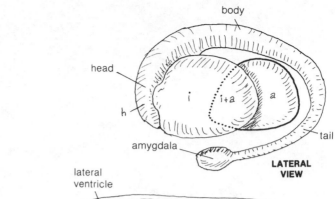

body
head
amygdala
tail
LATERAL VIEW

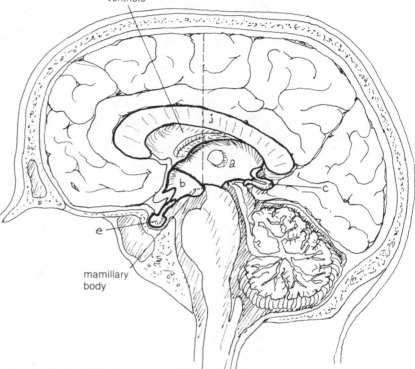

lateral ventricle
mamillary body
MIDSAGITTAL VIEW

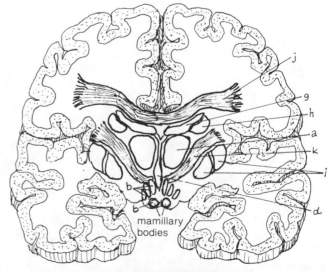

mamillary bodies
FRONTAL VIEW
(cross section through cerebrum
at level indicated by dotted line
in drawing above)

PLATE 124
see also 123, 12, 119

NERVOUS SYSTEM
BRAINSTEM/CEREBELLUM*

CN 18

1. First color the parts of the midbrain in all three illustrations, then color the parts of the hindbrain in order of their titles. Then color the related structures, taking note of their relationship to the structures just colored.

MIDBRAIN.
MESENCEPHALON*
CEREBRAL PEDUNCLES a
CEREBRAL AQUEDUCT b
SUPERIOR COLLICULI c
INFERIOR COLLICULI d
SUPERIOR CEREBELLAR PEDUNCLE e

HINDBRAIN.
METENCEPHALON*
PONS f
FOURTH VENTRICLE g
CEREBELLUM h
ARBOR VITAE i
MIDDLE CEREBELLAR PEDUNCLES j

MYELENCEPHALON (MEDULLA) k
PYRAMIDS L
FOURTH VENTRICLE g
INFERIOR CEREBELLAR PEDUNCLES m

RELATED STRUCTURES*
MAMILLARY BODIES (HYPO-
THALAMUS) n
OPTIC CHIASMA o
STALK OF HYPOPHYSIS p
SPINAL CORD q

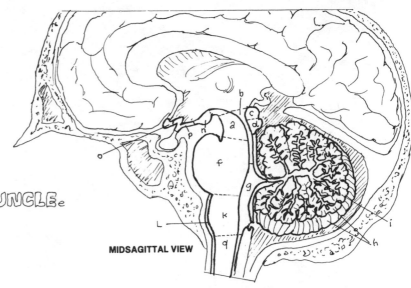

MIDSAGITTAL VIEW

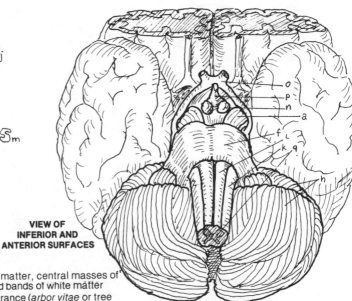

**VIEW OF
INFERIOR AND
ANTERIOR SURFACES**

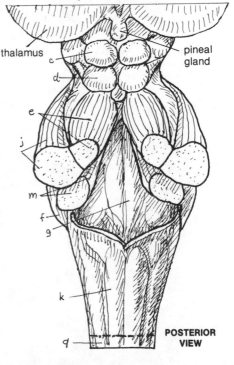

thalamus

pineal gland

**POSTERIOR
VIEW**

The *brainstem* consists of all portions of the brain less the cerebral and cerebellar hemispheres. All regions of the brainstem except certain parts of the diencephalon (see previous plate) are to be colored on this plate. The *midbrain* includes two *cerebral peduncles* separated from the *superior/inferior colliculi* by the *cerebral aqueduct*. The peduncles consist of: (1) two columns of axons conducting motor-related impulses from the cerebral cortex to the pons, medulla, or spinal cord; and (2) a deeper group of nuclei/tracts concerned with cranial nerves III and IV, relay of impulses between lower and higher centers, and facilitation/inhibition of somatic and visceral motor-related impulses. The cell bodies of the superior colliculus are the centers for visual reflexes, and those of the inferior colliculus for auditory reflexes (e.g., response to a loud, startling noise).

Derivatives of the metencephalon consist of the *pons* connected to the *cerebellum* by the *middle cerebellar peduncles*, which, in company with superior/inferior cerebellar peduncles, cross the waters of the *fourth ventricle*. The pons consists of (1) tracts descending from the midbrain (cortex to lower centers); (2) masses of cell bodies that synapse with certain tracts of cortical origin and whose axons constitute the middle cerebellar peduncle; (3) nuclei that relate to cranial nerves VI, VII, and VIII; (4) several ascending tracts arising from the medulla and spinal cord; and (5) a network of polysynaptic neurons that provide facilitation/inhibition influences on somatic and visceral reflexes as well as forming a mechanism for arousal, wakefulness, and alertness. The *cerebellum* con-

sists of a cortex of gray matter, central masses of motor-related nuclei, and bands of white matter forming a treelike appearance (*arbor vitae* or tree of life). The cerebellum is attached to the brainstem by three paired stalks of white matter: superior (from midbrain), middle (from pons), and inferior (from medulla) cerebellar peduncles. Input to the cerebellum comes in mainly via the inferior and middle peduncles; its influence on motor activity is directed out the superior peduncle. The cerebellum is concerned with equilibrium and position sense, control of muscle tone, and overall coordination of muscular activity.

The *medulla* and the lower part of the *fourth ventricle* are derivatives of the early myelencephalon. The medulla, continuous with the deep pons above and the spinal cord below, generally consists of (1) central masses of cell bodies forming relay nuclei (for descending/ascending tracts), association nuclei (continuation of the network of polysynaptic neurons), and cranial nerve nuclei (part of VIII, and IX, X, XI, and XII), and (2) peripheral bundles of white matter coming up from and going down to the spinal cord. The two bundles of fibers projecting out on the anterior surface of the medulla (L) are the *pyramids* consisting of the cortex-to-spinal cord (corticospinal) tract conducting impulses relating to voluntary, skilled movement. 80% of these fibers cross just below the pyramids to the opposite side of the medulla/spinal cord. The association nuclei of the medulla are concerned primarily with such visceral reflexes as heart rate, respiratory, and vasomotor (degree of constriction of blood vessels) control.

PLATE 125
see also 13, 116,
119, 115

NERVOUS SYSTEM
SPINAL CORD*

CN 18

1. Color the layers covering the spinal cord in the diagram at right. The pia mater covers the spinal cord entirely. Note that the lumbar cistern (subarachnoid space, c) is broken up by the emergence of spinal nerves. Color in those remaining strands of nerves (g) cut away to show the lumbar cistern. Color a, b, d as in Plate 119 (where d is labeled c).
2. Color in gray the gray matter portion of the four representative sections of the spinal cord and their titles.

DURA MATER a
ARACHNOID b
SUBARACHNOID SPACE c•
SPINAL CORD / PIA MATER d
2ND LUMBAR VERTEBRA e*
CONUS MEDULLARIS f
CAUDA EQUINA g
FILUM TERMINALE h
2ND SACRAL VERTEBRA i*

Beginning at the foramen magnum of the skull, the *spinal cord* is the distal continuation of the central nervous system. At the level of the 2nd lumbar vertebra (L2), it terminates as the *conus medullaris*. It bulges slightly in the lower cervical and lumbar regions (enlargements), giving evidence of increased numbers of neurons relating to the upper and lower limbs. Ensheathed in meninges, the spinal cord floats in CSF. The *pia mater* continues distal to the conus as the *filum terminale* and joins with the *dura mater* at the 2nd sacral vertebra (S2). Here the dura ends, forming the dural sac filled with CSF (lumbar cistern). The lower spinal nerves, reaching for the sacral intervertebral foramina and floating within the lumbar cistern, form a collection of fibers called the *cauda equina*.

The spinal cord consists of a central mass of gray matter arranged into the form of an H and a peripheral array of white matter forming descending and ascending tracts. As the cord progresses distally, the amount of white matter is reduced relative to the amount of gray matter, indicating that more and more axons are used up as the cord proceeds downward.

REGIONS OF SPINAL CORD.

GRAY MATTER *
POSTERIOR HORNS j
ANTERIOR HORNS k
LATERAL HORNS l
INTERMEDIATE ZONE m
GRAY COMMISSURES n

WHITE MATTER +
POSTERIOR FUNICULUS o
LATERAL FUNICULUS p
ANTERIOR FUNICULUS q
WHITE COMMISSURES r

POSTERIOR MEDIAN SULCUS s
ANTERIOR MEDIAN FISSURE t
CENTRAL CANAL u +

The gray matter of the spinal cord consists of *posterior horns* (central processes of sensory neurons, association neurons), *anterior horns* (cell bodies of motor neurons, association neurons), *intermediate zones* (mostly association neurons and some motor neurons), *lateral horns* (autonomic motor neurons in T1–L2, S2–4 levels) and axons of various neurons crossing in the *commissures*. Here in the gray matter, sensory neurons of the peripheral nervous system integrate with, and motor neurons of the peripheral nervous system conduct, the summated impulses from the central nervous system. The white matter of the cord is divided arbitrarily into columns or *funiculi*. Each funiculus contains a number of specific tracts: ascending long tracts (sensory), descending long tracts (motor), and short, intersegmental tracts. The long tracts conduct impulses to and from the brainstem and higher centers; the short tracts jump from segment to segment taking part in various spinal reflexes involving more than one level of the cord.

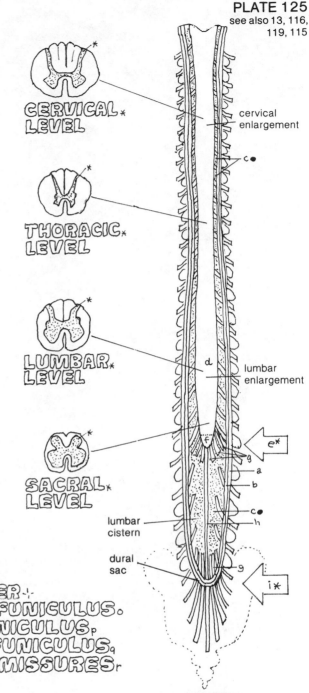

CERVICAL LEVEL *

cervical enlargement

THORACIC LEVEL *

LUMBAR LEVEL *

lumbar enlargement

SACRAL LEVEL *

lumbar cistern

dural sac

POSTERIOR VIEW OF SPINAL CORD AND MENINGES

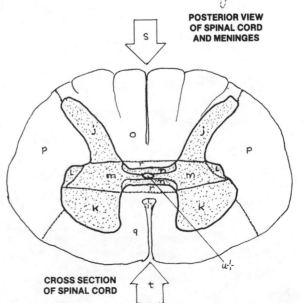

CROSS SECTION OF SPINAL CORD

PLATE 126
see also 125, 124, 105, 123, 122

NERVOUS SYSTEM
ASCENDING (SENSORY) TRACTS*

CN 3

1. Color the various orders of neurons for each of the four pathways shown. Complete each pathway and its titles before going on to the next.
2. Note that the spinocerebeller tracts (c², c³) each pass through their respective superior/inferior cerebellar peduncle (e, d). The middle cerebellar peduncles are not shown.

PAIN PATHWAY a

SENSORY NEURON (1ST ORDER) a'
LATERAL SPINOTHALAMIC TRACT (2ND O.) a²
THALAMUS *'
THALAMOCORTICAL TRACT (3RD O.) a³
POST CENTRAL GYRUS *²

Pain/temperature receptors generate an impulse that travels to the spinal cord through a *sensory neuron* whose central process enters the posterior horn and synapses with the *2nd order neuron* (association neuron belonging to a sensory pathway or system) whose axon crosses the anterior white commissure to enter the lateral funiculus and turn upward. Collections of such fibers in the lateral funiculus constitute the *lateral spinothalamic tract,* which ascends to the *thalamus.* There the 2nd order neuron synapses with relay neurons whose axons traverse the internal capsule and corona radiata to reach the *postcentral gyrus* of the cerebral cortex. Axons of the anterior spinothalamic tract (not shown) convey sensations of light touch.

TOUCH/PRESSURE PATHWAY b

SENSORY NEURON (1ST ORDER) b'
(IN FASCICULI CUNEATUS b", GRACILIS b''')
NUCLEUS CUNEATUS/GRACILIS (MEDULLA) b²
INTERNAL ARCUATE FIBERS (2ND O.) b³
MEDIAL LEMNISCUS (2ND O.) b⁴
THALAMUS *'
THALAMOCORTICAL TRACT (3RD O.) b⁵
POSTCENTRAL GYRUS *²

Touch/pressure receptors generate an impulse that travels to the spinal cord through a *sensory neuron* whose central process enters the posterior horn, passes into the posterior funiculus, and ascends to the medulla. Collections of such fibers in the posterior funiculus constitute the *fasciculi cuneatus* (laterally) and *gracilis* (medially). The axons of these *1st order neurons* synapse with *2nd order neurons* in the *medulla* (nuclei cuneatus gracilis, b²). Their axons sweep to the opposite side (as *internal arcuate fibers*) to form a bundle called the *medial lemniscus,* which terminates in the thalamus. There these axons synapse with relay neurons (3rd order) whose axons reach for the *postcentral gyrus* of the cerebral cortex via the internal capsule and corona radiata. The fasciculus cuneatus is not present in the lower half of the spinal cord.

MUSCLE/POSITION SENSE PATHWAY c

SENSORY NEURON (1ST ORDER) c'
ANTERIOR SPINOCEREBELLAR TRACT c² (2ND O.) c
POSTERIOR SPINOCEREBELLAR TRACT c³
INFERIOR CEREBELLAR PEDUNCLE d
SUPERIOR CEREBELLAR PEDUNCLE e
CEREBELLUM (CORTEX) f*

Stretch receptors and position sense receptors generate impulses that travel to the spinal cord through *sensory neurons* whose central processes enter the gray matter. Tendon stretch impulses pass to a *second order neuron* (c³) whose axon turns to the lateral funiculus (posterior aspect) of the same side and ascends as part of the *posterior spinocerebellar tract.* Position sense impulses pass to a second order neuron (in the posterior horn) whose axon crosses to the opposite lateral funiculus (anterior side), bends upward and becomes part of the *anterior spinocerebellar tract* (c²). The posterior tract (c³) enters the *inferior cerebellar peduncle* and synapses with cells of the *cerebellum.* The anterior tract (c²) ascends to and enters the *superior cerebellar peduncle* to synapse with cells of the cerebellum.

FRONTAL SECTION
(through thalamus)

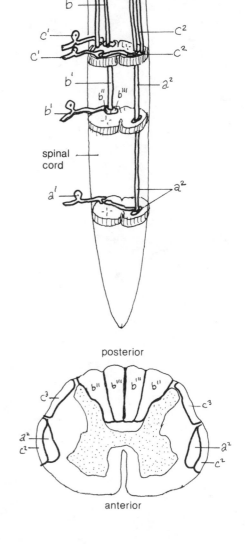

cerebellum

spinal cord

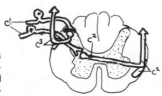

posterior

anterior

PLATE 127
see also 121–126

NERVOUS SYSTEM
DESCENDING (MOTOR) TRACTS*

CN 14

1. Color in the four descending pathways (g, h, i, j) one at a time from beginning to end, including the lower illustration (cross section of spinal cord.

2. Begin with lateral corticospinal tract (g, dotted). For easy identification, color it black and simultaneously color the structures of the brain (a–f) through which it passes.

PRECENTRAL GYRUS a
CORONA RADIATA b
INTERNAL CAPSULE c
CEREBRAL PEDUNCLE d
PONS e
MEDULLARY PYRAMIDS f
(DECUSSATION) f'
LATERAL CORTICOSPINAL TRACT g•
ANTERIOR CORTICOSPINAL TRACT h
MEDIAL RETICULOSPINAL i
LATERAL RETICULOSPINAL j
ASSOCIATION NEURON k

FINAL COMMON PATHWAY L
(MOTOR NEURON) L
FACILITATING EFFECT m
INHIBITING EFFECT n
EFFECTOR o

There are basically two long descending tracts or tract systems of the CNS (that is, tracts that pass through both brainstem and spinal cord): one goes through the pyramids of the medulla (corticospinal or pyramidal tract) and one does not (extrapyramidal tract of which the reticulospinal tracts are a part). The corticospinal tract commences with upper motor neurons whose cell bodies are located in the *precentral gyrus* of the frontal cortex. Axons of these upper motor neurons make up part of the *corona radiata, internal capsule,* and *cerebral peduncles* in their descent. Passing through the *pons* without interruption, these axons form the *pyramids* on the anterior surface of the *medulla*. 80% of these fibers *decussate* (cross) to the opposite side just below the pyramids to form the *lateral corticospinal tract* in the lateral funiculus of the spinal cord. The other 20% do not cross and form the *anterior corticospinal tract* on the same side as the originating cell bodies and the motor neurons with which they will synapse. Axons of the lateral (and anterior) spinothalamic tract enter the gray matter of the spinal cord at the appropriate level and synapse with the *motor neurons* of the anterior horn, or with their intermediaries, the *association neurons*. This pathway is responsible for generating voluntary, skilled, and discrete movements from skeletal muscle activity.

The extrapyramidal pathways are myriad and complex. They involve a multitude of polysynaptic networks from basal nuclei to spinal cord. Some of the results of their activities (facilitation/inhibition) are brought to bear upon the anterior horn (and lateral horn) motor neurons. The *reticulospinal tracts* are some of the pathways that conduct facilitating and inhibiting influences to the lower motor neurons resulting in the generation of unconscious, imprecise, postural adjustments; conscious, learned reflexes basic to everyday activities (eating, walking); and minute changes in muscle tone (resistance to stretch). The cerebral cortex, basal nuclei, brainstem nuclei, and the cerebellum all feed impulses into this descending system.

The medial tract arises among neurons in the medulla; the lateral tract arises from neurons in the deep pons. These neurons are subjected to direct inputs from the brainstem network of polysynaptic neurons (reticular formation). Passing into the anterior and lateral funiculi of the spinal cord, these reticulospinal tracts enter the gray matter at the appropriate levels to terminate about motor and intermediate neurons.

These and many other tracts rain down upon motor neurons of the anterior horn. The result of their *facilitory* and *inhibitory* influences is conducted through these motor neurons to the *effector:* skeletal muscle. These lower *motor neurons* are the *final common pathway* for the ultimate expression of all nervous activity: muscular contraction.

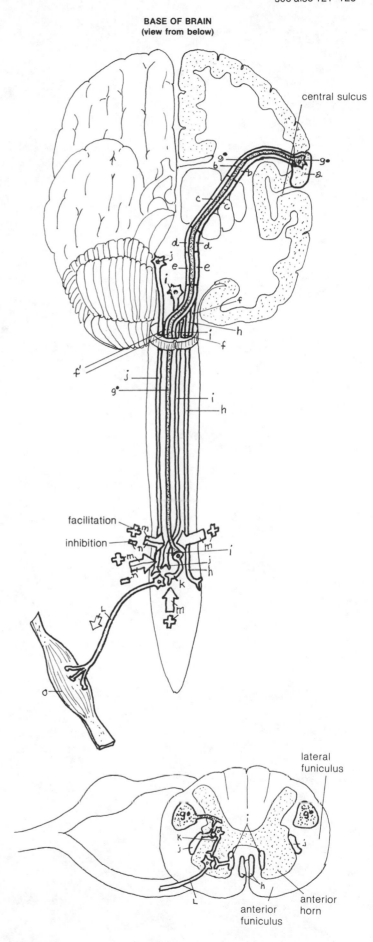

BASE OF BRAIN
(view from below)

central sulcus

facilitation

inhibition

lateral funiculus

anterior funiculus

anterior horn

NERVOUS SYSTEM
SPINAL NERVES d

PLATE 128
see also 116, 114, 115, 119, 125

CN 9

1. Color all three illustrations simultaneously. In the upper draw-ing, color the two pairs of nerves passing through the vertebral column as well as the exposed nerve and its roots above.
2. In the lower drawing, the motor cell bodies (i) are outlined by a dotted line to suggest their concealed position in the anterior horn of the spinal cord. Color them a different color from the cord (a) itself.
3. Use the colors used on similar structures on Plate 115 under different identification letters. Note that dorsal root ganglion (g), sensory cell bodies (h) and motor cell bodies (i) receive separate colors on this plate (on Plate 115 they received the color of the entire axon).
4. Autonomic neurons and their relations to spinal nerves are not included on this plate.

SPINAL CORD a
GRAY MATTER b*
WHITE MATTER c

SPINAL NERVES d
DORSAL (POSTERIOR) ROOT e
SENSORY AXONS f
DORSAL ROOT GANGLION g
SENSORY CELL BODIES h
MOTOR CELL BODIES (IN CNS) i
VENTRAL (ANTERIOR) ROOT j
MOTOR AXONS k

Spinal nerves are collections of axons in the peripheral nervous system. The roots of spinal nerves arise from the spinal cord. Each axon of a spinal nerve is part of a sensory or motor neuron. Most spinal nerves and their branches include the axons of both sensory and motor (mixed) neurons. There are about 31 pairs of spinal nerves issuing from the spinal cord bilaterally and sequen-tially (segmentally). The mixed axons of spinal nerve branches form a pattern of innervation in touch with virtually every musculo-skeletal, fascial, and skin area in the body. The *sensory axons* (peripheral processes) within the spinal nerve head toward the spinal cord from peripheral areas of the body. As they approach the cord within the tunnel of the intervertebral foramen, the axons bend dorsally to form the *dorsal (sensory) root* of the spinal nerve. Within that root the unipolar *cell bodies* of the sensory neurons form a distinct swelling: the *dorsal root ganglion.* The central processes of these sensory neurons continue on into the poste-rior horn of the spinal cord where they synapse or bend to enter the white matter. The *motor axons* within the spinal nerve arise from multipolar *motor cell bodies* within the anterior horn of the spinal cord. Collections of these axons form the *ventral root* of the spinal nerve. The ventral and dorsal roots emerge from inter-vertebral foramen or vertebral canal to form the spinal nerves.

Through the vehicle of peripheral nerves (spinal and cranial): (1) information concerning the dynamic state of one's external and internal environment and the spatial orientation of the body in that environment is conveyed to the central nervous system, and (2) appropriate motor responses can be forwarded from the central nervous system to effectors (muscle) for action.

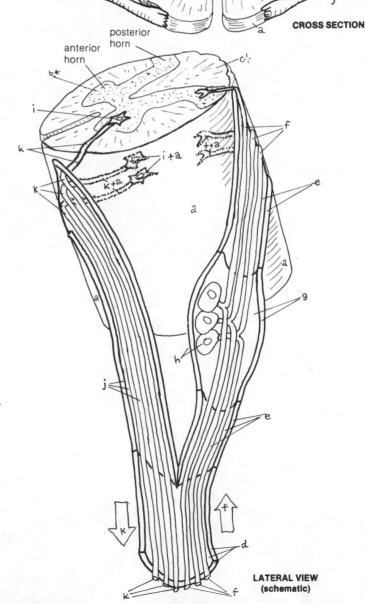

ANTERIOR-LATERAL VIEW

intervertebral foramen

CROSS SECTION

posterior horn
anterior horn

LATERAL VIEW
(schematic)

CN 14

1. Color the coverings of the peripheral nerve first. Notice the axon (and its covering of endoneurium) protruding from the nerve.
2. Color the surrounding muscles (o) in a light brown, and the superficial fascia in yellow, if colors approximating their natural color are desired. Leave the outer rim of skin uncolored.
3. Color e, f, and g the colors they received on Plate 128 under different identification letters.

COVERINGS OF PERIPHERAL NERVE*

EPINEURIUM a
PERINEURIUM b
ENDONEURIUM c
AXON d

TYPICAL THORACIC SPINAL NERVE*

DORSAL ROOT e
VENTRAL ROOT f
SPINAL NERVE g
POSTERIOR RAMUS h
MUSCULAR BRANCH i
CUTANEOUS DIVISION j
ANTERIOR RAMUS k
MUSCULAR BRANCHES l
LAT. CUTANEOUS DIVISION m
ANT. CUTANEOUS DIVISION n

RELATED STRUCTURES*

SKELETAL MUSCLES o
SUPERFICIAL FASCIA p
SKIN q -/-

Spinal nerves and their branches consist of axons of sensory and motor neurons intricately bound in fibrous connective tissue: delicate, fine collagenous fibers (*endoneurium*) surround each axon and its immediate coverings (myelin and/or neurilemma); thicker fibrous tissue (*perineurium*) ensheathes each of the bundles of axons within the nerve; and the fibrous *epineurium* binds all the bundles together in a single unit, the peripheral nerve. These fibrous layers physically support the axons as well as their nutrient capillaries. The epineurium is adjacent to and continuous with the surrounding deep or superficial fascia.

Each spinal nerve breaks up into a fairly typical pattern of distribution after leaving the spinal cord. Essentially, the spinal nerve, formed from *dorsal* and *ventral* roots, splits into anterior and posterior *rami* (large branches). Each of these has a number of smaller *muscular* branches and *cutaneous* branches. The muscular branches supply skeletal muscle with motor fibers, smooth muscle of arteries with autonomic motor fibers, and sensory fibers for various receptors associated with muscles and tendons. The *cutaneous* branches supply the overlying skin and fascia with sensory fibers for receptors and motor (autonomic) fibers for the smooth muscle of cutaneous arteries, erector-of-the-hair (smooth) muscles, and sweat glands. The posterior ramus supplies the back (deep) muscles and the overlying skin and fascia; the anterior ramus covers the rest of the body. Note how the anterior ramus courses between muscle layers, supplies them with muscular branches, and then gives off cutaneous divisions whose branches ramify in the superficial fascia and reach for the skin. Note further the potential for overlap among the cutaneous branches ensuring that no area of skin is without sensory receptors. The plan you have colored here applies only to the thoracic and abdominal walls. In the limbs, the pattern is basically similar except that the anterior rami form plexuses of nerves from which muscular and cutaneous branches emerge in a definite pattern (see next two plates).

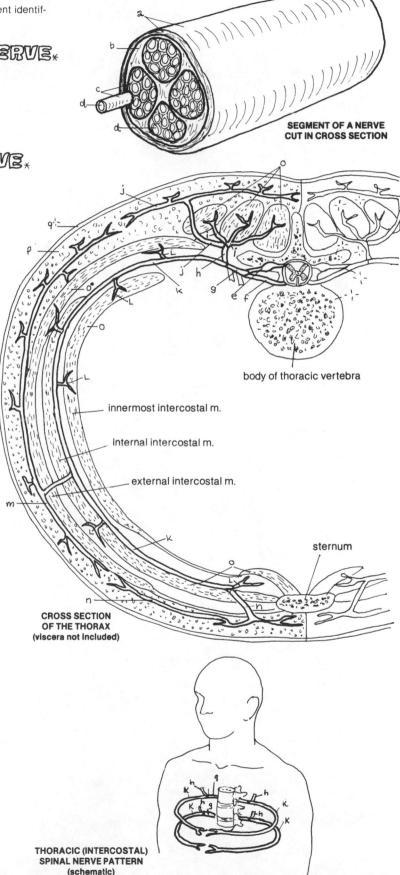

SEGMENT OF A NERVE
CUT IN CROSS SECTION

body of thoracic vertebra

innermost intercostal m.

internal intercostal m.

external intercostal m.

sternum

CROSS SECTION
OF THE THORAX
(viscera not included)

THORACIC (INTERCOSTAL)
SPINAL NERVE PATTERN
(schematic)

PLATE 130
see also 116, 128, 132

NERVOUS SYSTEM
NERVES TO THE UPPER LIMB*
BRACHIAL PLEXUS*

CN 9

1. Color the various parts of the diagram of the brachial plexus (a–d), coloring the posterior cord and related divisions (c² and d³ dotted areas) a little lighter than the others. The dotted nerves lie deeper (more posterior) than the other parts of the plexus. Do not color the unlettered, untitled branches of the plexus.
2. Color the terminal nerves leaving the plexus (the dotted area which is colored gray) and their route in the view of the entire limb below.

BRACHIAL PLEXUS*
ROOTS (5): C5-T1 a
TRUNKS (3): UPPER b¹ MIDDLE b² LOWER b³
DIVISIONS (6): 3 ANTERIOR c¹ 3 POSTERIOR c²
CORDS (3): LATERAL d¹ MEDIAL d² POSTERIOR d³

TERMINAL NERVES*
MUSCULOCUTANEOUS N. e
AXILLARY N. f
RADIAL N. g
MEDIAN N. h ROOTS h¹
ULNAR N. i

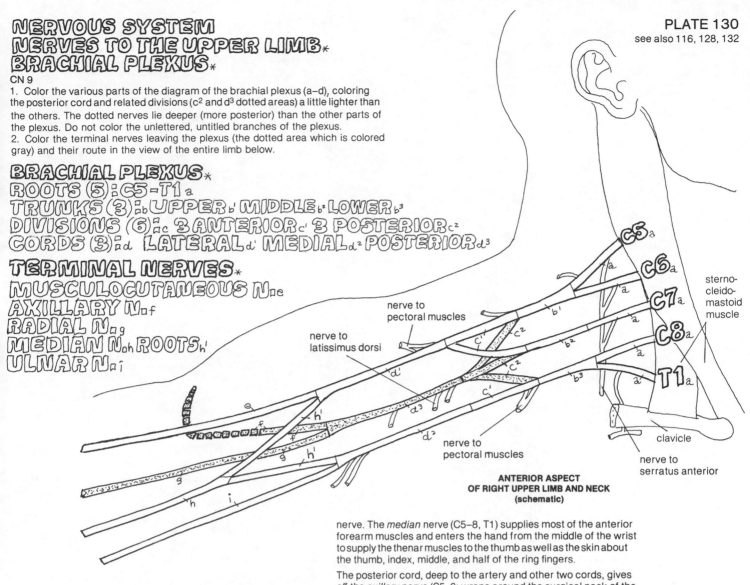

nerve to pectoral muscles
nerve to latissimus dorsi
nerve to pectoral muscles
sterno-cleido-mastoid muscle
clavicle
nerve to serratus anterior

**ANTERIOR ASPECT
OF RIGHT UPPER LIMB AND NECK
(schematic)**

The nerves supplying the musculoskeletal structures of the upper limb are derived from the anterior rami of the 5th–8th cervical and 1st thoracic spinal nerves (C5–T1). These anterior rami form a network or pattern in the neck called the *brachial plexus* found buried among the deep muscles of the lateral neck, under the clavicle and in the axillary space below the shoulder. In the axilla, three cords are formed about the axillary artery: the lateral supplies the lateral aspect of the limb and some of the superficial muscles of the back, the medial supplies the anterior aspect of the limb, and the posterior supplies the posterior aspect of the limb including two muscles of the superficial back. Major nerves of the lateral cord are the *musculocutaneous* (C5, 6, 7; supplying muscles of the anterior aspect of the arm including biceps brachii and becoming the lateral cutaneous nerve of the forearm) and a contribution to the median nerve. The major nerves of the medial cord are the *ulnar* (C8, T1; passing down the arm to the medial epicondyle and into the medial side of the anterior forearm to supply two muscles nearby and on into the hand to supply the hypothenar and deep muscles as well as the skin about the little (5th) and half of the ring (4th) fingers) and a contribution to the median

nerve. The *median* nerve (C5–8, T1) supplies most of the anterior forearm muscles and enters the hand from the middle of the wrist to supply the thenar muscles to the thumb as well as the skin about the thumb, index, middle, and half of the ring fingers.

The posterior cord, deep to the artery and other two cords, gives off the *axillary* nerve (C5, 6; wraps around the surgical neck of the humerus to supply deltoid and teres minor) and the *radial* (C5–8, T1; supplies triceps brachii, takes a half turn about the humerus, and passes into the posterior forearm to supply brachioradialis and other muscles [mostly extensors] in that region).

Nerves that pass close to the surface or around a bone are often candidates for injury: radial nerve close to the mid-humerus (fracture there can harm the nerve resulting in wrist drop), axillary nerve around the surgical neck of the humerus (fracture there can lacerate nerve resulting in loss of deltoid), median nerve often just deep to the skin of the anterior wrist (deep laceration can go through nerve resulting in sensory deficits in fingers and partial reduction in thumb mobility), and the ulnar nerve passing round the medial epicondyle (fracture there can harm the nerve resulting in a partial clawlike configuration of the hand, especially with respect to fingers 4 and 5).

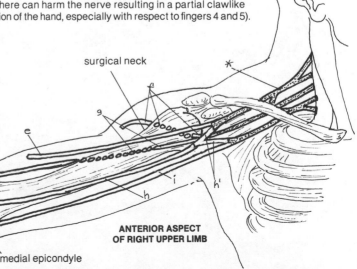

surgical neck

medial epicondyle

**ANTERIOR ASPECT
OF RIGHT UPPER LIMB**

NERVOUS SYSTEM
NERVES TO THE LOWER LIMB*

CN 14

1. Note that the roots of the lumbar and sacral plexuses are to be colored in 2 shades of gray.

LUMBAR PLEXUS a*
FEMORAL N. b
OBTURATOR N. c
LATERAL FEMORAL CUTANEOUS N. d
LUMBOSACRAL TRUNK e

SACRAL PLEXUS f•
SUPERIOR GLUTEAL N. g
INFERIOR GLUTEAL N. h
PUDENDAL N. i
SCIATIC N. j
POSTERIOR FEMORAL CUTANEOUS N. k
TIBIAL N. l
MED./LAT. PLANTAR N. m
COMMON PERONEAL N. n
SUPERFICIAL PERONEAL N. o
DEEP PERONEAL N. p

PLATE 131
see also 116, 128, 132

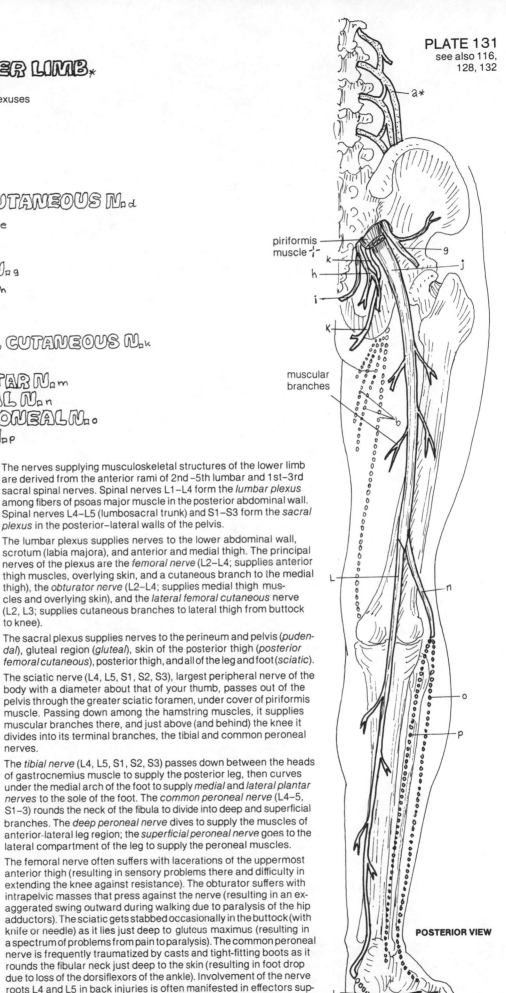

piriformis muscle

muscular branches

POSTERIOR VIEW

The nerves supplying musculoskeletal structures of the lower limb are derived from the anterior rami of 2nd–5th lumbar and 1st–3rd sacral spinal nerves. Spinal nerves L1–L4 form the *lumbar plexus* among fibers of psoas major muscle in the posterior abdominal wall. Spinal nerves L4–L5 (lumbosacral trunk) and S1–S3 form the *sacral plexus* in the posterior–lateral walls of the pelvis.

The lumbar plexus supplies nerves to the lower abdominal wall, scrotum (labia majora), and anterior and medial thigh. The principal nerves of the plexus are the *femoral nerve* (L2–L4; supplies anterior thigh muscles, overlying skin, and a cutaneous branch to the medial thigh), the *obturator nerve* (L2–L4; supplies medial thigh muscles and overlying skin), and the *lateral femoral cutaneous* nerve (L2, L3; supplies cutaneous branches to lateral thigh from buttock to knee).

The sacral plexus supplies nerves to the perineum and pelvis (*pudendal*), gluteal region (*gluteal*), skin of the posterior thigh (*posterior femoral cutaneous*), posterior thigh, and all of the leg and foot (*sciatic*).

The sciatic nerve (L4, L5, S1, S2, S3), largest peripheral nerve of the body with a diameter about that of your thumb, passes out of the pelvis through the greater sciatic foramen, under cover of piriformis muscle. Passing down among the hamstring muscles, it supplies muscular branches there, and just above (and behind) the knee it divides into its terminal branches, the tibial and common peroneal nerves.

The *tibial nerve* (L4, L5, S1, S2, S3) passes down between the heads of gastrocnemius muscle to supply the posterior leg, then curves under the medial arch of the foot to supply *medial* and *lateral plantar* nerves to the sole of the foot. The *common peroneal nerve* (L4–5, S1–3) rounds the neck of the fibula to divide into deep and superficial branches. The *deep peroneal nerve* dives to supply the muscles of anterior-lateral leg region; the *superficial peroneal nerve* goes to the lateral compartment of the leg to supply the peroneal muscles.

The femoral nerve often suffers with lacerations of the uppermost anterior thigh (resulting in sensory problems there and difficulty in extending the knee against resistance). The obturator suffers with intrapelvic masses that press against the nerve (resulting in an exaggerated swing outward during walking due to paralysis of the hip adductors). The sciatic gets stabbed occasionally in the buttock (with knife or needle) as it lies just deep to gluteus maximus (resulting in a spectrum of problems from pain to paralysis). The common peroneal nerve is frequently traumatized by casts and tight-fitting boots as it rounds the fibular neck just deep to the skin (resulting in foot drop due to loss of the dorsiflexors of the ankle). Involvement of the nerve roots L4 and L5 in back injuries is often manifested in effectors supplied by those roots (resulting in pain down to the foot and even foot drop).

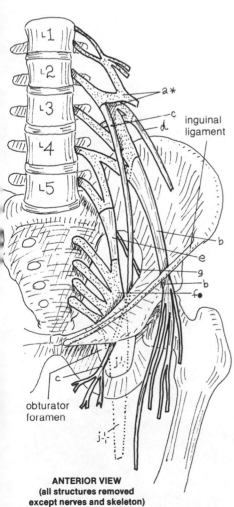

inguinal ligament

obturator foramen

ANTERIOR VIEW
(all structures removed except nerves and skeleton)

PLATE 132
see also 129, 130, 131, 116

NERVOUS SYSTEM
DERMATOMES*

CN 4

1. Color the complete titles below in four separate colors. Then color the corresponding dermatomes in both front and back figures. While coloring each of the four sets, keep in mind the plexuses (cervical, C1–C4; brachial C5–T1; lumbar L1–L4; sacral, L5–S3) and intercostal nerves that give off most of the nerves supplying these dermatomal areas. Dermatomes of the back from C2–C4, T2–L2, and S3–S5 are supplied by posterior rami of those spinal nerves.
2. Use contrasting colors for adjacent sets (cervical, thoracic, and so on) of dermatomes to emphasize the borders between them. You may wish to alternate the bands T2 through T12 with a dark and light application of that color.
3. Note that the face is not to be colored as it is supplied by the trigeminal nerve (cranial V) and not one of the segmental spinal nerves. Its sensory pattern can be seen on the following plate.

DORSAL ROOTS OF CERVICAL NERVES C2 - C8

DORSAL ROOTS OF THORACIC NERVES T1 - T12

DORSAL ROOTS OF LUMBAR NERVES L1 - L5

DORSAL ROOTS OF SACRAL NERVES S1 - S5

An area of skin (cutaneous area) whose sensory receptors/ axons feed into a single dorsal root of a spinal nerve is called a *dermatome*. This human dermatomal map is derived from a number of experimental, clinical, and surgical experiences. There is, by no means, universal agreement as to the precise area covered by one dorsal root. This is largely due to the considerable overlap that occurs between adjacent dermatomes (as many as 3 or 4 dorsal roots may receive inputs from a single dermatome). Still, such a map of dermatomes is a valuable asset to the clinician concerned with complaints of pain and reduced loss of sensations. The answer to the question "where does it hurt?" is applied to the physician's awareness of dermatomes. Certain nerve injuries and CNS diseases are reflected in exaggerated/diminished sensations in specific dermatomes. Visceral pain, such as appendicitis, inflammation of the gall bladder, and obstructive stones in the urinary tract are frequently "referred" to specific cutaneous areas. This phenomenon of referred pain is based on the fact that both visceral and cutaneous areas are served by the spinal cord; inevitably, certain viscera and dermatomes share a *common* spinal cord segment. For reasons that are not yet clear, the brain may interpret as cutaneous pain that which is, in fact, visceral pain. Thus kidney pain may be referred to dermatomes T10–T11, and inflammation of the pleura over the diaphragm (innervated by the phrenic nerve [C3–C5]) may be referred to the tip of the shoulder (dermatomes C3–C5), and spasms of heart muscle (supplied with sensory axons from T1–T5) may be referred to cutaneous areas of the left medial arm (T2 dermatome). While coloring the dermatomes, note that (1) the 1st cervical nerve has no dermatome, for it essentially has no dorsal root; (2) the C4 and T2 dermatomes appear to overlap on the chest wall because dermatomes C5 to T1 are essentially committed to the upper limbs; (3) the L2–S2, and L3–S3 dermatomes appear to overlap because dermatomes L3 to S2 are essentially committed to the lower limbs.

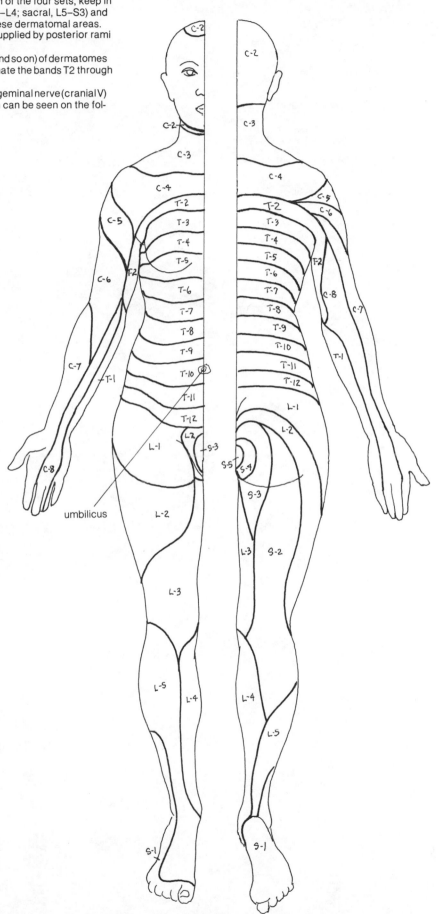

umbilicus

PLATE 133
see also 116

NERVOUS SYSTEM
CRANIAL NERVES*

CN 12

1. Use each of the 12 colors to color the title, the nerve, the functional drawings, and the Roman numerals in their three locations. Also include the arrows in the large illustration; these indicate whether they are primarily motor (pointing away) or sensory (pointing toward) or both.
2. Before coloring each nerve, read the summary of function. Due to space limitations, only major functions are mentioned.

OLFACTORY I
OPTIC II
OCULOMOTOR III
TROCHLEAR IV
TRIGEMINAL V
ABDUCENS VI
FACIAL VII
VESTIBULOCOCHLEAR VIII
GLOSSOPHARYNGEAL IX
VAGUS X
ACCESSORY XI
HYPOGLOSSAL XII

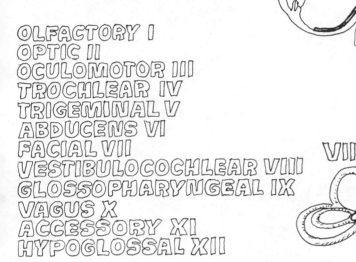

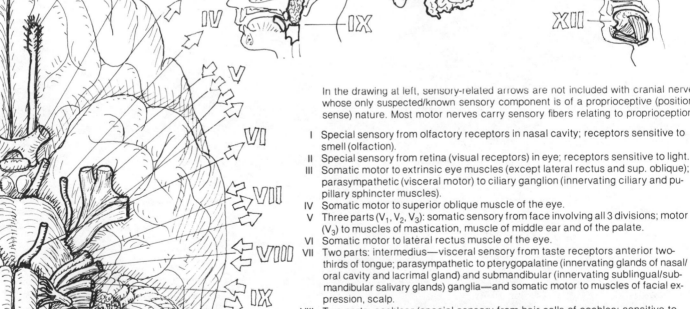

In the drawing at left, sensory-related arrows are not included with cranial nerves whose only suspected/known sensory component is of a proprioceptive (position sense) nature. Most motor nerves carry sensory fibers relating to proprioception.

I Special sensory from olfactory receptors in nasal cavity; receptors sensitive to smell (olfaction).

II Special sensory from retina (visual receptors) in eye; receptors sensitive to light.

III Somatic motor to extrinsic eye muscles (except lateral rectus and sup. oblique); parasympathetic (visceral motor) to ciliary ganglion (innervating ciliary and pupillary sphincter muscles).

IV Somatic motor to superior oblique muscle of the eye.

V Three parts (V_1, V_2, V_3): somatic sensory from face involving all 3 divisions; motor (V_3) to muscles of mastication, muscle of middle ear and of the palate.

VI Somatic motor to lateral rectus muscle of the eye.

VII Two parts: intermedius—visceral sensory from taste receptors anterior two-thirds of tongue; parasympathetic to pterygopalatine (innervating glands of nasal/oral cavity and lacrimal gland) and submandibular (innervating sublingual/submandibular salivary glands) ganglia—and somatic motor to muscles of facial expression, scalp.

VIII Two parts: cochlear (special sensory from hair cells of cochlea; sensitive to sound); vestibular (special sensory from inner ear equilibrium receptors).

IX Visceral sensory from taste receptors posterior one-third of tongue; general sensory from mucosa about posterior tongue and tonsils; special sensory from carotid sinus (at bifurcation of common carotid) sensitive to blood pressure; parasympathetic to otic ganglion (innervating parotid salivary gland); motor to 2 muscles of pharynx.

X General sensory from part of ear and auditory meatus; visceral sensory (except pain) from pharynx, larynx, trachea, esophagus, thoracic and abdominal viscera; parasympathetic to ganglia innervating thoracic and abdominal viscera; motor to pharynx and larynx.

XI Two parts: spinal (motor to sternocleidomastoid and trapezius muscles) and cranial (joins vagus to innervate larynx).

XII Motor to extrinsic and intrinsic muscles of tongue.

PLATE 134

NERVOUS SYSTEM
AUTONOMIC NERVOUS SYSTEM.
SYMPATHETIC DIVISION.

CN 8

1. Work this plate with the next two, using the same colors.
2. Color structure g white or light gray; color h a darker gray.
3. Carefully color the splanchnic nerves (i), which link the sympathetic chain (d) to the prevertebral ganglia (e) in the drawing to the far right and in the region marked 3 below.

PREGANGLIONIC CELL BODY LOCATIONS (T1-L2) a¹
PREGANGLIONIC CELL BODIES a
PREGANGLIONIC AXONS b
POST GANGLIONIC CELL BODIES c
SYMPATHETIC CHAIN OF GANGLIA d
PREVERTEBRAL GANGLIA e
POSTGANGLIONIC AXONS f

WHITE RAMUS COMMUNICANS g *
GRAY RAMUS COMMUNICANS h ●
SPLANCHNIC N. i

The autonomic nervous system (ANS) is that part of the peripheral nervous system (PNS) that innervates smooth muscle and glands of visceral organs as well as the cardiac muscle of the heart. Thus it is a motor system. It functions largely independent of your will; it is autonomic, not automatic. The ANS is segregated from the rest of the PNS (in terms of classification) on structural as well as functional grounds: the CNS-to-effector pathway involves two neurons. The first (preganglionic) neuron arises in the CNS, as you would suspect. Its axon travels to a peripheral ganglion where it synapses with the second (postganglionic) neuron, whose axon proceeds to the effector. Since sensory neurons of visceral organs are structurally/functionally no different than their somatic counterparts, they are not considered part of the ANS. In effect, sensory neurons of visceral organs and the ANS constitute a visceral nervous system.

The ANS consists of two divisions: sympathetic and parasympathetic. The sympathetic division is concerned with responses to fight/flight situations, making possible dilation of the pupil, increased heart and respiratory rates, increased blood flow to skeletal muscles, sweating, and other reactions appropriate to such emergencies. The parasympathetic division is more concerned with vegetative reactions, similar to those experienced following a large meal. These enhance digestion and absorption of nutrients (increased secretomotor activity), draining of the urinary bladder, reduced heart/respiratory rates, and shunting of blood from skeletal muscle to digestive viscera. Structurally, a major difference between the two divisions lies in the position of the ganglia and how the nerves get to and leave them. Concentrating on the *sympathetic division*: the *cell bodies* of the *preganglionic neurons* (a^1) are in the lateral horns of the spinal cord from *T1* through *L2* (a) only (thus the sympathetic division is also known as the thoracolumbar division). Their *axons* (b) pass through the anterior roots of the spinal nerves T1–L2, join the axons of the spinal nerves, and then abruptly turn into the *sympathetic chain of ganglia* (d) located along and outside the vertebral column from C1 to the coccyx. In doing this, they form the *white ramus communicans* (g); white because they are myelinated. Once in the chain, the preganglionic axon may take one of 3 options: (1) it can synapse with the *postganglionic cell body* (middle c) at the same level it entered; (2) it can move up/down the chain one or more segments to synapse with a postganglionic cell body (upper c); or (3) it can pass right through the chain without synapsing, form part of the *splanchnic nerve* (i) (a collection of sympathetic preganglionic axons) destined for cell bodies of postganglionic neurons (lower c) in *prevertebral ganglia* (e) located in front of the vertebral column in the abdominal cavity. The *axons of postganglionic neurons* (f) leave the chain via *gray rami communicans* (h) (unmyelinated) to join spinal nerves, or leave the chain directly to join blood vessels sharing a common destination of viscera (not shown on this plate—see f and f^1 next plate), or leave the prevertebral ganglia with neighboring blood vessels also traveling to a common destination, in this case, abdominal viscera. The next plate puts this division into a greater perspective.

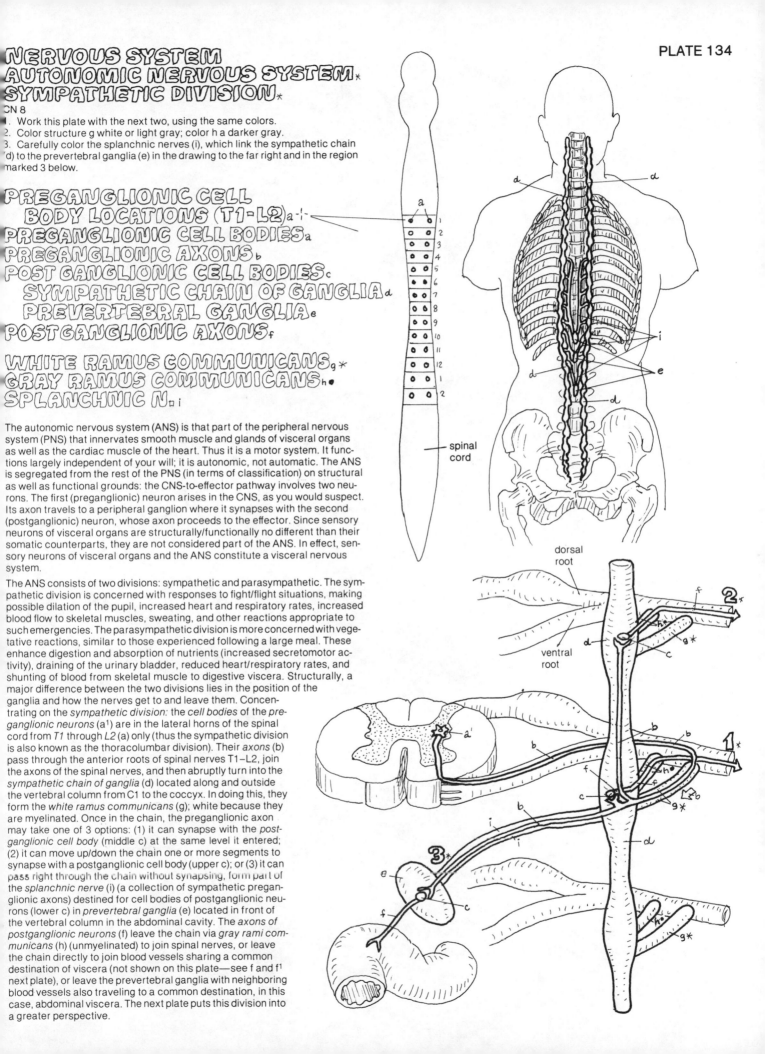

spinal cord

dorsal root

ventral root

PLATE 135
see also 134, 129, 104

NERVOUS SYSTEM
AUTONOMIC NERVOUS SYSTEM٭
SCHEME OF SYMPATHETIC DIVISION٭

CN 7

1. Orient yourself to this diagram: note that the spinal cord is in the middle with sympathetic chains on left and right sides. All connections of both chains are not shown (in the body, left and right chains are duplicates of one another; space considerations prevent us from duplicating them here). On the left, only those pathways to skin (f^2) are represented; on the right, pathways to head/neck and body cavities are shown.
2. Carefully color all structures of a single heading (in order from the uppermost title to the lowest) before going on to the next. Read the corresponding text as you color.
3. Note that the preganglionic axons (b) synapsing at prevertebral ganglia (e) are components of the splanchnic nerve (i) and receive both colors. Do not color the organs.

PREGANGLIONIC NEURONS٭
CELL BODIES a
AXONS b
SPLANCHNIC N. i

POSTGANGLIONIC NEURONS٭
CELL BODIES c
AXONS TO HEAD & NECK f
TO THORACIC VISCERA f'
TO SKIN: a f²
SWEAT GLANDS f²
ARRECTOR PILI f²
BLOOD VESSELS f²
TO ABDOMINAL VISCERA f³
TO PELVIC/PERINEAL VISC. n f⁴

SYMPATHETIC CHAIN d
PREVERTEBRAL GANGLIA e
SPINAL NERVES j٭

This plate concentrates primarily on postganglionic organization; the previous plate emphasized preganglionic structure. The postganglionic axons of this division have four basic regions to supply: head and neck, thorax, cutaneous areas, abdomen, and pelvis and perineum.

Consider the *postganglionic axons to the head/neck:* these axons (f) leave the sympathetic chain at the superior cervical ganglion, join carotid arteries (not shown) en route and supply dilator muscle in the iris, glands of the eye, nasal and oral cavities (reduction of secretion), smooth muscle of blood vessels (vasoconstriction), sweat glands (increase secretion), and arrector pili muscles (erect hairs on surface of skin).

Consider the *postganglionic axons to thoracic viscera:* these axons (f¹) leave the *chain* (d) directly to join/form the cardiac, pulmonary, and esophageal plexuses of nerves (not shown). The sympathetic axons of this mixed autonomic plexus supply the SA and AV nodes of the heart/coronary arteries (increased heart rate/coronary dilation), lungs and bronchi (vasodilation and bronchodilation), and esophagus (inhibited peristaltic activity).

Consider the *postganglionic axons to the skin:* these axons (f²) leave the chain via the gray rami (not shown) at each and every level of the spinal cord to join the spinal nerves (j). These axons will branch along with its somatic counterparts (not shown) to supply arteries associated with skeletal muscle (vasodilation) and cutaneous areas (increased sweat gland activity, erection of hairs, and vasoconstriction).

Consider the *postganglionic axons to abdominal viscera:* the *prevertebral ganglia* (e) consist of three major sets of cell bodies arranged about major branches of the abdominal aorta (not shown); the cell bodies are named relative to the neighboring artery. Preganglionic axons arrive at these gan-

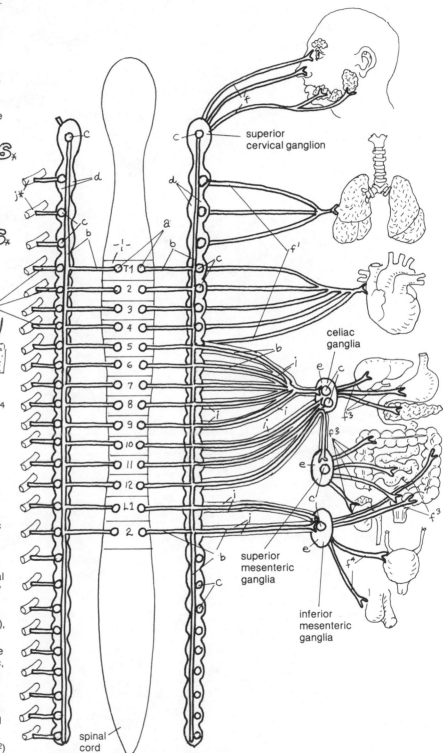

glia via *splanchnic nerves* (i). Postganglionic axons (f³) leave each of the three ganglia to supply the smooth muscle and glands of the viscera indicated as well as the smooth muscle of their arteries (reduced peristalsis and glandular secretion, increased sphincter activity, and vasoconstriction).

The *postganglionic axons to the pelvis and perineum* (f⁴) leave the inferior mesenteric ganglia in a downward direction to a network of autonomic fibers (not shown) from which axons reach for the smooth muscle, glands, and vascular smooth muscle of the lower intestinal tract, pelvic and perineal organs.

superior cervical ganglion

celiac ganglia

superior mesenteric ganglia

inferior mesenteric ganglia

spinal cord

PLATE 136
see also 135, 133

NERVOUS SYSTEM
AUTONOMIC NERVOUS SYSTEM *
SCHEME OF PARASYMPATHETIC DIVISION *

CN 4

1. This diagram shows the parasympathetic scheme on one side of the body only. Note that there are preganglionic cell bodies in both cranial and sacral areas.

2. The text will follow the order of the titles. Color all structures of a single heading before going on to the next and read the corresponding parts of the text. Do not color the organs.

PREGANGLIONIC NEURONS: b
CELL BODIES a
AXONS WITH: III CRANIAL N. b¹
VII CRANIAL N. b² IX CRANIAL N. b³
X CRANIAL N. b⁴
AXONS FROM: S2, S3 & S4 b⁵

GANGLIA: e
CILIARY e¹
PTERYGOPALATINE e²
SUBMANDIBULAR e³
OTIC e⁴
INTRAMURAL e⁵

POSTGANGLIONIC AXONS: f
CELL BODIES c
AXONS TO: EYE f¹ NASAL/ORAL
CAVITIES f² SALIVARY
GLANDS f³ THORACIC/ABDOM-
INAL VISCERA f⁴ PELVIC/
PERINEAL VISCERA f⁵

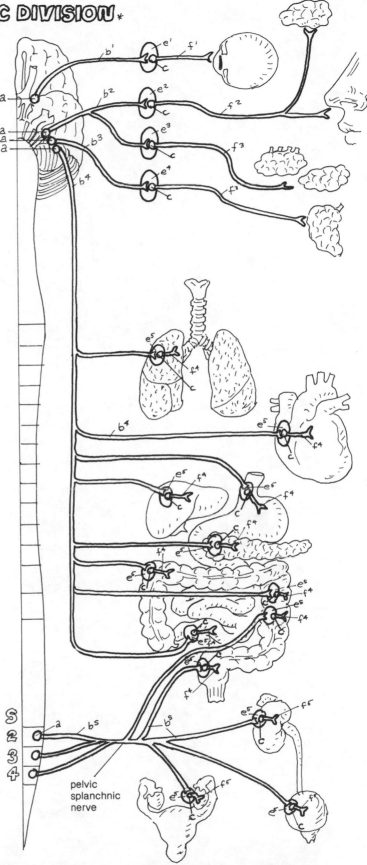

Parasympathetic *preganglionic neurons* arise in the brainstem and in the sacral part of the spinal cord. In the head region, the preganglionic axons join with somatic axons of the oculomotor (*III*), facial (*VII*), and glossopharyngeal (*IX*) cranial nerves to reach their ganglia. Preganglionic fibers of the vagus (*X*) pass down the neck to the larynx, trachea, bronchi, and below (as shown) to the level of the descending colon. Their ganglia are located in the visceral organs they supply. In the thorax, the vagal fibers join with the sympathetics in the cardiac and pulmonary plexuses (not shown) and disperse. The vagal fibers remaining form a plexus about the esophagus (not shown) to go through the diaphragm and enter the abdomen where they form a mix with sympathetics about the prevertebral ganglia, from which they follow arteries to the organs they supply. *Sacral* preganglionic axons, arising from cell bodies in the lateral horns of the spinal cord (segments S2 through S4) leave via the anterior roots, join the spinal nerves for a few millimeters, then bend away toward the pelvic interior. Collections of these nerves constitute the pelvic splanchnic nerves that form a plexus with the sympathetic axons (from the inferior mesenteric ganglia) on the rectum. The axons then follow the arteries to the viscera they supply.

The parasympathetic *ganglia* of the head are discrete bodies slightly smaller than the head of a pin. The *ciliary ganglion* is located just behind the eyeball, the *pterygopalatine ganglion* is located in the lateral wall of the nasal cavity near the nasopharynx; the *otic ganglion* is located in the infratemporal fossa just deep to the vertical portion of the mandible; and the *submandibular ganglion* is located deep to the submandibular salivary gland under the mandible. The *intramural ganglia* (associated with the vagus and sacral preganglionics), located in the submucosa and muscular tunics of visceral organs, are of microscopic dimensions. From these masses of cell bodies issue the short postganglionic axons.

Postganglionic axons to the eye supply the ciliary muscle of the eye (alters lens shape) and the pupillary sphincter (reduces the size of the pupil). Postganglionics from the pterygopalatine ganglion supply glands (increased secretion) of the *eye* and *nasal and oral cavities;* those fibers from the submandibular ganglion (both ganglia receive preganglionics from cranial nerve VII) supply the submandibular/sublingual *salivary glands* (increased secretion). Postganglionic axons from intramural ganglia in thoracic, abdominal, pelvic, and perineal viscera are very

short and supply the smooth muscle and glands (increased secretion/ muscular activity, decreased heart rate, bronchoconstriction) therein. You will note that the parasympathetics do not generally supply blood vessel musculature, sweat glands, and arrector pili muscles; therefore, they are not generally found in peripheral nerves as are sympathetic postganglionic axons.

pelvic
splanchnic
nerve

PLATE 137
see also 11, 135, 136

NERVOUS SYSTEM
VISUAL SYSTEM ∗ (1)

CN 21

1. Note the nature of the neighboring structures of this vertical section of the eye which are not to be colored. The 3-dimensional character of the eyeball can be appreciated by looking at Plate 139.
2. Use a light color for i, j, and j¹. Use red for h.

LAYERS OF THE EYE ∗

SCLERA a
  CORNEA a¹
CHOROID b
  CILIARY BODY c
    CILIARY PROCESSES c¹
    IRIS d
RETINA e
    FOVEA CENTRALIS f
OPTIC DISC g
    RETINAL ARTERIES h

SPACES / FLUIDS ∗

VITREOUS BODY i
AQUEOUS HUMOR j
  ANTERIOR CHAMBER j
  POSTERIOR CHAMBER j¹

LENS k
  SUSPENSORY LIGAMENT L
PUPIL m
CONJUNCTIVA n
OPTIC NERVE o
MUSCLES OF EYEBALL p

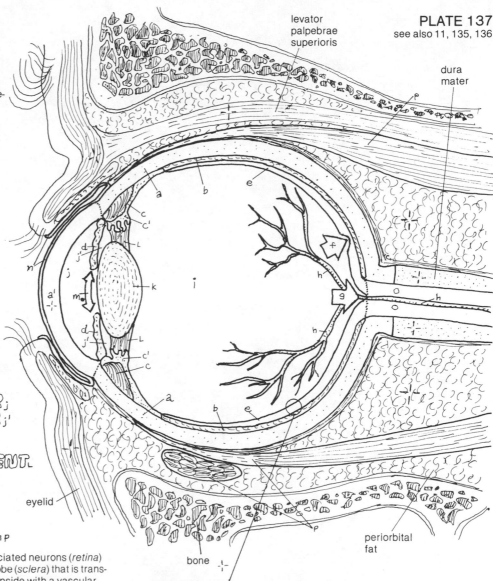

levator
palpebrae
superioris

dura
mater

eyelid

bone

periorbital
fat

The eye is a layer of photoreceptor cells and associated neurons (*retina*) packaged within a fibrous, rubberlike protective globe (*sclera*) that is transparent in front (*cornea*). The sclera is lined on the inside with a vascular, highly pigmented layer (*choroid*) that absorbs light and prevents scattering. Most of the other structures *within* the eyeball are concerned with light waves. Light, traveling in straight lines, must be bent (refracted) as it enters the eye (through the *pupil*) to converge on a focal point in front of the retina. The *cornea* (layers of fine fibers encapsulated with epithelial cells), *lens* (tightly packed epithelial cells with a high degree of elasticity), *vitreous humor* (a gel of water and mucoprotein), and *aqueous humor* (an extracellular fluid filling the anterior/posterior chambers of the eye) are the media that refract the light waves, listed here in order of their functional significance.

The choroid thickens anteriorly to form the *ciliary body* (pigmented connective tissue with smooth muscle fibers) from whose *processes* the *suspensory ligaments* are directed to the lens. These ligaments passively put a tension (circumferentially) on the lens, flattening it. The ciliary muscle of the ciliary body, acting under parasympathetic stimulation, takes the tension off the ciliary processes and suspensory ligaments, resulting in the lens rounding up due to its inherent elasticity and permitting close-up vision.

The *iris* is an extension of the ciliary body and forms a circular, adjustable rim about the lens. The space within the circular rim is the pupil. The diameter of the pupil may be altered by muscles in the iris that are oriented in two directions. The dilator pupillae muscle pulls the iris back toward the ciliary body, dilating the pupil; the sphincter pupillae muscle draws the iris down around the front of the lens, constricting the pupil. The color of the iris is largely a function of the amount of pigment within.

The retina consists of several layers of cell bodies (nuclear layer) and fibers (plexiform layers). The *rods* (highly sensitive to light and insensitive to color) and *cones* (sensitive to color and provide highest visual acuity) constitute the *photoreceptor neurons;* the rods generally hold a population edge of 20:1. An exception here occurs at the *fovea centralis* (a slight depression in a yellow, circular area of the retina), where only cone cells and related neurons appear. This point on the retina is in the optical pathway of direct light; thus the greatest visual acuity can be gained by looking directly at an object, under proper light. The *optic disc* (where optic nerve fibers stream to the outside behind the eyeball) is without rods/cones and is, in fact, a blind spot.

LAYERS OF RETINA ∗

INTERNAL LIMITING MEMBRANE e¹
AXONS (OPTIC N. FIBERS) o¹
GANGLION NEURONS q
BIPOLAR NEURONS r
PHOTORECEPTOR NEURONS ∗
  RODS s CONES t
PIGMENTED EPITHELIUM u
LIGHT RAYS ∗ NERVE IMPULSE ●

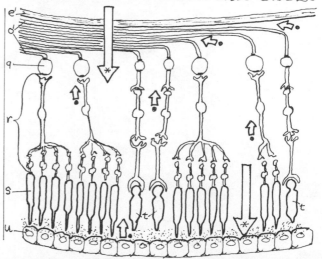

PLATE 138
see also 137, 72, 136

NERVOUS SYSTEM
VISUAL SYSTEM * (2)
CN 15

1. Color the upper illustration with the colors used on the preceding plate. Complete the entire illustration even though not all structures are identified on this plate.
2. Note that structure (n) is to be colored in both illustrations and with the same color.
3. Do not color arrows representing circulation of aqueous humor.
4. In lower illustration, the letter identifications refer to structures different from above. Color the directional arrows gray.

SECRETION/DRAINAGE OF AQUEOUS HUMOR

SCLERA a / CORNEA a'
CILIARY BODY c / PROCESSES c'
POSTERIOR CHAMBER j
IRIS d
ANTERIOR CHAMBER i
CANAL OF SCHLEMM v

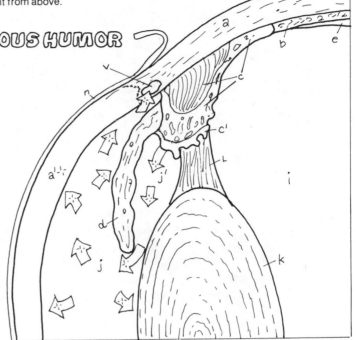

Aqueous humor (fluid) is an extracellular fluid, somewhat like cerebrospinal fluid in composition, secreted by epithelial cells of the *ciliary body* into the *posterior chamber* of the eye. The fluid circulates through the pupil into the *anterior chamber* to be absorbed by a small *canal of Schlemm* that circles the eye at the *iris-sclera* junction. The fluid is then absorbed by small veins connected to the canal. The rate of secretion of aqueous humor normally seems to be a function of the rate of absorption by the canal. The aqueous humor creates an intraocular pressure necessary for the mechanical stability of intraocular structure (lens, ciliary body, retina, and so on). It also provides nutrients for the avascular lens. On occasion, aqueous humor is not properly drained at the canal—possibly due to back pressure in the draining veins or an obstruction. An increase in intraocular pressure is generally created to such an extent that serious eye damage results over a period of time. This condition, glaucoma, can now be prevented by checking intraocular pressure with a tonometric device. Chemotherapy or surgical intervention can often restore proper circulation.

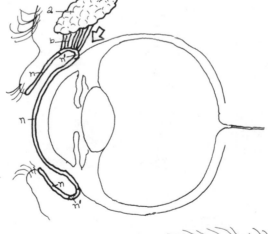

LACRIMAL APPARATUS *

LACRIMAL GLAND a
LACRIMAL DUCTS b
CONJUNCTIVA n FORNIX n'
LACRIMAL PUNCTA c
LACRIMAL CANALS d
LACRIMAL SAC e
NASOLACRIMAL DUCT f
INFERIOR MEATUS g
(NASAL CAVITY) g

The *lacrimal apparatus* provides a mechanism for secretion/drainage of fluid lubricating the movement of eyelids over the cornea. The inner surface of the eyelids are lined with a vascular, epithelial-lined layer called the *conjunctiva*. This layer reflects (bends) at the corners of the eyelid and sclera to overlie the cornea. Irritation of this membrane (conjunctivitis) is popularly known as "red eye." The *lacrimal gland* in the upper lateral aspect of the orbit sends several ducts into and through the conjunctival corners (*fornix*). Lacrimal fluid (tears), a watery fluid much like the serous secretions of certain salivary glands, pours over the conjunctiva lined cornea and pools in lakes at the medial edge of the lower eyelid. The fluid is drained by *lacrimal canals* whose orifices open at the medial edge of both eyelids (*puncta*). The fluid drains into the *lacrimal sacs*, flows down the *nasolacrimal ducts* into the *inferior meatuses of the nasal cavity*. Increases in emotional tension often induce parasympathetic stimulation of the lacrimal gland during the act of crying.

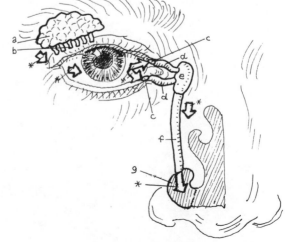

PLATE 139
see also 137, 138, 133, 124

NERVOUS SYSTEM
VISUAL SYSTEM ✻ (3)

CN 9

1. Color each muscle (but not its tendon) and at the same time color the movement it produces by coloring the respective arrow. Color the intrinsic muscles including the arrows indicating the movement of the iris.

2. Use only 2 colors in the diagram below. Read each title, coloring it in gray, and then color the portions of the pathway to which it refers with either of the two colors.

MUSCLES OF THE EYE.

EXTRINSIC ✻
SUPERIOR RECTUS a
INFERIOR RECTUS b
LATERAL RECTUS c
MEDIAL RECTUS d
SUPERIOR OBLIQUE e
INFERIOR OBLIQUE f

INTRINSIC ✻
CILIARY g
IRIS ✻
    SPHINCTER PUPILLAE h
    DILATOR PUPILLAE i

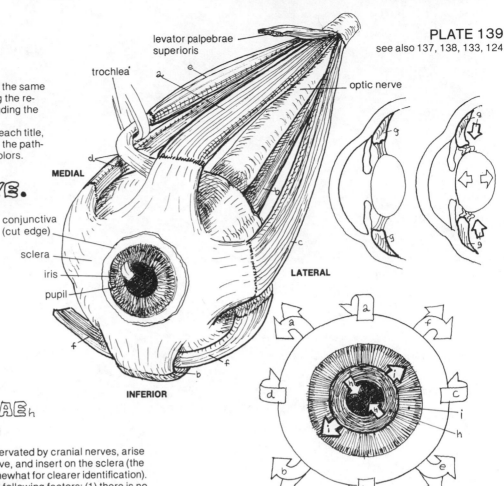

The *extrinsic skeletal muscles* of the eye are innervated by cranial nerves, arise from a circular tendon surrounding the optic nerve, and insert on the sclera (the muscles here have been raised off the sclera somewhat for clearer identification). Their functions are complex, complicated by the following factors: (1) there is no way to measure specific function of an isolated muscle of the eye, and (2) the axis of the eyeball (center of pupil to the optic disc) is not the same as the optical path of light (center of the pupil to the fovea centralis). Generally, however, it is agreed that the eye is capable of elevation (a), depression (b), abduction (c), and adduction (d). The rotary movements (inward [e] and outward [f]) are considerably more controversial. It is important to remember that any one eye movement involves all 6 muscles to one degree or another; therefore, these rotary movements may be "absorbed" in the more classical movements of the eye. The muscle levator palpebrae superioris lifts the eyelid and is not attached to the sclera.

Intrinsic muscles of the eye are smooth, innervated by autonomic nerves riding with cranial nerves, and arise/insert within the eye. The actions of these muscles have been discussed in the previous plate.

VISUAL PATHWAYS.
VISUAL OBJECT j, k
LIGHT WAVES j', k'
RETINA j², k²
OPTIC: NERVE j³, k³ CHIASMA j⁴, k⁴ TRACT j⁵, k⁵
LATERAL GENICULATE BODY j⁶, k⁶
SUPERIOR COLLICULI j⁷, k⁷
OPTIC RADIATIONS j⁸, k⁸
VISUAL CORTEX j⁹, k⁹

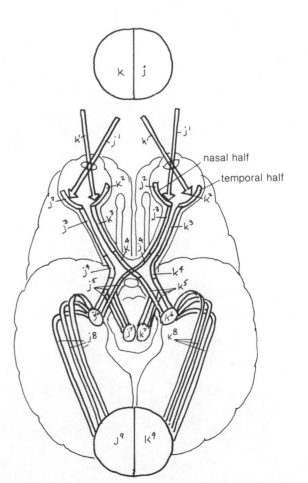

Light waves impinge on the *retina*, stimulating the photoreceptors to discharge electrochemical "impulses." These impulses are directed from the retina to the *occipital (visual) cortex* according to the scheme shown at right. Note how the optic fibers from the outer (temporal) retina do not cross at the *optic chiasma*, but the inner (nasal) fibers do. As the *optic tract* extends to the *lateral geniculate bodies* (nuclei) of the thalamus, certain fibers are directed to the *superior colliculi*, where visual reflexes are initiated. Impulses from the colliculi are conducted to cranial and spinal nerve motor cell bodies and related intermediate centers in response to a threatening visual stimulus. Impulses arriving at the visual cortex create a visual image that is spatially oriented and made meaningful with the aid of related association centers. Note that the image received at the occipital lobe is reversed to that actually visualized. Integration of impulses (both visual and memory) at the occipital cortex results in perception of the image as actually seen.

PLATE 140
see also 12, 133

NERVOUS SYSTEM
AUDITORY SYSTEM * (1)

CN 26

1. Complete each drawing before proceeding to the one below it. Read the text as you color each part.
2. Note that the organ of Corti (V) is shown as one unit of structure in figure D; its component parts are to be colored in figure E.

EXTERNAL EAR *
AURICLE a
EXT. AUDITORY MEATUS b
TYMPANIC MEMBRANE c

MIDDLE EAR *
MALLEUS d
INCUS e
STAPES f
AUDITORY (EUSTACHIAN) TUBE g

INTERNAL EAR *
BONY LABYRINTH h
VESTIBULE i
OVAL WINDOW j
SEMICIRCULAR CANALS k
COCHLEA L
SCALA VESTIBULI m
SCALA TYMPANI n
ROUND WINDOW o

MEMBRANOUS LABYRINTH p
SACCULE q / UTRICLE q'
ENDOLYMPHATIC DUCT r
SEMICIRCULAR DUCTS s
COCHLEAR DUCT t
TECTORIAL MEMBRANE u
ORGAN OF CORTI v
####### HAIR CELLS w
####### SUPPORTING CELLS x
####### BASILAR MEMBRANE y
####### SPIRAL GANGLION z
####### & VIII CRANIAL N. z'

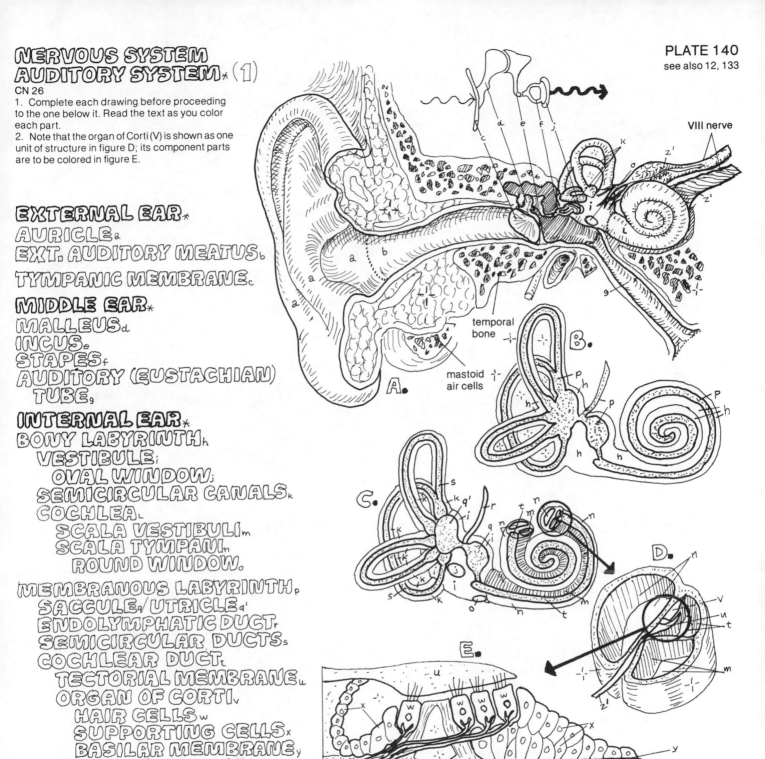

VIII nerve

temporal bone

mastoid air cells

A.

B.

C.

D.

E.

Auditory and vestibular structures can be found within the ear. The ear consists of an *external* part (*auricle* [a] and *meatus* [b] concerned with collecting and channeling sound energy into the head), a *middle* part (tympanic cavity primarily concerned with converting the sound energy into mechanical energy, amplifying it, and conducting it to the next inner chamber), and an *internal* part (concerned with both auditory and vestibular stimuli). Sound energy causes the *tympanic membrane* (c) to vibrate. These vibrations are transferred through the 3 ossicles (*malleus, incus, stapes*—all connected by synovial joints) to the *oval window* (j) (partly separating middle and internal cavities). The middle ear cavity, lined with respiratory mucosa and located within the petrous portion of the temporal bone, is open to the nasopharynx via the *auditory tube* (permits adjustment of pressures between cavity and outside) and to the mastoid air cells via an opening in the posterior wall of the cavity (not shown).

The internal ear, carved out within the petrous portion of the temporal bone, consists of a series of interconnecting chambers or passages (*bony labyrinth*) filled with fluid (perilymph). Within the bony labyrinth is a series of membranous chambers and passages (*membranous labyrinth*) also filled with fluid (endolymph). The relationship of these two labyrinths can be ap-

preciated after coloring figure B.

Referring to figure C, the bony labyrinth consists of *vestibule* (i), *semicircular canals* (k), and *cochlea* (L, best seen in figure A as a whole unit). In figures C and D, the cochlea can be seen to consist of two tubes, one adjacent to the other: the *scala vestibuli* (m), continuous with the vestibule; and the *scala tympani* (n), terminating at the *round window*. These two canals are continuous with one another at the tip of the cochlea.

The membranous labyrinth, seen in figure C, consists of *saccule* and *utricle* with their *endolymphatic duct* (q, q[1], r) located in the vestibule, *semicircular ducts* (s) within the semicircular canals, and the *cochlear duct* (t), located within the scala vestibuli of the cochlea. The endolymphatic duct terminates as a blind tube under the dura mater covering the temporal bone. Within the winding cochlear duct, supported by bone and *basilar membrane,* is a ribbon of specialized receptor (*hair*) cells and *supporting cells* covered with a *tectorial membrane*. This complex, the *organ of Corti,* is responsible for converting mechanical energy into electrochemical energy that can be conducted down the auditory portion of cranial nerve VIII via *spiral ganglia* to the brain for interpretation. The functions of the vestibular structures and the sequence of auditory function are discussed on the following plate.

PLATE 141
see also 140, 133

NERVOUS SYSTEM
AUDITORY SYSTEM *(2)
VESTIBULAR SYSTEM*

CN 8

1. Use the same colors from the preceding plate for structures repeated here.
2. Do not color the arrows in the upper drawing except for the one labeled z.
3. Color the structures as you read the text. It may be helpful to review the text in the previous plate.
4. The illustration at right is a highly schematic view of the auditory structures and is presented here to show the sequence of events resulting in the development of auditory impulses. The more anatomically correct cochlea (with its 2½ turns) can be seen in Plate 140.
5. Because 3 new colors (1–3) are needed below, color in any structure from a–z first, repeating the colors used for them on Plate 140. Then color 1–3 with new colors or any of those colors from Plate 140 that are not needed.

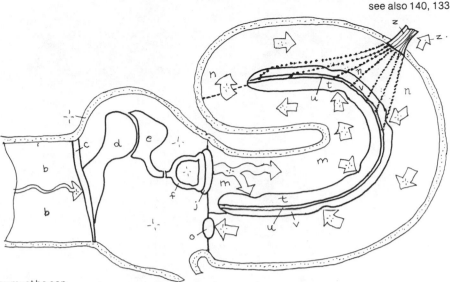

The brain has no receptors for sound, therefore sound energy must be converted to mechanical energy that can be converted to electrochemical stimuli—impulses the brain can deal with. In part, this explains the apparent complexity of the hearing mechanism. The external ear collects sound waves, which are brought to the tympanic membrane through the external auditory meatus. The tympanic membrane, acting as a resonator, transmits the energy to the ossicles, converting it from sound to mechanical energy. Within the middle ear, the amplitude of the energy is increased considerably. The vibratory movements of the ossicles are transmitted to the vestibule by way of the oval window. The perilymph of the bony labyrinth is set in motion, creating waves in the scala vestibuli to the cochlear tip and back down the scala tympani to the round window, where the vibra-

tions are dampened. The fluid motion in the scala vestibuli creates oscillations in the membranous roof of the cochlear duct, which creates endolymph motion within the duct itself. (Refer to figures D and E of the previous plate.) Endolymph motion stirs the tectorial membrane lying over the organ of Corti, bending the hairlike processes of the receptor cells to the point of discharging electrochemical impulses out the sensory processes. The impulses pass through the bipolar spiral ganglia and on to the cochlear nuclei of the medulla via the auditory division of cranial nerve VIII. Stimulation of the hair cells at the *base* of the cochlea produces a perception of high pitched sounds; stimulation of hair cells at the *tip* of the cochlea produces a perception of low pitched sounds.

VESTIBULAR SYSTEM / EQUILIBRIUM*

AMPULLA₁.
CRISTA*
CUPOLA₂.
HAIR CELLS w'
NERVE FIBERS z'
SUPPORTING CELLS x'

SACCULE q / UTRICLE q'
MACULA*
GELATINOUS LAYER 2'
OTOLITHS 3
HAIR CELLS w'
NERVE FIBERS z'
SUPPORTING CELLS x'

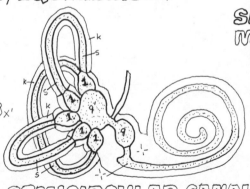

SEMICIRCULAR CANALS k
SEMICIRCULAR DUCTS s

The vestibular system consists of the *semicircular canals* (oriented at 90° to one another), their membranous *ducts*, and the *utricle/saccule* within the vestibule. The membranous semicircular ducts, floating in perilymph, are continuous with the saccule and the utricle. Within these membranous chambers flows endolymph. One end of each duct (and canal) is enlarged, forming an *ampulla*. Within the ampullae can be found ampullary crests or *crista*, consisting of receptor hair cells, supported by neighboring nonsensory cells. The hairlike processes of these receptor cells are embedded in a sugarprotein mass looking like an inverted cup (*cupola*). Movement of endolymph, in response to head turning, pushes these cristae to one side, bending the hair cells, which fire an impulse in response. The impulses travel out the vestibular portion of cranial nerve VIII to the vestibular nuclei of the medulla.

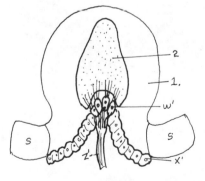

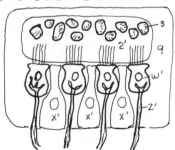

Within the utricle and saccule walls are located *maculae*, which operate on basically the same principle as cristae. The macula consists of a long row of hair cells and their supporting elements. The hairlike processes are embedded in a *gelatinous* (protein-sugar) layer with calcium salts (*otoliths*). Movement of endolymph pushes these otoliths, causing bending of the hair processes and the discharge of nerve impulses. The effect of these vestibular receptors is to influence eye movements and body positioning—an adaptive process during changes in spatial orientation.

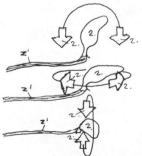

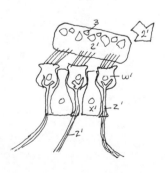

PLATE 142
see also 11, 12, 71, 79, 133

NERVOUS SYSTEM
TASTE & OLFACTION*

CN 15

1. The filiform papillae (c) in the drawing of the tongue are the smallest, light-lined circles.
2. The olfactory mucosa (i) below is enclosed within the dotted area. Note that structures (j) penetrate gaps in (m).

PAPILLAE*
CIRCUMVALLATE a
FUNGIFORM b
FILIFORM c

TASTE BUDS d
PORE CANAL e
RECEPTOR CELLS f
SUPPORTING CELLS g
NERVE FIBERS h

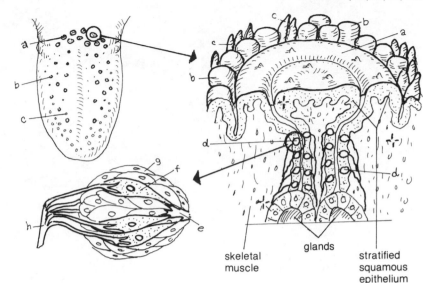

skeletal muscle   glands   stratified squamous epithelium

Taste receptors (*taste buds*) are located within the epithelial lining of the sides (moats) of the circumvallate papillae on the tongue, as well as the soft palate, oral pharynx, and epiglottis. Each "bud" consists of a number of sensory receptor cells surrounded by supporting cells. The apex of the taste bud (facing the moat) is the *pore canal* (e) through which dissolved food material must pass to reach the receptors. The base of the bud consists of sensory fibers (h) that become part of cranial nerve VII or IX, depending on its location. Material to be tasted must be in solution. Although experiments have shown there to be four basic tastes (sour, salt, sweet, bitter), there appears to be no significant difference in structure among the taste buds. Sensory cells of taste buds, like many other epithelial tissues, undergo frequent mitoses (every few days). Each new daughter cell must then form a new synapse with the sensory nerve process.

Discrimination among tastes by the gourmet is actually a product of taste sensations, temperature, smell, and the texture of the food. The taste of food is significantly affected by the reduced sense of smell (as with a cold—a phenomenon attributable to the more sensitive olfactory apparatus described below. Interpretation of taste occurs in taste centers of the cerebral cortex.

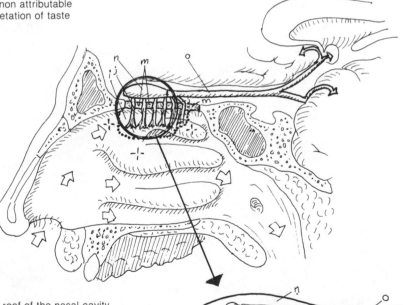

OLFACTION (SMELL)*
OLFACTORY MUCOSA i
OLFACTORY NEURONS j
OLFACTORY HAIRS (CILIA) k
SUPPORTING CELLS l
CRIBRIFORM PLATE m
OLFACTORY BULB n
OLFACTORY TRACT o

Olfactory receptors are located within the *olfactory mucosa* at the roof of the nasal cavity. The olfactory sensors are true bipolar sensory *neurons* (unlike most receptors, which synapse with sensory fibers). Their *supporting cells* come in two varieties, one of which is typically respiratory in character (pseudostratified columnar). That end of the neuron facing the surface of the nasal cavity forms a rounded tip that projects into the mucus of the nasal cavity. From this tip extend several *olfactory cilia,* which are believed to be responsible for initiating the excitation in response to olfactory stimuli. Olfactory stimuli (things that smell) are brought into the nasal cavity during inhalation (large arrows indicate air flow). Once dissolved in the mucus, the particles stimulate the olfactory cilia to fire electrochemical impulses through the olfactory neurons (j) (the direction these impulses take is indicated by the small arrows). The more central end of the neuron projects its axon up through the *cribriform plate* of the ethmoid bone in company with other axons. Within the *olfactory bulb* the axons of the primary sensory neurons synapse with cells whose axons form the *olfactory tracts* going to the temporal (medial and inferior surfaces) and frontal (inferior surface) cortices of the cerebral hemisphere and related centers.

abdominis	ab-**dom**-in-iss
abducens	ab-**doo**-sens
acetabulum	ah-see-**tab**-yoo-lum
acini	**as**-ih-nee
acromion	ah-**kroh**-mee-on
adrenal	ad-**ree**-nal
afferent	**af**-er-ent
alar	**ay**-lar
albicans	**ahl**-bih-kahns
albuginea	ahl-bew-**jin**-ee-ah
alimentary	al-ih-**men**-tor-ee
allantois	ah-**lan**-toh-iss
alveolar	al-**vee**-oh-lar
amorphous	ah-**mor**-fus
ampulla	am-**pew**-lah
anastomosis	ah-nas-toh-**moh**-siss
anconeus	an-**koh**-nee-us
anguli	**ang**-yoo-ly
ani	**ay**-ny
anococcygeal	ay-noh-kok-**sij**-ee-al
anus	**ay**-nus
aorta	ay-**or**-tah
apical	**ayp**-ih-kal
aponeurosis	ah-poh-noo-**roh**-siss
appendices	ah-**pen**-dih-sees
epiploica	ep-ih-**ploy**-ih-kah
appendicular	ah-pen-**dik**-yoo-lar
aqueous	**ay**-kwe-us
arachnoid	ah-**rahk**-noyd
arbor vitae	**ar**-bor **vy**-tee
arcuate	**ar**-kew-at
areola	ah-**ree**-oh-la
arrector pili	ah-**rek**-tor **pee**-ly
arytenoid	ah-**reh**-tih-noyd
atretic	ah-**treht**-ik
atrium	**ay**-tree-um
atrophy	**at**-roh-fee
auricle	**ah**-rih-k'l
axillary	**ak**-sih-lar-ee
azygos	**ahz**-ih-gaws
basal	**bay**-sal
basilic	bah-**sil**-ik
biceps brachii	**by**-ceps **brayk**-ee-i
bicipital	by-**sip**-ih-tal
blastocoele	**blast**-toh-seel
blastomere	**blast**-toh-meer
brachialis	**bray**-kee-ay-liss
brevis	**breh**-viss
bronchiole	**bron**-kee-ohl
buccinator	**buk**-sih-nay-tor
bulbospongiosus	bul-boh-**spon**-jee-oh-sus
bulbourethral	bul-boh-yoo-**ree**-thral
bursa	**bur**-sah
calcaneus	kal-**kay**-nee-us
calyces	**kal**-ih-sees
calyx	**kay**-liks
canine	**kay**-nyn
capillary	kap-ih-**layr**-ee
carotid	kah-**rot**-id
carpi	**kar**-py
cauda equina	**kaw**-dah eh-**kwy**-nah
cecum	**see**-kum
celiac	**see**-lee-ak
centriole	**sen**-trih-ohl
cephalic	seh-**fal**-ik
cerebellum	ser-eh-**bel**-um
cerebrum	**ser**-ee-brum
chiasma	ky-**as**-ma
choana	koh-**ah**-nah
cholecystokinin	koh-leh-siss-toh-**kyn**-in
chondro-	**kon**-dro
chordae	**kord**-ee
chorion	koh-**ree**-on
choroid	koh-**royd**
chromatin	**krohm**-ah-tin
chromosome	**krohm**-oh-sohm
ciliary	**sil**-ee-air-ee
cisterna chyli	siss-**ter**-nah **ky**-lee
clavicle	**klav**-ih-k'l
clitoris	**klih**-toh-riss
coccygeal	kok-**sij**-ee-al
coccyx	**kok**-siks
cochlear	**kok**-lee-ar
coelom	**see**-lom
colic	**kah**-lik
collagenous	kol-**lah**-jen-us
colliculi	kah-**lik**-yoo-ly
colon	**koh**-lon
commissure	**kom**-ish-ur
concha	**kon**-ka
condyle	**kon**-dyl
conus medullaris	**koh**-nus **med**-yoo-lar-iss
coracoid	**kor**-ah-koyd
cornea	**kor**-nee-ah
cornua	**kor**-noo-ah
corona	koh-**roh**-nah
radiata	**ray**-dee-ah-tah
coronal	koh-**roh**-nal
corpus callosum	**kor**-pus kah-**loh**-sum
corrugator	**kor**-uh-gay-tor
cranial	**kray**-nee-al
cremaster	kree-**mas**-ter
cribriform	**krib**-rih-form
cricoid	**krih**-koyd
cruciate	**kroo**-she-ayt
crus	krooz
crypt	kript
cuneatus	**koo**-nee-ayt-us
cuneiform	koo-**nee**-ih-form
cupola	**kuh**-poh-lah
cutaneous	kew-**tay**-nee-us
cystic	**sis**-tik
-cyte	site
decidua	dee-**sid**-yoo-ah
decussation	dee-kus-**say**-shun
deglutition	dee-gloo-**tih**-shun
diaphragm	**dy**-ah-fram
diaphysis	dy-af-**ih**-siss
diencephalon	dy-en-**sef**-ah-lon
digiti	**dij**-ih-tee
dilator	dy-**lay**-tor
ductus deferens	**duk**-tus **def**-er-ens
duodenum	doo-oh-**dee**-num
efferent	**ef**-er-ent
endocrine	**en**-doh-krin
endometrium	en-doh-**mee**-tree-um
eosinophil	ee-oh-**sin**-oh-fil
epicondyle	ep-ih-**kon**-dyl
epidermis	ep-ih-**der**-mis
epididymis	ep-ih-**did**-ih-miss
epiglottis	ep-ih-**glot**-iss
epimysium	ep-ih-**mys**-ee-um
epineurium	ep-ih-**noo**-ree-um
epiphyseal	ep-ih-**fiz**-ee-al
epiphysis	eh-**pif**-ih-siss
epithelium	ep-ih-**thee**-lee-um
erythrocyte	eh-**rith**-roh-site
esophagus	eh-**sawf**-ah-gus
estrogen	**es**-troh-jen
ethmoid	**eth**-moyd
eustachian	yoo-**stay**-kee-an
exocrine	**eks**-soh-krin
facial	**fay**-shal
falciform	**fal**-sih-form
fallopian	fal-**loh**-pee-an
falx cerebri	falks sih-**ree**-bry
fascia	**fash**-ee-ah
fasciae	**fash**-ee
fascicle	**fas**-ih-k'l
fasciculi	fah-**sik**-yoo-ly
femoral	**fem**-or-al
femur	**fee**-mur
fetus	**fee**-tus
fibula	**fib**-yoo-lah
fibroblast	**fy**-broh-blast
filum terminale	**fy**-lum ter-mih-**nal**-ee
foramen	foh-**ray**-men
fourchette	for-**shet**
frenulum	**fren**-yoo-lum
frontalis	fron-**tah**-liss
fungiform	**fun**-jih-form
funiculus	**fuh**-nik-yoo-lus
fusiform	**few**-sih-form
ganglion	**gang**-glee-on
gastrocnemius	gas-trok-**nee**-mee-us
gastroepiploic	gas-tro-ep-ih-**ploh**-ik
gemellus	jem-**el**-us
genicular	jih-**nik**-yoo-lar
gingiva	**jin**-jih-vah
glomerulus	gloh-**mayr**-yoo-lus
glucagon	**gloo**-kah-gon
gluteus	**gloo**-tee-us
golgi	**gohl**-jee
graafian	**graf**-ee-an
gracilis	**gras**-il-iss
gyri	**jy**-ry
gyrus	**jy**-rus
hallucis	**hal**-us-iss
haustra	**haws**-trah
hemiazygos	**hem**-ee-ahz-ih-gaws
hemorrhage	**hem**-or-ij
hemorrhagicum	hem-or-**rahj**-ih-kum
hiatus	hy-**ay**-tus
hilus	**hy**-lus
humerus	**hew**-mer-us
hyaline	**hy**-ah-lin
hyoglossus	hy-oh-**gloss**-us
hyoid	**hy**-oyd
hypophysis	hy-**pof**-ih-siss
hypothalamus	hy-poh-**thal**-ah-mus
ileum	**il**-ee-um
iliacus	il-ee-**ak**-us
iliopsoas	il-ee-oh-**soh**-as
incus	**ing**-kus
inguinal	**ing**-gwih-nal
innervation	in-er-**vay**-shun
integument	in-**teg**-yoo-ment
intercostal	in-ter-**kos**-tal
interosseous	in-ter-**ahs**-ee-us
interstitial	in-ter-**stish**-al
intestine	in-**test**-in
iris	**i**-riss
ischium	**iss**-kee-um
jejunum	jeh-**joo**-num
jugular	**jug**-yoo-lar
kinetochore	kih-**net**-toh-kor
labia	**lay**-bee-ah
labii	**lay**-bee-i
labyrinth	**lab**-ih-rinth
lactiferous	lak-**tif**-er-us
lacrimal	**lak**-rih-mal
lacuna	lah-**koo**-nah
lamina	**lam**-ih-nah

PRONUNCIATION GUIDE

Langerhans	**lahng**-er-hanz
larynx	**lar**-inks
latae	**lah**-tee
latissimus	lah-**tiss**-ih-mus
lemniscus	lem-**niss**-kus
lenticular	len-**tik**-yoo-lar
leukocyte	**loo**-koh-site
levator	ley-**vay**-tor
linea aspera	**lin**-ee-ah **ahs**-per-ah
lingual	**ling**-gwal
lumbrical	**lum**-brih-kal
luteum	loo-**tee**-um
lysosome	**ly**-soh-sohm
macrophage	**mak**-roh-fahj
macula	**mak**-yoo-lah
malleolus	mal-**ley**-oh-lus
malleus	**mal**-ee-us
mandible	**man**-dih-b'l
manubrium	mah-**noo**-bree-um
masseter	**mas**-seh-ter
mater	**mah**-ter
meatus	mee-**ay**-tus
mediastinum	mee-dee-as-**ty**-num
meningeal	meh-**nin**-jee-al
meniscus	meh-**niss**-kus
mesencephalon	mes-en-**sef**-ah-lon
mentalis	men-**tah**-liss
mesentery	**mes**-en-ter-ee
mesovarium	mes-oh-**vay**-ree-um
metastasis	meh-**tass**-tah-siss
metencephalon	met-en-**sef**-ah-lon
mitochondria	my-toh-**kon**-dree-ah
mitosis	my-**toh**-siss
morula	**mor**-yoo-lah
mucosa	mew-**koh**-sah
multifidus	mul-**tif**-ih-dus
myelin	**my**-eh-lin
mylohyoid	my-loh-**hy**-oyd
myofibril	my-oh-**fy**-bril
-mysium	**mys**-ee-um
navicular	nah-**vik**yoo-lar
neurilemma	noo-rih-**lem**-mah
nodule	**nod**-yool
nuchal	**noo**-kal
nucleolus	noo-**klay**-oh-lus
oblique	ob-**leek**
obturator	**ob**-too-ray-tor
occipital	awk-**sip**-ih-tal
olecranon	oh-**lek**-rah-non
omentum	oh-**men**-tum
oogenic	oh-oh-**jen**-ik
ophthalmic	off-**thal**-mik
opponens	oh-**poh**-nens
orbicularis	or-**bik**-yoo-lar-iss
oculi	**awk**-yoo-ly
otolith	**oh**-toh-lith
ovulation	ohv-yoo-**lay**-shun
oxytocin	awk-see-**toh**-sin
pacinian	pah-**sin**-ee-an
palate	**pal**-at
palatine	**pal**-ah-teen
palmaris	pah-**mah**-riss
pampiniform	pam-**pin**-ih-form
pancreas	**pan**-kree-as
papillary	**pap**-ih-ler-ee
parietal	pah-**ry**-eh-tal
parotid	pah-**rot**-id
patella	pah-**tel**-lah
pectineus	**pek**-tih-nee-us
pectoral	**pek**-toh-ral
peduncle	**pee**-dung-k'l
penis	**pee**-niss
pericardium	pair-ih-**kar**-dee-um
perineum	pair-ih-**nee**-um
periosteum	pair-ee-**oss**-tee-um
peripheral	peh-**rif**-er-al
peritoneum	pair-ih-toh-**nee**-um
peroneus	pair-**oh**-nee-us
petrosal	peh-**troh**-sal
phalanges	fah-**lan**-jeez
pharynx	**fair**-inks
phrenic	**fren**-ik
pia mater	**pee**-ah **mah**-ter
pineal	**py**-nee-al
pinocytotic	pee-noh-sy-**tot**-ik
piriformis	peer-ih-**form**-iss
pisiform	**py**-sih-form
pituitary	pih-**too**-ih-tair-ee
placenta	plah-**sen**-tah
plasma	**plaz**-mah
platelet	**playt**-let
platysma	plah-**tiz**-mah
pleura	**ploor**-ah
pleurae	**ploor**-ee
pollicis	**pawl**-iss-iss
popliteal	pop-**lit**-ee-al
prepuce	**pree**-poos
procerus	proh-**seh**-rus
progesterone	pro-**jess**-ter-ohn
pronation	pro-**nay**-shun
propria	**proh**-pree-ah
pseudo-	**soo**-doh
psoas	**soh**-as
pterygoid	**ter**-ih-goyd
pudendal	pew-**den**-dal
Purkinje	pur-**kin**-jee
pylorus	py-**loh**-rus
quadratus	kwad-**rah**-tus
ramus	**ray**-mus
Ranvier	rahn-vee-**ay**
raphe	**rah**-fee
renal	**ree**-nal
rete	**reh**-teh
reticulum	reh-**tik**-yoo-lum
retina	**ret**-ih-nah
retinaculum	ret-ih-**nak**-yoo-lum
rhomboid	**rawm**-boyd
ribosome	**ry**-boh-sohm
risorius	rhiz-**or**-ee-us
rugae	**roo**-gee
saccule	**sak**-yool
sacrum	**say**-krum
sagittal	**saj**-ih-tal
saphenous	sah-**feh**-nus
sarcolemma	sar-koh-**lem**-ah
sartorius	sar-**tor**-ee-us
scalenus	skah-**lee**-nus
scaphoid	**skaf**-oyd
scapulae	**skap**-yoo-lee
sciatic	**sy**-at-ik
sclera	**skleh**-rah
scrotum	**skroh**-tum
sebaceous	seh-**bay**-shus
sella turcica	**sel**-ah **tur**-sih-kah
semimembranosus	seh-my-mem-bran-**oh**-sus
seminiferous	seh-mih-**nif**-er-us
serosa	seh-**roh**-sah
serratus	ser-**ray**-tus
soleus	**sohl**-ee-us
spermatozoan	sper-mah-toh-**zoh**-on
sphenoid	**sfee**-noyd
sphincter	**sfingk**-ter
spinae	**spy**-nee
spinalis	spy-**nay**-liss
splanchnic	**splank**-nik
splenic	**splen**-ik
splenius	**splee**-nee-us
squamous	**skway**-mus
stapes	**stay**-peez
sternocleido-	ster-noh-**kly**-doh
stratum basale	**stra**-tum bass-ah-**lee**
subclavian	sub-**klay**-vee-an
sulcus	**sul**-kus
supination	soo-pih-**nay**-shun
suprarenal	soo-prah-**ree**-nal
symphysis	**sim**-fih-siss
synapse	**sin**-aps
synovial	sih-**noh**-vee-al
taenia	**tay**-nee-ah
tendinae	**ten**-din-ee
tensor fasciae	**ten**-sor **fah**-shee
latae	**lah**-tee
tentorium	ten-**toh**-ree-um
cerebelli	ser-ih-**bel**-ly
teres	**teh**-reez
tertius	**ter**-shee-us
testes	**tes**-teez
testicular	tes-**tik**-yoo-lar
testosterone	tes-**toss**-ter-ohn
thalamus	**thal**-ah-mus
thenar	**thee**-nar
thoracic	thoh-**ras**-ik
thyrotropin	thy-roh-**tro**-pin
trabeculae	trah-**bek**-yoo-lee
trachea	**tray**-kee-ah
trapezium	trah-**pee**-zee-um
trapezoid	**trap**-eh-zoyd
tricuspid	try-**kus**-pid
trigeminal	try-**jem**-ih-nal
triquetrum	try-**kwee**-trum
trochanter	troh-**kan**-ter
trochlea	**trohk**-lee-ah
trophoblast	**trohf**-oh-blast
tunica	**too**-nik-kah
turcica	**tur**-sih-kah
ulna	**ul**-nah
umbilical	um-**bil**-ih-kal
unipennate	yoo-nee-**pen**-ayt
ureter	yoo-**ree**-ter
urethra	yoo-**ree**-thrah
uriniferous	yoo-rih-**nif**-er-us
urogenital	yoo-roh-**jen**-ih-tal
uterus	**yoo**-ter-us
utricle	**yoo**-treh-k'l
uvula	**yoo**-vew-lah
vacuole	**vak**-yoo-ohl
vagina	vah-**jy**-nah
vagus	**vay**-gus
vastus	**vas**-tus
vein	vayn
vena cava	**vee**-nah **kah**-vah
venous	**vee**-nus
ventricle	**ven**-trih-k'l
vermiform	**ver**-mih-form
vertebra	**ver**-teh-brah
vibrissae	vy-**bris**-see
villi	**vil**-ly
viscera	**viss**-er-ah
vitreous	**vit**-ree-us
xiphoid	**zih**-foyd
zona pellucida	**zoh**-nah pel-**loo**-sid-ah

BIBLIOGRAPHY

Anthony, C. P., and N. J. Kolthoff. *Textbook of Anatomy and Physiology,* 9th ed. St. Louis: C. V. Mosby Co., 1975.

Arey, L. B. *Developmental Anatomy,* 7th ed. Philadelphia: W. B. Saunders Co., 1965.

Benson, R. C., ed. *Current Obstetric and Gynecologic Diagnosis and Treatment.* Los Altos, CA: Lange Medical Publications, 1976.

Bloom, W., and D. W. Fawcett. *A Textbook of Histology,* 10th ed. Philadelphia: W. B. Saunders Co., 1975.

Chusid, J. G. *Correlative Neuroanatomy and Functional Neurology,* 16th ed. Los Altos, CA: Lange Medical Publications, 1976.

Clemente, C. D. *A Regional Atlas of the Human Body.* Philadelphia: Lea and Febiger, 1975.

De Robertis, E. D. P., F. A. Saez, and E. M. F. De Robertis, Jr. *Cell Biology.* Philadelphia: W. B. Saunders, Co., 1975.

Elson, L. M. *It's Your Body.* New York: McGraw-Hill Book Co., 1975.

Frohse, F., M. Brodel, and L. Schlossberg. *Atlas of Human Anatomy.* New York: Barnes and Noble, 1961

Ganong, W. F. *Review of Medical Physiology,* 7th ed. Los Altos, CA: Lange Medical Publications, 1975.

Gardner, E., D. J. Gray, and R. O'Rahilly. *Anatomy,* 4th ed. Philadelphia: W. B. Saunders Co., 1974.

Goss, C. M., ed. *Gray's Anatomy of the Human Body,* 28th ed. Philadelphia: Lea and Febiger, 1966.

Grant, J. C. B. *An Atlas of Anatomy,* 6th ed. Baltimore: Williams and Wilkins, 1972.

Guyton, A. C. *Textbook of Medical Physiology,* 5th ed. Philadelphia: W. B. Saunders Co., 1976.

Haymaker, W., and B. Woodhall. *Peripheral Nerve Injuries,* 2nd ed. Philadelphia: W. B. Saunders Co., 1953.

Hollingshead, W. H. *Textbook of Anatomy,* 3rd ed. New York: Harper & Row, 1974.

Lockhart, R. D., G. F. Hamilton, and F. W. Fyfe, *Anatomy of the Human Body,* 2nd ed. Philadelphia: J. B. Lippincott Co., 1965.

Netter, F. H. *Nervous System,* Ciba Collection of Medical Illustrations, vol. 1. Summit, NJ: Ciba Pharmaceutical Products, 1953.

Noback, C. R. *The Human Nervous System.* New York: McGraw-Hill Book Co., 1967.

Romanes, G. J., ed. *Cunningham's Textbook of Anatomy,* 11th ed. New York: Oxford University Press, 1972.

Shapiro, D., F. Belamarich, and C. Levy. *Human Anatomy and Physiology,* New York: Holt, Rinehart and Winston, 1974.

Tortora, G. J., and N. P. Anagnostakos. *Principles of Anatomy and Physiology.* San Francisco: Canfield Press, 1975.

Truex, R. C., and M. B. Carpenter. *Neuroanatomy,* 7th ed. Baltimore: Williams and Wilkins, 1974.

Turner, C. D., and J. T. Bagnara. *General Endocrinology,* 6th ed. Philadelphia: W. B. Saunders Co., 1976.

Warwick, R., and P. L. Williams, ed. *Gray's Anatomy,* 35th British ed. Philadelphia: W. B. Saunders Co., 1973.

Williams, R. H., ed. *Textbook of Endocrinology,* 5th ed. Philadelphia: W. B. Saunders Co., 1974.

———. *Atlas of Body and Mind.* New York: Rand McNally, 1970.

ANSWER KEYS

to Plates 60 and 65

Plate 60   Arteries

a. Aorta
b. Brachiocephalic
c. R./L. Common Carotid
d. External Carotid
e. Internal Carotid
f. Subclavian
g. Axillary
h. Brachial
i. Radial
j. Ulnar
k. Superficial Palmar Arch
l. Deep Palmar Arch
m. Digital
n. Internal Thoracic
o/o'. Anterior/Posterior Intercostal
p. Superior Epigastric
q. Inferior Epigastric
r. Celiac
s. Renal
t. Superior Mesenteric
u. Testicular/Ovarian
v. Inferior Mesenteric
w. Common Iliac
x. Internal Iliac
y. External Iliac
z. Femoral
1. Popliteal
2. Anterior Tibial
3. Posterior Tibial
4. Peroneal
5. Lateral Plantar
6. Arcuate
7. Dorsalis Pedis
8. Medial Plantar
9. Digital
10. Pulmonary Trunk/Arteries

Plate 65   Veins

a. Digital
b/b'. Dorsal/Palmar Network
c. Basilic
d. Cephalic
e. Radial
f. Ulnar
g. Brachial
h. Axillary
i. Subclavian
j. Brachiocephalic
k. Superior Vena Cava
l. External Jugular
m. Internal Jugular
n. Azygos
o. Intercostal
p. Thoracoepigastric
q. Inferior Mesenteric
r. Superior Mesenteric
s. Splenic
t. Gastric
u. Hepatic Portal
v/v'. Digital/Plantar Venous Arch
w. Dorsal Venous Arch
x. Great Saphenous
y. Lesser Saphenous
z/z'. Med./Lat. Plantar
1. Dorsal
2. Anterior Tibial
3. Posterior Tibial
4. Popliteal
5. Femoral
6. External Iliac
7. Internal Iliac
8. Common Iliac
9. Inferior Vena Cava
10. Renal
11. Testicular/Ovarian
12. Hepatic
13. Pulmonary